THE PLAYWRIGHT'S COMPANION 1989

A Submission Guide to Theatres & Contests in the U.S.A.

Compiled and introduced

by

Mollie Ann Meserve

FEEDBACK THEATREBOOKS

Manufactured in the United States of America.

Feedback Theatrebooks
305 Madison Avenue, Suite 411
New York, NY 10165

Distributed by:

Samuel French Trade
7623 Sunset Blvd.
Hollywood, CA 90046

ISSN   0887-1507
ISBN   0-937657-03-4

Contents

Introduction

Power to the Playwright:
a survey, a manifesto, a challenge

by Dennis J. Reardon

There are only two states of being in which it is possible to write good plays. One is a condition of unfettered ignorance, a realm of grace and innocence usually found only in absolute novices. (One thinks of Georg Buchner and *Woyzeck*.) If you are presently residing within that zone of experiential virginity, please read no further, and good luck to you.

The other creatively energized state is the condition of heightened self-awareness some call wisdom. It is harder to attain than innocence, but much easier to sustain. As in any profession, a playwright's wisdom is a function of hard-won experience and self-conscious reflection upon that experience. One must have written and been produced and lived to tell the tale. One must have read extensively, both in the creative literature and the theoretical. One must have studied both the errors and the successes of one's peers and predecessors. One must have learned humility without compromising self-esteem.

Above all, one must passionately love to write for the sake of writing itself. Nothing is more self-destructive than to conceive of writing as a means to an end, whether that end be riches, renown, or merely therapy. Write because it is fun, and satisfying. Write as if the entire world is waiting to read your next word, but be content if no one but yourself ever reads that word. And make sure it's the best word.

If you're a playwright, it is useful for you not only to love writing but to love the Theater as well, infirm old lady that she is. Love her as if she were your mother, and retain as much hope for her as if she were your first-born child. This is not easily accomplished. Playwrights, with gigantic exceptions such as Moliere and Shakespeare, are often not "theater people." Rather, they are a sub-species of writer who periodically stumble out of their self-imposed creative isolation long enough to endure a three or four-week long rite of public passage called a "production." When that ordeal is over, the light-blinded playwright staggers back to his study, grateful for the healing silence of what Georges Blanchot calls his "essential solitude." By contrast, the director and the performers immediately move on to the next production, perhaps four or five of them in a single year. Meanwhile, the playwright can expect to spend anywhere from half a year to two years merely recovering from the stress of the production, no matter how successful it was, and at least that long in turning out a new script. And that is why the playwright must try to love the Theater: because it is so punishing.

Do not expect the Theater to love you back. Producers will not love you because, like all playwrights, you tend to be indigent, and that makes you either irascible or servile. Actors and actresses will avoid you because you are less handsome than they, you grind your teeth during rehearsals, and you generally are not much fun. Agents will love you for up to three years, but not enough to return your phone calls. Critics will either disdainfully ignore you or make you wish they had. Directors will hate you because you act like you wrote the damn play. Saddest of all, you will probably have few close friends among your fellow playwrights, those kindred spirits best able to understand the unique and terrible pressures of your anachronistic profession. It may well be that no playwright ever truly liked another playwright's script. Perhaps that's an indictment of our capacity for charity and selflessness. Perhaps that's just the Law of the Jungle. Either way, it's a shame.

For myself, though I love very few playwrights up close and personal, I cherish them all in the abstract. I wish every one of them complete, unqualified success every time out even though I am keenly aware of what a quixotic and empty benediction that is. The painful truth is that playwrights work in a medium which guarantees at least partial failure every time, and nearly total failure most of the time.

This extraordinarily high failure ratio is partly a problem inherent within language itself. German theorist Wolfgang Iser puts it succinctly: "What is meant can never be totally translated into what is said." Between the Signifier and the Signified is an abyss of indeterminacy common to all art. "The pigmented canvas or the carved stone," writes Roman Ingarden, "never fully 'realize' the work of art." Or, as Iser axiomatically declares, "All forms of dialogue and communication run the continual risk of failure."

But if this hermeneutical "risk" is the common plight of all artists everywhere, reflect for a moment upon how much graver the risks are for playwrights. The dramatist-in-performance forsakes the luxury of a contemplative Reader, a meditative soul communing silently with the Author at his own interpretive pace, re-reading at will, free to savor a particularly piquant turn of phrase. What the *angst* - filled playwright sees on Opening Night is an assembled mob of humanity, mostly strangers to one another, all of whom have paid an outrageous price for their evening. They expect to be transported and transformed, preferably while laughing heartily throughout. For now, before Curtain, they gossip, they yawn, they read their programs, they wait to pass judgment. When the stage lights come up or the curtain opens, this heterogeneous mass of fiercely opinionated humanity must instantly set about becoming of one mind with the author solely through the power of his score of Word and Gesture as transmitted through the bodies of living, breathing, error-prone actors. The experience is diachronic and ephemeral. At any moment a key "thought-bearing" line can be snuffed out by a cough or a sneeze, thereby jeopardizing an entire scene.

Merely to get to this highly problematic opportunity to communicate, the playwright and his manuscript have undoubtedly already endured a "developmental" process capable of turning pumpernickel into Wonder Bread, a process, in fact, designed to do precisely that. What the playwright "means to mean" is first filtered through the minds and bodies of agents, hired readers, producers, directors, actors, designers, backers, "workshop" audiences--a gauntlet which tends to transform the profoundest sentiments into sentimental pap. The entropy between a playwright's conception and its execution is enormous, far beyond that experienced by print poets or fictionalists. All of which is why Herbert Blau can write

I don't much like going to plays. They are

viii

almost invariably—especially if the Text is great—so much less than a reductive shadow of the magnitude of the mind.

Or why Samuel Beckett can proclaim, "The best possible play is one in which there are no actors, only text."

It is this "heat loss," this _aporia_ between the initial "felt thought" of the stage poet and the apparition of that thought we see in the flesh of the actors gliding through the illusion of the stage, that makes Opening Night such exquisite torture for a playwright. More often than not, what represents itself to the theater-going public as an accurate physical embodiment of the playwright's work bears almost no resemblance to the playwright's primal text, the Text of the Mind which the playwright courageously seeks and invariably fails to transcribe onto the paper of his original draft manuscript, the Text which he relentlessly pursues through each subsequent rewrite until he feels he has it exactly where he wants it—or as close to that impossibility as he will ever get.

It is at this precise moment of exactitude that the playwright surrenders his deeply private manuscript to that master manipulator, the Director. And it is at this moment that our dramatist begins the battle for control of the Text, a struggle which most playwrights still apprehend only on a subliminal level. This is why I can unaffectedly claim to love all playwrights. Most of them are so innocent, so vulnerable. Think of it: After months, perhaps years of solitary labors, they wander into a theater, a place built to deconstruct reality in interesting ways, and they say to a strange person who has been designated the Director, "Here is what I thought and felt and said. I went to a lot of trouble with it and I've finally got it just right. Now you think it and feel it and say it, and while you're at it, teach all those other strangers, those high-strung actors and actresses over there, to think it and feel it and say it just the way it looks on my paper."

At this point the experienced director will assure the upstart clod of a playwright that SANDS OF ZANZIBAR (or whatever) is the most affecting, the most cogent script he's seen _ever,_ and that he will personally mutilate any actor so indulgent as to omit even a pause in a stage direction. And so begins the process of seducing the Text away from the playwright. It will continue, generally with great deference and courtesy and much talk of the "collaborative process" and praise for the playwright's "professionalism" and "flexibility" in acceding to demands for rewrites and revisions until, on that inexorable Opening Night, the Director's play premieres. Aghast, the Playwright belatedly discovers that he has unwittingly participated in the communal trivialization of what may once have been a powerful manuscript.

This internecine war between Director and Playwright for control of the Text is not a recent development. Patrice Pavis, the French semiotician, notes that the Director was "smart enough to seize his chance at the end of the 19th century . . . and the director has not relinquished his hold on the text."

> He plays the 'modest' role of servant to the text, yet never loses an opportunity of recalling the providential nature of his appearance . . . he aims, through his stage discourse, to control entirely the theatre event, and therefore also the text rewritten by the magic baton of this conductor of the stage.

In this connection, it is useful to bear in mind that when a director speaks of "the Text," he may well be referring not to letters on a page but to an entire complex of competing and complementary signifying systems encompassing gesture, lighting, costumes, sound, image, and only incidentally including dialogue.

The ulitmate production question is, "Who's in charge of meaning?" The Director? The Actor? The Producer? The Spectator? Or--radical notion--the Playwright? Remember this: All signifying systems are not created equal. Blau expresses that thought this way:

> . . . a single gesture is not, despite the popular wisdom and some acting theory, worth a thousand words, for that still depends on the words, and your sense of language as a gesture."

x

No signifying system yet devised is as efficient a conveyor of meaning as language. Language is the model humans use to interpret their reality, including reality as construed by image and metaphor. As Pavis puts it, "We read the image according to the segmentation imposed by language."

It is time for the playwright to reassert the primacy of the Word. Playwrights know intuitively what is now decreed by many--all we have is language. This being the case, the playwright's text is more than a mere "blueprint" for a production, a trampoline off which "auteurist" directors can bounce "concepts" and performance ensembles can endlessly improvise. Moreover, the Play as Text exists as an irrefutable artistic entity even wthout an audience. The exceptions to the rule once again serve primarily to validate the rule: the theatrical event begins with the playwright, the person in charge of words and hence the person most responsible for the dispersal of meaning. After his initial work is done, a mad interpretive scramble ensues in which the playwright must play an aggressive role as guardian of the guiding vision. Not to do so is an abdication of creative responsibility, the punishment for which is forfeiture of the right to complain about the end product, the Play-as-Performance.

Every so often the Theater tries to turn her back on her playwrights. She quickly becomes anemic, and soon welcomes back what used to be called the Dramatic Poet. We are now at such a juncture. This is a propitious moment for the emergence of a truly gifted and original playwright. There is a vacuum that wants to be filled. The directors are tired and confused and increasingly dispirited. The performance ensembles have succumbed to predictable reiteration. For years they have untongued themselves, worshipping surface in lieu of depth, and now they find themselves with nothing more to say. Even their once startling repertoire of Gesture has grown depleted and conventionalized. Over the past thirty years, the avant-garde has successfully challenged the primacy of Representation, but it now appears they have replaced it with nothing, thereby creating a crisis. Never has the Theater seemed more fragmented and directionless. But this temporary exhaustion should not inspire depression or despair. It is an opporturnity waiting to be seized by a creative genius, and my bet is that new force will be a wordsmith, a Playwright.

But all bets are open, especially stylistically. There are no rules anymore unless it is this one: Make it work. To make it work, today's playwright must be far more knowledgeable than his predecessors. He must know theory, and I am not talking about the usual "How To Write a Play" manuals. All they will tell you is how formulaic plays used to be written. Very, very few of them will even mention a concept fundamental to an understanding of 20th century drama--distance, perhaps the central determinant of style. Daphne Ben-Chaim, in her work on aesthetics of audience response, comments that the

> dramatist today chooses a theatrical style, and therefore a general distance norm, for his or her play, just as he or she chooses characters and situations . . . not only have the fixed canons of genre fallen in the theater, so have the fixed canons of style . . . The deliberate manipulation of distance is, to a great extent, the underlying factor that determines theatrical style in this century.

Ben-Chaim concludes by calling for a "new level of self-consciousness both for the artist and the spectator."

Pavis has written that "the avant-garde fears the Text like the plague." By the same token most playwrights have an equally morbid dread of theory. It must be overcome. Perhaps it will help if one realizes that every line of dialogue or stage direction the playwright inscribes is a theoretical statement, whether he likes it or not. Every play is a critique of reality. The playwright cannot evade this, nor should he seek to do so. To present alternative illusions for the illusion of actuality is why the playwright exists. It is not a trivial calling, nor an easy one. How can a contemporary playwright any longer sit down to his work of solitude without sensing that his true task is to redefine Theater? But, since that is an oppressively grandiose *raison d'être*, the working playwright must repress the burden of the day's emotional, formal, and intellectual anarchy while his play is in process. His practical day-to-day chore is daunting enough: to make thousands of choices per play, from the macrocosmic to the microscopic.

xii

And the only rules he has to guide him are all self-constructed. It is in this sense that writing a play is a bit like juggling; if you stop to think about what you're doing, everything comes crashing down on your head. Thus the average playwright's fear of theory.

Underlying it is the superstitious dread that the creative "magic" will disappear if it is examined. Weigh that unverifiable nightmare against the certain consequences of a continued "know-nothingism." For starters, American playwrights will learn nothing from the often inspiring research of the avant-garde over the past several decades. They will continue to find themselves at the mercy of canny directors thoroughly conversant with the theatrical and philosophical currents of their times. And, despite their best efforts, American playwrights will continue to be vulnerable to a charge recently made by Richard Gilman that we are turning out plays that

> seem detached from real issues, not just political or ideological ones, but questions of language, metaphysics, the shape and coloration of the human world.

It is certain that the world no longer requires an endless succession of trivial dramas dressed in the threadbare garb of decrepit forms, styles, and language. It needs rich and profound texts, bold new syntheses, and sophisticated, ego-stable playwrights capable of being both Poet and Painter, masters equally of verbal and visual image. In short, as Andre Gregory muses in *My Dinner With Andre,*

> We need a new language, a language of the heart . . . a new kind of poetry . . . another kind of perception, in which you have that sense of being united to all things, and you suddenly understand everything.

This new language must leave room for mystery, for that is the life-pulse of theater. "If the mystery is not there," writes Blau, "whatever else it may be, it will not be theater." In his final analysis, and mine, it all comes back to the Word :

xiii

Whether or not the words acquire the luster
they once had, the strategies of theatre over
the next fifteen years will be conceived after
the spacious model of language . . . .

All playwrights should pray that Blau is right. If he is, and if
the Theater indeed has a future, that future belongs to the
Playwright.

Seize the day.

(Dennis J. Reardon is author of such plays as *The Leaf People*,
The Happiness Cage and *Steeple Jack*. He is a teacher of
playwriting and a winner of the National Play Award, the
Weissberger Foundation Award, a CAPS Award and a National
Endowment for the Arts Playwriting Fellowship.)

Quotations used in the above essay are from the following
sources:

Adams, Hazard and Leroy Searle, eds. *Critical Theory Since
1965*. Tallahassee, FL: Florida State Univ. Press, 1986.

Bain, D. *Samuel Beckett*. New York: Harcourt, Brace,
Jovanovich, 1978.

Ben-Chaim, Daphne. *Distance in the Theatre: The Aesthetics
of Audience Response*. Ann Arbor, MI: UMI Research Press,
1984.

Blau, Herbert. *Blooded Thought*. New York, Performing Arts
Journal Publications, 1982.

Gilman, Richard. "Off-Broadway: Qualities of Morale." *The
Village Voice*, 26 May 1987.

Pavis, Patrice. *Languages of the Stage: Essays in the
Semiology of Theatre*. New York: Performing Arts
Journal Publications, 1982.

Shawn, Wallace and André Gregory. *My Dinner with André*.
New York: Grove Press, 1981.

Spotlight: The Playwriting Program at the College of William and Mary

The Department of Theatre and Speech at the College of William and Mary in Williamsburg, Virginia, is "firmly rooted in the liberal arts tradition," says Dr. Louis E. Catron, professor of playwriting. The department offers the Bacherlor of Arts degree in theatre. With as many as forty students taking courses each year, the department has eleven faculty members, all of whom hold the Ph.D. or another terminal degree. A roll-call of alumni would include such names as Linda Lavin, Scott Glenn, Justin Deas and Glenn Close.

Catron, 1988 winner of the Virginia State Council for Higher Education Outstanding Faculty Award, came to William and Mary in 1966 to develop the department's playwriting program. Under his guidance, as many as twenty new, student-written one-act and full-length plays, theatrical monologues and television scripts are produced each year through the Premiere Theatre project. The project is part of the department's Second Season program which Catron supervises, "annually consisting of some thirty to forty student and faculty directed one-act and full-length productions."

The Studio Theatre is a large television studio, complete with a soundproof production booth from which, in the company of playwright, director and other interested students, Catron views each Premiere Theatre production and critiques the work as it is being performed. By observing audience reactions from this vantage point, Catron is able to illuminate specific problems that the author might otherwise overlook.

Catron compares Premiere Theatre productions to Grotowsky's "poor theatre." "I stress to the director: 'Your job is to work with actor and script.'" Original works are staged in front of a black curtain using generic properties and building blocks. Production budgets are provided by William and Mary alumni donations, and students whose works are produced receive an honorarium of ten dollars. Premiere Theatre audiences are made up largely of students, "with a beautiful representation of parents."

Theatre majors are required to complete thirty-six credit hours in the department, which specifies that thirty-two must be in acting, directing, design and literature. Three semesters of playwriting coursework are available, with options of repeating courses and studying playwriting as a special project. At least one playwriting course is offered each semester, "usually three sections a year with enrollment limited to ten students per section." Every student writes two one-act plays of approximately thirty-five pages, which are revised three times. Catron also requires students to write theatrical monologues of approximately five typed pages. Catron believes the theatrical monologue to be "both a valid artistic project and an excellent training ground for playwrights" and is in the process of writing a textbook on the theatrical monologue for playwrights, actors and directors.

For the first time, Catron is teaching a Production Seminar, an experimental course in which twenty students work on acting, directing and playwriting projects. "Each student is writing a monologue or one-act. We talk about how to act and direct each work." The concept for the course is based on Catron's belief that "in an age when the specialist is honored, we need to look at the essences which are virtually similar in acting, directing and playwriting." The requirement that acting and directing students work on playwriting projects, Catron believes, has inspired a positive attitude toward both the playwriting process and playwrights in the department. "With so many students writing plays and talking about their works, other students and faculty members understand that the playwright has sweated and bled over the creation of the play. Having an active playwriting program gives students both knowledge of play analysis and respect for all playwrights' work."

Catron cites several reasons for aspiring playwrights to come to William and Mary for training, including "an awful lot of good, individualized attention and strong, positive support of playwrights."

The playwriting program has produced a number of successful dramatic writers: Karen Hall has been story editor for such television programs as *MASH, Hill Street Blues* and *Moonlighting* and has written movies such as *The Betty Ford*

Story, Lisa Seidman is story editor for *Falcon Crest*; Barbara Bruno is an assistant director in Hollywood; Debbie Pryor has written plays such as *Burrhead* and *Wetter 'N Water,* which have been produced off Broadway and in regional theatres.

The faculty is distinguished. Catron is author of *Writing, Producing, and Selling Your Play,* and his article "One to One: The Art and Science of Writing Monologues" appeared in the October 1988 issue of *Dramatics* (see listings in The Playwright's Library). His latest book, published in February 1989 by Mayfield Publishing Company, is entitled *The Director's Vision* and *Writer's Digest* will soon publish an article which he entitled "Foreshadowing: The Writer's IOU to the Writer." Bruce McConachie is co-editor (with Daniel Friedman) of *Theatre for Working Class Audiences.* Richard Palmer, author of *The Lighting Art* and an upcoming book, *The Critics' Canon,* recently received an award for his contributions to the Virginia Educational Theatre Association. "With our faculty's focus on the classroom, these achievements are extra bonuses," Catron says.

The department produces four mainstage shows each academic year, directed by faculty members and frequently featuring performances by the professors. The 1988-89 season consists of *Three Penny Opera, A Christmas Carol, The Country Wife* and *House of Blue Leaves.* The Virginia Shakespeare Festival, which is affiliated with the department, produces four plays in repertory each summer.

Financial aid is available from the College of William and Mary in the form of scholarships, loans and work-study programs. The department offers a work-study program in technical theatre, allowing students to assist various touring shows mounting productions on campus.

Interested students should write to the Department of Theatre and Speech, College of William and Mary, Williamsburg, Virginia 23185. The department phone number is (804) 253-4395 or 253-4273.

Professional Playscript Format

It is no secret among playreaders--although it too often seems a fairly well-guarded one among playwrights--that the scripts which, out of hundreds or even thousands of submissions, most appeal to the eye are inevitably the first to receive the mind's fullest attention. No playwright should take lightly the admonition that a few courtesies--simple in implementation--will encourage a prompt and attentive preliminary reading. Along with a neatly-typed, high-quality copy of the play, securely bound in a clean new folder, the use of professional playscript format is of foremost importance in what *The Playwright's Companion* terms proper "Submission Etiquette." Here, then, are guidelines to professional format:

Scripts should be typed on one side only of 8.5"x11" white paper. Pica type is preferred by most playreaders, but a clear elite type is acceptable provided the page does not appear "crowded." If the script is prepared on a word-processor, photocopies of dot-matrix print-outs should be avoided.

The left margin of each page of script is set at 15 pica spaces (1.5 inches) from the left edge of the paper in order to accommodate binding in a folder; the right margin should be 1 inch from the right edge.

On the title page, the play's title, in all-caps and underscored, is centered approximately 20 single spaces from the top of the page. Below the underscore line, at 2 single-space intervals, the description (e.g., "A Play in Two Acts"), the word "by" in lower case and the playwright's name appear. The Copyright notice--if the play is registered--is typed in the lower left corner at the margin, and the author's contact information in the lower right.

On the page immediately following, entitled "Cast of Characters," the character list is double spaced with character names typed at the left margin, underscored and followed by colons. A description of each character follows on the same line. The tab setting for the descriptions is at the playwright's discretion. If space permits on this page, the descriptions of time and place may be centered below the character list; if not, a separate page should be used for these descriptions.

At the opening of each scene, set descriptions, under the titles of "SETTING" and "AT RISE" typed at the left margin and followed by colons, are set at 40 pica spaces (4 inches) from the left edge. "SETTING" refers to the appearance of the stage; "AT RISE" refers to the situation and activity on stage as the lights come up or the curtain rises.

Except between speeches by different characters, the text is single spaced. Character titles, which identify the speaker, are typed in all-caps and aligned at 40 pica spaces from the left edge. When a speech continues onto the following page, the character title is retyped at the standard setting and followed by the abbreviation "(Cont.)." When two characters speak simultaneously, both speeches occupy the same line, and tab settings for character titles are at the playwright's discretion, depending upon the length of each line of dialogue.

JOHN	JOAN
Hello, Joan. It's me again!	Oh, not you again!

Character names appearing in stage directions are typed in all-caps. Stage directions, unless they are one-word descriptions of the characters' manner of delivering the lines, are typed on a separate line and begin at a 27 pica tab setting; they should not occupy more than 2.5 inches per line.

Stage directions which are one-word descriptions of manner may follow the character title:

JOAN (sarcastically)
How charming to see you so soon.

All stage directions are enclosed in parentheses. Those directions which are complete sentences are punctuated as such. Stage directions falling within a speech are single spaced within the speech; those which fall between speeches by different characters are set off by double spaces.

Lines of dialogue are the only lines in the body of the script which run from left to right margin.

For emphasis on certain words of dialogue, underscoring, not all-caps, is used.

Page numbers are typed in the upper right corner, 4 or 5 single spaces from the top of the page. In a one-act play, only consecutive Arabic numbers are used. If the play is divided into acts, the act number is typed in Roman numerals and precedes the page number. Thus, ACT I, Page 15 would be typed as "I-15." If the acts are broken into scenes, the scene number is typed in Arabic or lower case Roman numerals and is placed between act and page numbers. ACT III, Scene 3, Page 81 would be typed as "III-3-81" or "III-iii-81." Page numbers run consecutively throughout the script, without regard to act or scene. Every act and every scene begins on a new page, with act and scene designations centered 8 single spaces from the top of the page. Act designations are typed in all-caps; scene designations are typed in lower case and are located 2 single spaces below the act designations. Both designations use a 40 pica tab setting as their left margin and are underscored:

ACT I

Scene iv

When a scene ends, "(BLACKOUT)" or "(CURTAIN)" is typed at the 40 pica tab setting, and in the same style 2 single spaces below this is the designation "(END OF ACT)" or "(END OF SCENE)." On the last page of the script, this final designation reads simply "THE END."

The following three pages provide a sample, reduced in size and not to exact scale, of a title page, character page and first page of text of a play typed in professional script format.

CHARMING JOHN

A Play in Two Acts

by

Ann Woods

Box 606,
Nashville, IN 47448
(812) 555-0000

Cast of Characters

Joan Allen:	A widow in her early 40's.
John Parker:	Her ex-husband, 46.
Edith Murphy:	Her best friend and neighbor, approaching 50.
Mr. Sims:	A man of indeterminate age.
Glynnis:	John's secretary, in her 20's.

Scene

Joan Allen's home in suburban St. Louis.

Time

Summer, 1985.

ACT I

Scene 1

SETTING: We are in JOAN ALLEN's
living room. The fur-
nishings are elegant,
expensive and eclectic and
include a sofa, chairs and a
coffee table. Doors lead to a
foyer, to the dining room
and to a patio which can be
seen through a large
picture window.

AT RISE: Afternoon. JOAN, carrying
a vase of flowers, enters
from the dining room, sets
the vase on a table and exits
to the dining room. JOHN
appears on the patio and
tries to peer in through the
window.

JOAN
(off)
I said, "I don't care what you <u>think</u>, Mr. Sims!
(She enters, followed by EDITH.)
You do the grounds. I do the house."

(JOHN ducks out of sight.)

EDITH
You let him have his say once, and now . . .
(making herself comfortable
on the sofa)
You're like that, you know. Treat people too nice.
Where -- I ask you -- where does it get you?

The Playwright's Checklist

A query/synopsis should include the following materials:

☐ A brief, polite and business-like cover letter addressed to an individual, introducing the play, explaining why it may be appropriate for this particular theatre, publisher or program and indicating a willingness to provide the script upon request.

☐ A 1-2 page script synopsis, briefly identifying all characters, indicating the number of acts and scenes, describing locales and set changes—as well as any unusual technical demands—and providing a succinct summary of the play's action.

☐ A script history, giving details of previous productions, workshops or readings of the play and of any awards the play has won.

☐ A carefully selected 10-page dialogue sample. (We recommend that—unless specifically requested—playwrights not send opening scenes as samples.)

☐ The playwright's resume and any available reviews of the play.

☐ A stamped, self-addressed business envelope (#10), or, if requested, a self-addressed postcard, for the reader's response.

A script submission to a theatre, publisher or special program should include the following materials:

☐ A brief and business-like cover letter.

☐ A clear copy (not the original) of the script, typed in proper playscript format, and securely bound in a sturdy folder.

☐ A cassette tape, recorded if possible by professional musicians and/or vocalists, of original music used in the play.

☐ A succinct synopsis and a script history.

☐ The playwright's resume.

☐ A stamped, self-addressed postcard for notification of receipt or for the reader's response.

☐ A stamped, self-addressed mailer for return of the script. (Note: <u>This mailer is essential if the playwright wishes any submitted materials returned</u>. Playwrights should be aware that Special 4th Class Mail is the most economical means of mailing scripts and should compare the cost of copying and binding a script with the cost of the mailer and return postage.)

☐ Any additional materials requested by the recipient.

A request for information, guidelines and/or application form should include the following materials:

☐ A polite letter requesting the desired information and materials.

☐ A stamped, self-addressed business envelope.

A script entry mailed to a contest should include the following materials:

☐ A brief and business-like cover letter, indicating the playwright's intention to enter the play in the competition.

☐ As many typed, securely bound copies of the script as required by the contest. (Note: some contests require that all information identifying the playwright be removed from the script prior to submission; in such instances, a second title page with the playwright's name, address and phone number should be attached to the cover letter.)

☐ A cassette tape of any original music.

☐ All completed application forms, written statements, entry fees and other materials required by the contest.

☐ A script history and the author's resume, if required.

☐ A stamped, self-addressed postcard for notification of receipt of submission.

☐ A stamped, self-addressed business envelope for notification of the play's status.

☐ A stamped, self-addressed mailer for return of the script.

Using *The Playwright's Companion 1989*

Again this year, we are grateful to the hundreds of literary managers, artistic directors, contest and program coordinators, editors and others who help us keep *The Playwright's Companion* up-to-date by responding to our annual survey. Without their continued assistance, publication of this book would not be possible.

As in years past, we have attempted to arrange the listings in a manner that will be both clear and easy to use. The listings in each section are arranged in alphabetical order, using the first letter of the organization name or contest or program title. Articles are not considered, unless they constitute a vital part of the name or title. When an organization, contest or program bears the name of an individual, the listing is alphabetized under the first letter of the first name.

The listings are divided into five major sections: Theatres, Contests, Special Programs, Publishers and Agents. The theatre section includes those theatres, and some producing companies, expressing an interest in new plays for production and/or readings along with a few theatres interested in second productions exclusively. The contest section lists competitions offering cash prizes, productions, staged readings or publication and a few competitions offering commissions.

A special list at the end of the theatre section provides information on theatres which have recently issued calls for new scripts.

This year our special program section focuses mainly upon programs specifically for playwrights, including membership, service and support organizations and resource information services; play development programs; professional appointments; script services; sources of financial suppport; and writers' colonies. The publisher section has been limited to those publishers expressing a particular interest in plays.

Our section on agents includes only contact information. Playwrights wishing to secure the services of an agent should send a query with script synopsis, resume and script history. Scripts should be sent only upon the agent's request.

We believe the information included in the listings to be for the most part self-explanatory, but some clarification is necessary.

Each theatre is classified according to type, such as "professional not-for-profit." This classification does not refer to contractual agreements or tax status; its purpose is to suggest the kind of production a playwright might expect at each theatre.

In the theatre and publisher sections the heading entitled "Policy" or "Policies" provides information on the proper submission of new scripts. In the contest and special programs sections this heading is entitled "Procedure" and explains the accepted manner of entering the competition or applying for or participating in the program. In the special program section this heading is often omitted; unless a listing specifically states otherwise, playwrights should request guidelines and application forms from any program before submitting materials.

Whether they are mentioned in a listing or not, certain appropriate materials must accompany each submission, entry or application (see The Playwright's Checklist)—except in the instances of contests and programs which specify other procedures. To our knowledge, no one listed in this book will return scripts not accompanied by adequately stamped, self-addressed mailers; many will not respond to requests for information that do not include stamped, self-addressed business envelopes.

In the theatre section the heading "Best time" refers to the months or seasons when each theatre prefers to receive submissions. Unless a listing specifically states otherwise, it may be assumed that the theatre accepts submissions at other times throughout the year but considers the stated time optimal. The "Response" heading refers to the length of time the readers normally require in replying to either a query or a script submission. If both scripts and queries are accepted and only one response time is indicated, the response time applies to both types of submissions.

In the contest and special program sections, "Deadline," unless followed by the word "postmark," indicates the date by which entries or applications must be received. "Notification" refers to the date when contest winners or program participants will be notified of their status. For all contests and programs it is advisable to request information well in advance, as policies and dates may change without notice.

In considering remuneration, playwrights are advised to understand the exact terms of payment resulting from production or publication—and any future commitments required by a producer or publisher—prior to entering into any kind of agreement or contract. The Dramatists Guild, listed in Special Programs, provides free contractual advice to its members.

In the heading "Your chances" the information appears in abbreviated form. The first number refers to the approximate number of new scripts received by a theatre or publisher each year or the number of plays normally entered in a competition. In the theatre and publisher sections the second number indicates the number of new plays given full productions each season or published each year. In the contest section, the second number indicates the number of judges normally involved, and the third number suggests how many readings each entry is likely to receive.

In most instances, the "Program" or "Programs" heading in the theatre section provides information on those special programs for playwrights offered in addition to full productions.

Suggestions quoted under the heading "Advice" are intended to assist the playwright in approaching each particular theatre, contest or publisher and should not be interpreted as general recommendations on the subject of playwriting or applied to any other theatre, contest or publisher.

The listings in *The Playwright's Companion 1989* are based upon newly received or approved information and include as many quotations from respondents to our annual survey as space allows. In no instance has the intent of a response been altered by editing.

With each edition of *The Playwright's Companion*, accuracy is our primary goal. Should you find outdated or erroneous information in this book, please let us know.

M.A.M.

Note: Inclusion of a theatre, contest, program, publisher, agent or publication in *The Playwright's Companion 1989* does not constitute endorsement or recommendation by Feedback Services or Feedback Theatrebooks, nor does exclusion imply a lack of endorsement or recommendation.

Playwright's Submission Record

In order to avoid submitting a play twice to the same market, playwrights devise various record-keeping systems. We suggest use of a submission file containing a record sheet for each play, as shown below:

Play title: _____

Draft: _____

Submitted query:_____, script:_____
                     (date)   (date)

To: _____
_____

Response expected: _____, received: _____
                       (date)   (date)

Follow-up: _____

Result: _____

Comment: _____

*

Draft: _____

Submitted query:_____, script:_____
                     (date)   (date)

To: _____
_____

Response expected: _____, received: _____
                       (date)   (date)

Follow-up: _____

Result: _____

Comment: _____

xxx

Theatres

Guidelines for submitting materials to the theatres listed in *The Playwright's Companion 1989* :

Read each listing thoroughly and carefully and follow any advice offered.

Do not expect a theatre to make an exception in the works it produces, its exclusive interests or its specifications in order to produce your play.

Comply exactly with each theatre's stated submission policy.

Be sure that appropriate materials accompany every submission (see The Playwright's Checklist).

Do not expect any theatre to return materials, or respond to any correspondence, not accompanied by self-addressed mailers or envelopes, adequately stamped and large enough to accommodate the materials to be mailed.

ABOUT FACE THEATRE COMPANY
AT THE NAT HORNE THEATRE
442 W. 42nd St., New York, NY 10036
(718) 956-5960 **Contact:** Sean Burke, Co-Artistic Director **Theatre:** off off Broadway **Works:** full-length plays, one-acts, adaptations, musicals **2nd productions:** no **Special interests:** "Original American plays only. We are a social and political theatre company, interested in plays that explore and reinterpret the American myth and ideology." **Specifications:** "No plays set in New York apartments; no single-set plays." **Tours:** yes **Stage:** proscenium, 99 seats **Audience:** "Young—20-40 years of age." **Policies:** query/synopsis with resume; commission **Best times:** Dec.-Jan. for one-act; Jul.-Aug. for full-length play **Response:** 5 months **Your chances:** one-acts: 225/6 plus 16 workshops and 30 readings; full-length plays: 190/3 plus 8 workshops and 15 readings **Remuneration:** negotiable **Programs:** readings, staged readings, workshop productions, development

ACACIA THEATRE

Box 11952, Milwaukee, WI 53211 (414) 962-2380
Contact: Alan Atwood, Artistic Director **Theatre:** professional not-for-profit **Works:** full-length plays, one-acts, translations, adaptations, musicals **2nd productions:** yes **Special interest:** "Plays with biblical or spiritual themes. A comedy based on a biblical story would be great." **Maximum cast:** 8 **Tours:** yes **Stage:** arena, 281 seats **Audience:** "Most are Christians from a variety of denominations." **Policies:** unsolicited script; professional recommendation; "word of mouth/perusal copy" **Best times:** spring, fall **Your chances:** 3-4/1 **Remuneration:** $500 **Advice:** "We are looking for plays written from a Christian World View."

ACADEMY THEATRE

Box 77070, 173 14th St. NE, Atlanta, GA 30357 (404) 873-2518 **Contact:** Linda Anderson, Literary Manager **Theatre:** professional not-for-profit **Works:** full-length plays, one-acts, adaptations, children's plays **2nd productions:** "If not previously produced in the Southeast." **Special interests:** "Non-traditional plays with elements of poetic language and surrealism; plays that deal with important issues in imaginative ways." **Specifications:** maximum cast: 8; simple set **Stages:** modified thrust, 389 seats; flexible, 250 seats; flexible, 80 seats **Audience:** "A cross-sampling of Atlantans interested in alternative theatre-going and good acting." **Policies:** query/synopsis with dialogue sample; unsolicited script from local writer only **Best time:** Oct.-May **Response:** 1 month query; 4 months script **Your chances:** 300/5 **Remuneration:** "Varies with type of production." **Programs:** quarterly readings for students in theatre's playwriting classes; Theatre for Youth (plays for grades 3-12); Black Box Theatre: New Play Program for local writers **Advice:** "The Academy Theatre looks for plays that show writers have found their own voice and are not imitating current theatrical trends. We get excited by writers who have a facility with language along with the ability to disburb, amuse and interest an audience in theatrical, dramatic ways."

A CONTEMPORARY THEATER SOUTHWEST
4949 E. Shaw Butte, Scottsdale, AZ 85254
(602) 996-3333 Contact: Ric Alpers, Executive Director
Theatre: community not-for-profit **Works:** children's plays
Specifications: unit set; some limitations on lighting
Tours: "Not generally." **Stage:** proscenium, 150 seats
Audience:"We aim toward a family audience." **Policy:**
unsolicited script **Your chances:** "very few/none"
Remuneration: no **Programs:** classes; DramaQuest
competition for student playwrights in grades 1-12 in Mariposa
County, deadline Dec. 10, 1989 (inquire) **Comments:** "We
are not currently seeking new plays outside our own
organization. Our contest for young playwrights received 80
entries, and 6 were produced." Formerly Associated
Children's Theatre of Scottsdale.

A CONTEMPORARY THEATRE
100 W. Roy St., Seattle, WA 98119
(206) 285-3220 Contact: Jeff Steitzer, Literary
Manager **Theatre:** professional not-for-profit **Works:** full-
length plays, translations, adaptations, musicals, children's
plays **2nd productions:** yes **Tours:** children's plays
Stage: thrust, 450 seats **Audience:** "Very mixed."
Policies: query/synopsis; professional recommendation;
agent submission **Response:** 1 month query; 3 months script
Your chances: 500/1 **Remuneration:** "Royalties
arranged; often residency for rehearsals." **Program:**
Songworks: workshop productions for small-scale musicals
(inquire)

THE ACTING COMPANY
Box 898 Times Square Station, New York, NY 10108
(212) 564-3510 Contact: Rob Bundy, Staff Repertory
Director **Theatre:** professional not-for-profit **Works:**
full-length plays, one-acts, translations, adaptations, musicals
Special interest: works suitable for an ensemble of 10
men and 4 women, 20-45 years of age **Specifications:**
simple set **Tours:** yes **Stage:** proscenium, 287 seats
Policy: professional recommendation **Best time:** Nov.-Jan.
Response: 8-10 weeks

THE ACTING GROUP
Box 1252 Old Chelsea Station, New York, NY 10011
(212) 645-1459   **Contact:** Celia Barrett, Producing Artistic Director **Theatre:** professional **Works:** full-length plays, one-acts **Special interests:** comedy, drama **Specifications:** maximum cast: 10; no more than 2 sets; "we are an ensemble company of actors, playwrights, directors--major age range 25-45" **Stages:** "Rented per show--in Manhattan only." **Policies:** query/synopsis with resume; professional recommendation; agent submission; may accept unsolicited script **Best time:** spring for following fall/winter **Response:** 10-12 months script **Your chances:** 2000+/5 **Remuneration:** "Usually $50 per one-act." **Programs:** staged readings, development; "a few playwright members work with us year-round" **Advice:** "Be patient; we're very small but do high quality Equity Showcases. Slow in response."

ACTORS ALLEY REPERTORY THEATRE
4334 Van Nuys Blvd., Sherman Oaks, CA 91403
(818) 986-2278   **Contact:** Alvin Ross, Literary Manager **Theatre:** professional not-for-profit **Works:** full-length plays, one-acts **Special interests:** "World, American and West Coast premieres; provocative works." **Policy:** unsolicited script with synopsis **Program:** Actors Alley Repertory Theatre Annual New Play Competition (AART; see Contests) **Comment:** "Any full-length play submitted is automatically considered for the AART Competition."

ACTORS' ALLIANCE, INC.
AAI, JAF Box 7370, New York, NY 10116
(718) 768-6110 **Contact:** Melanie Sutherland, Juanita Walsh, Co-Artistic Directors **Theatre:** off off Broadway **Works:** full-length plays, one-acts, translations, adaptations **2nd productions:** yes **Tours:** yes **Stage:** proscenium, 99 seats (Nat Horne Theatre) **Audience:** "Subscription list of 4000 in NY, NJ and PA." **Policy:** unsolicited script **Response:** 2 months **Your chances:** 50/1-2 **Remuneration:** "Expenses and small stipend." **Programs:** readings, staged readings, workshop productions **Advice:** "This is a membership company. Playwrights may submit plays

and join the organization, which has a small fee." **Comment:** See Actors' Alliance, Inc. listing in Special Programs.

ACTORS ALLIANCE THEATRE
30800 Evergreen, Southfield, MI 48076 (313) 642-1326 Contact: Annette Madias, Artistic Associate **Theatre:** professional not-for-profit **Works:** full-length plays, adaptations, musicals **2nd productions:** yes **Special interests:** "Women's plays, contemporary issues, gay and lesbian themes." **Stages:** flexible, 150 seats; various spaces, 500-1500 seats **Audience:** "Black/white—urban, upper middle class." **Policy:** query/synopsis **Response:** 3 months query; 6-9 months script **Your chances:** 30-60/1 **Remuneration:** negotiable **Program:** internships

THE ACTORS' COMPANY OF PENNSYLVANIA
Box 1153, Lancaster, PA 17603 (717) 397-1251 Contact: Jeanne Clemson, Producing Director **Theatre:** professional not-for-profit **Works:** full-length plays, one-acts, translations, adaptations, musicals, children's plays **Specifications:** simple production requirements **Stages:** proscenium, 800 seats; thrust, 200 seats **Policy:** query/synopsis **Best time:** summer **Response:** 6 months if interested in query; 3 months script

ACTORS FOR THEMSELVES
Matrix Theatre, 7657 Melrose Ave., Los Angeles, CA 90046 (213) 852-1445 Contact: Joseph Stern, Producer **Theatre:** professional not-for-profit **Works:** full-length plays **2nd productions:** yes **Special interests:** "Contemporary issues, literary merit, strong roles for actors." **Stage:** thrust **Policy:** professional recommendation **Best times:** Jan.-Feb., Aug.-Sept. **Response:** 2 months

ACTORS LAB ARIZONA
7624 E. Indian School Rd., Scottsdale, AZ 85251 (602) 990-1739 Contact: Jan Sickler, Artistic Director **Theatre:** professional not-for-profit **Works:** full-length plays, translations, adaptations, children's plays **Specifications:** small cast, simple set **Stage:** thrust,

120 seats **Policy:** query/synopsis **Response:** 2 weeks query; 4–6 months script

ACTORS LABORATORY THEATRE
**Avila College, 11901 Wornall Rd.,
Kansas City, MO 64114 (816) 942–8400 ext. 290**
Contact: Buck Baker, Producer **Theatre:** university/college **Works:** full-length plays, one-acts, musicals, children's plays **Specifications:** maximum cast: 7; single set preferred **Stages:** thrust; arena **Audience:** middle-class families **Policy:** query/synopsis with resume **Response:** 4 months **Your chances:** 15/0-1 **Remuneration:** no

ACTORS OUTLET THEATRE
120 W. 28th St., New York, NY 10019
(212) 807-1590 Theatre: off off Broadway **Works:** full-length plays, one-acts, translations, adaptations, musicals **Specifications:** maximum cast: 25; no more than 2 sets **Tours:** no **Stage:** flexible, 99 seats **Audience:** "General." **Policies:** professional recommendation; agent submission **Your chances:** 100/3 **Remuneration:** negotiable **Programs:** readings, staged readings, workshop productions

ACTORS' REPERTORY COMPANY
308 S. Dixie Hwy., West Palm Beach, FL 33401
(305) 655-2122 Contact: Nona Lloyd, Artistic Director **Theatre:** professional not-for-profit **Works:** full-length plays, one-acts **2nd productions:** "Not required." **Specifications:** maximum cast: 8; single set **Stage:** arena, 99 seats **Policy:** query/synopsis **Best times:** Jun.-Jul., Nov., Feb.-Mar. **Response:** 6 months **Remuneration:** negotiable royalty **Programs:** readings, staged readings **Comments:** Company attempts to produce 1 new play each season. Formerly Actors' Workshop and Repertory Company.

THE ACTORS SPACE
250 W. 54th St., New York, NY 10019
(212) 757-5900 Contact: Scott Klavan, Literary Manager **Theatre:** professional not-for-profit **Works:** full-length plays, one-acts, translations, adaptations, musicals **2nd**

productions: "Sometimes." **Special interest:** "High stakes plays in which characters have strong, clear objectives." **Specifications:** simple set preferred; "actors aged 20's-40's preferred but older okay" **Stages:** black box; rented spaces, 50 or more seats **Policies:** query/synopsis with resume preferred; unsolicited script with resume **Response:** 3 months **Your chances:** 50-100/3 plus staged readings **Programs:** staged readings, workshop productions, development **Advice:** "Hard hitting/social issues."

ACTORS THEATRE OF LOUISVILLE
316 W. Main St., Louisville, KY 40402
(502) 584-1265 Contact: Michael Bigelow Dixon, Literary Manager **Theatre:** professional not-for-profit **Works:** full-length plays, one-acts **2nd productions:** yes **Maximum cast:** 15 **Tours:** "Occasionally." **Stages:** thrust, 650 seats; thrust, 150 seats **Audience:** "A cross-section of the Louisville community." **Policies:** query/synopsis; professional recommendation; agent submission; unsolicited script of one-act only **Response:** 1 month query; 6-9 months script **Your chances:** 2500/30 **Remuneration:** "Royalties in accordance with Dramatists Guild/LORT contracts." **Program:** National One-Act Play Contest (see Contests) **Advice:** "Submit plays to the National One-Act Play Contest." **Comment:** See Breslin, Jimmy. 'TKO in Louisville" (*American Theatre*, Jun. 1988), 25-27, 57.

ACTORS THEATRE OF ST. PAUL
28 W. 7th Pl., St. Paul, MN 55102 (612) 297-6868
Contact: Michael Andrew Miner, Artistic Director **Theatre:** professional not-for-profit, LORT regional repertory company **Works:** full-length plays, one-acts, translations, adaptations, musicals **2nd productions:** yes **Special interest:** "High quality scripts." **Specifications:** maximum cast: 15; cast must suit casting needs of resident company **Stage:** proscenium **Audience:** "Varied." **Policies:** unsolicited script; query/synopsis; professional recommendation; agent submission **Best time:** Feb.-Jun. **Response:** 2 weeks query; 3 months script **Remuneration:** negotiable royalty **Programs:** staged readings, workshop productions, residencies **Advice:** "While we accept direct submissions, we believe that a carefully prepared query and synopsis can

save you postage and time. We solicit many of the scripts described in synopsis; discourage ones similar in theme to those we've recently produced, and often request an additional script from your resume."

ACTORS' WORKSHOP
295 E. Main #5, Ashland, OR 97520
(503) 482-9659 Contact: Michael O'Rourke, Artistic Director **Theatre:** professional not-for-profit **Works:** full-length plays, translations, adaptations, musicals, children's plays **2nd productions:** yes **Special interests:** "We are influenced by Carl Jung, Commedia, fantasy writers. Social issues with upbeat themes; plays that show the human spirit." **Specifications:** "It is very difficult to produce black plays, as there are next to no black actors in the area. No heavy, depressing, realistic drama." **Tours:** "Some." **Stage:** flexible, 42 seats **Audience:** "Very broad base; 30% tourists; most are rather adventurous." **Policy:** query/synopsis with dialogue sample and resume **Best time:** Jan.-Feb. **Response:** 3 months **Your chances:** 50/1-2 **Remuneration:** "Minimal. Some grant monies when available." **Programs:** readings, staged readings, workshop productions, development **Advice:** "Sincerity, simplicity; don't force the plot. Adaptations should remain as true to original as practicable. Must be willing to re-write. Imagination!"

ACTORS' WORKSHOP AND REPERTORY COMPANY
West Palm Beach, FL See Actors' Repertory Company.

THE ADELPHIAN PLAYERS
8515 Ridge Blvd., Brooklyn, NY 11209
(718) 238-3309 Contact: Russ Bonanno, President **Theatre:** professional not-for-profit **Works:** full-length plays, adaptations **2nd productions:** yes **Special interests:** "Urban problems, senior citizens' issues, contemporary comedies." **Specifications:** "Staff considerations." **Stage:** flexible **Audience:** "Senior citizen and general, Brooklyn-Urban area." **Policies:** unsolicited script with resume; professional recommendation **Best time:**

Nov.-Dec. **Response:** 3-4 weeks query; 5-6 weeks script **Remuneration:** no **Comment:** Theatre operates during summer only.

A.D. PLAYERS
2710 W. Alabama, Houston, TX 77098
(713) 526-2721 Contact: Carol Anderson, Literary Manager **Theatre:** professional not-for-profit **Works:** full-length plays, one-acts, translations, adaptations, musicals, children's plays **2nd productions:** yes **Exclusive interest:** "All our productions are from a Christian world view: God's reality in Man's everyday world. We are looking for children's shows." **Maximum cast:** 12 **Tours:** "Many." **Stage:** proscenium, 212 seats **Audience:** "Majority are conservative, from a wide range economically, ethnically and educationally." **Policies:** unsolicited script; query/synopsis **Response:** 2 weeks query; 2 months script **Your chances:** 100/1 **Remuneration:** negotiable royalty

ALABAMA SHAKESPEARE FESTIVAL
Box 20350, Montgomery, AL 36120-0350
(205) 272-1640 Contact: Lori Grifo, Artistic Associate **Theatre:** professional not-for-profit **Works:** full-length plays, translations, adaptations **2nd productions:** no **Special interest:** new translations of 17th-19th century European works **Specifications:** maximum cast: 18-20; no more than 3-4 sets **Stages:** modified thrust, 750 seats; flexible, 225 seats **Policy:** query/synopsis with dialogue sample **Best time:** Jun.-Sept. **Response:** 3 weeks query; 3-4 months script **Your chances:** 50-60/0 **Remuneration:** no

ALASKA REPERTORY THEATRE
P.O. Box 104700, Anchorage, AK 99510-4700
(907) 276-2327 Contact: Andrew J. Traister, Producing Artistic Director **Theatre:** professional not-for-profit **Works:** full-length plays, translations, adaptations, musicals, cabaret/revues **Stages:** proscenium, 800 seats; proscenium, 350 seats **Policy:** query/synopsis **Response:** 2 weeks query; 3-6 months script

ALCHEMY THEATRE COMPANY
515 E. 85th St., New York, NY 10028
(212) 744-4275 Contact: Gita Donovan, Artistic Director
Theatre: off off Broadway **Works:** full-length plays, one-acts, adaptations **2nd productions:** "If New York premieres." **Stages:** rented spaces **Audience:** "General public, well educated, literate; students; some appeal to ethnic constituency—depends upon the play." **Policies:** unsolicited script; query/synopsis; professional recommendation; agent submission; commission **Response:** 1 month **Your chances:** 300-400/2 full productions **Remuneration:** negotiable **Programs:** staged readings, workshop productions, development **Advice:** "We are open to your best work!"

ALHAMBRA DINNER THEATRE
12000 Beach Blvd., Jacksonville, FL 33216
(904) 641-1212 Contact: Tod Booth, Producer **Theatre:** Equity dinner **Works:** full-length plays, musicals **Special interests:** comedies, farces, star vehicles **Specifications:** maximum cast: 8; single set **Policy:** unsolicited script

ALLENBERRY PLAYHOUSE
Box 7 Rt. 174, Boiling Springs, PA 17007
(717) 258-3211 Contact: Michael Rothaarr, Producer **Theatre:** Equity dinner, stock **Works:** full-length plays, musicals **2nd productions:** yes **Special interests:** comedies, farces, musicals **Specifications:** cast of 5-7; single set; limited wing and fly space **Stage:** proscenium, 414 seats **Policy:** query/synopsis **Best time:** Jan.-Aug. **Advice:** "Comedies and family dramas; no offensive language or subject matter." **Comment:** "We do very few new plays but are always open."

ALLEY THEATRE
615 Texas Ave., Houston, TX 77002
(713) 228-9341 Contact: Robert Strane, Literary Manager **Theatre:** professional not-for-profit **Works:** full-length originals, translations, adaptations, musicals **2nd productions:** yes **Stages:** thrust, 800 seats; arena, 296 seats **Policy:** query/synopsis **Response:** 3 weeks query; 2-6 months script **Remuneration:** negotiable **Programs:** readings, staged readings, workshop productions, residencies

ALLIANCE THEATRE
1280 Peachtree St. NE, Atlanta, GA 30309
(404) 898-1119 Contact: Sandra Deer, Literary Manager
Theatre: professional not-for-profit **Works:** full-length plays, adaptations **Stages:** proscenium, 864 seats; flexible, 200 seats **Policy:** professional recommendation **Response:** 1-3 months

AMAS REPERTORY THEATRE
1 E. 10th St., New York, NY 10029
(212) 369-8000   Contact: Rosetta LeNoire, Artistic Director **Theatre:** professional not-for-profit **Works:** musicals **2nd productions:** if previous production was not by a professional theatre or if work has been substantially revised since production **Special interest:** musical biographies **Specifications:** maximum cast: 20 preferred; simple set; "works must be suitable for multi-racial casting and for the whole family" **Tours:** yes **Stage:** modified thrust, 99 seats **Audience:** "Multi-racial, from the entire New York metro area." **Policies:** unsolicited script; query/synopsis **Best time:** Jul.-Sept. **Response:** several weeks-months **Your chances:** 150/3 **Remuneration:** no **Programs:** workshop productions, internships, residencies **Comment:** "Many of our productions have gone on to receive potentially lucrative commercial productions."

AMERICAN CONSERVATORY THEATRE
450 Geary St., San Francisco, CA 94102
(415) 771-3880 Contact: Edward W. Hastings, Artistic Director **Theatre:** professional not-for-profit **Works:** full-length plays, translations, adaptations **Maximum cast:** 10 **Stage:** black box, 50-60 seats **Audience:** subscription **Policies:** query/synopsis preferred; unsolicited script **Response:** 2 months query; 6 months script **Program:** readings **Advice:** "Please inquire first." **Comment:** Theatre receives 100-150 new scripts each year.

AMERICAN ENSEMBLE COMPANY
Box 972 Peck Slip Station, New York, NY 10272
(212) 571-7594   Contact: Mr. Kelly Masterson, Literary Manager   **Theatre:**   off   off   Broadway, professional not-for-profit **Works:** full-length plays, one-

acts, musicals **2nd productions:** only if not previously produced off off Broadway **Special interests:** "Socially significant plays written with a concern for language." **Specifications:** unit set; "not interested in avant garde" **Stage:** proscenium, 128 seats **Audience:** "General New York City." **Policy:** query/synopsis with dialogue sample **Response:** 2 months **Your chances:** 350/5 full productions, 8 staged readings **Programs:** staged readings, workshop productions, residencies **Comment:** "We hope to do 10 full productions and 15 readings with authors who live in the New York City area."

AMERICAN FOLK THEATER, INC.
230 W. 41st St. Suite 1807, New York, NY 10036
(212) 764-1267 Contact: David Newman, Literary Manager **Theatre:** professional not-for-profit **Works:** full-length plays **2nd productions:** no **Special interest:** "Plays which are socially relevant, thought-provoking, entertaining." **Specifications:** maximum cast: 5; multi-racial cast; "one set if realism or naturalism is required" **Stage:** thrust **Audience:** "College graduates, 20-50, all races, urban." **Policies:** query/synopsis; professional recommendation; agent submission **Best time:** late fall **Response:** 6 weeks query; 6 months script **Your chances:** 500/3 **Remuneration:** "As per option agreement." **Programs:** readings, staged readings, workshop productions, development, classes, internships **Advice:** "Plays that dramatically and musically explore the multi-cultural character of our changing American society. We are interested in plays of action, not only of words, and especially those with a heightened sense of theatrical realism."

AMERICAN JEWISH THEATRE
15 W. 28th St., New York, NY 10001
(212) 683-7220 Contact: Susan Nanus, Dramaturg **Theatre:** professional not-for-profit **Works:** full-length plays, translations, adaptations, musicals **Exclusive interest:** Jewish themes **Stage:** black box, 100 seats **Audience:** "Subscription, mainly middle-class Jewish." **Policies:** unsolicited script; professional recommendation;

agent submission **Response:** 3 months   **Your chances:**
150/4-5   **Program:** Jewish Women Playwrights Unit (inquire)

AMERICAN LIVING HISTORY THEATER
Box 2677, Hollywood, CA 90078   (213) 876-2202
Contact: Dorene Ludwig, Artistic Director   **Theatre:**
professional   not-for-profit   **Works:**   one-acts   **2nd
productions:**   yes   **Exclusive interest:**   "American
historical and literary characters and events/primary source
material." **Specifications:** maximum cast: 1-2 preferred;
"no set, some props"   **Tours:** "Throughout the U.S. on
per-performance basis." **Stages:** proscenium, thrust, arena,
flexible--"depending upon the client's space" **Audience:** "Ages
4 through over 70, all ethnic groups and white, all educational
levels." **Policies:** unsolicited script; query/synopsis with sas
postcard **Response:** 6 months **Remuneration:** "Depends
upon funding, and how produced--Equity, waiver, reading, etc."
Your chances: 12-15/0 **Program:** "Seminars and
consultation available to writers on request. Fees based on
services." **Advice:** "Do not send material that has nothing to
do with our interests. It wastes both the writer's and the
producer's time!" **Comment:** "We rarely produce work
outside the company: submissions are not historically
accurate/primary source; we have numerous playwrights
within the company."

AMERICAN MUSIC THEATRE FESTIVAL
One Franklin Plaza, Philadelphia, PA 19103
(215) 988-9050 Contact: Eric Salzman, Artistic Director
Theatre: professional not-for-profit **Works:** musicals **2nd
productions:** yes **Tours:** yes **Policies:** unsolicited script
with resume; professional recommendation **Best time:**
Nov.-Jun. **Response:** 9 months **Your chances:** 200/5
Programs: staged readings, workshop productions, Fall
Festival (inquire)

THE AMERICAN PLACE THEATRE
111 W. 46th St., New York, NY 10036
(212) 246-3730 Contact: Christopher Breyer, Literary
Manager **Theatre:** professional not-for-profit **Works:**
full-length plays, one-acts, adaptations, cabaret/revues **2nd
productions:** yes **Special interests:** "Innovative

works, humorous revues." **Specifications:** American playwrights only **Stages:** flexible, 299 seats; flexible, 100 seats; flexible cabaret, 100 seats **Policies:** unsolicited script from writer who has had professional productions; query/synopsis with up to 25-page dialogue sample from others **Best time:** Sept.–Jun. **Response:** 4 months **Programs:** American Humorist Series (2 programs per season of works by or about American Humorists); Jubilee (annual festival celebrating Black history)

AMERICAN RENAISSANCE THEATRE
112 Charlton St., New York, NY 10014
(212) 929-4718 Contact: Susan Gert, Literary Manager **Theatre:** off off Broadway, professional not-for-profit **Works:** full-length plays, one-acts, children's plays **2nd productions:** yes **Special interest:** American themes **Specifications:** maximum cast: 6; simple set **Stage:** flexible **Audience:** "Extremely varied." **Policies:** query/synopsis with dialogue sample and resume; professional recommendation; agent submission **Response:** 2-4 months **Remuneration:** "Equity Showcase scale." **Programs:** staged readings, readings, workshop productions, development

AMERICAN REPERTORY THEATRE
64 Brattle St., Cambridge, MA 02138
(617) 495-2668 Contact: R. J. Cutler, Director of New Plays **Theatre:** professional not-for-profit **Works:** full-length plays, one-acts, translations, adaptations, cabaret/ revues **Special interest:** plays with "poetic dimension" rather than "prosaic realism" **Maximum cast:** 15 **Stages:** proscenium, 350 seats; flexible, 556 seats **Policy:** query/synopsis with 10-page dialogue sample **Best time:** Sept.–Jun. **Response:** 2 weeks query; 4-5 months script **Programs:** readings, development

THE AMERICAN STAGE COMPANY
Box 1560, St. Petersburg, FL 33731
(813)   823-1600 Contact: Kathy Foley, Production Assistant **Theatre:** professional not-for-profit **Works:** full-length plays **Special interest:** works written in the last 10 years by American playwrights **Maximum cast:** 10 **Stage:** flexible, 110 seats **Policies:** query/synopsis with

1st 10 pages of script preferred; unsolicited script **Best time**: Jul.-Aug. **Response**: 2 months query; 4 months script

AMERICAN STAGE COMPANY
Box 336, Teaneck, NJ 07666
Contact: Jamie Milestone, Associate Producer **Theatre**: professional not-for-profit **Works**: full-length plays **2nd productions**: yes **Special interest**: American plays **Specifications**: maximum cast: 6; single set; low proscenium **Tours**: yes **Stage**: proscenium, 270 seats **Audience**: "New York suburban." **Policies**: query/synopsis with resume; professional recommendation **Best time**: spring **Your chances**: 200-300/3-4 **Remuneration**: no **Program**: readings

AMERICAN STAGE DIRECTIONS
San Francisco, CA This theatre is permanently closed.

AMERICAN STAGE FESTIVAL
Box 225, Milford, NJ 03055
(603) 673-7515, -3143 **Contact**: Larry Carpenter, Artistic Director **Theatre**: professional not-for-profit **Works**: full-length plays, musicals **Special interest**: innovative works on American society **Specifications**: maximum cast: 10 for plays, 6 with 5 musicians for musicals; no fly system **Stage**: proscenium, 480 seats **Policy**: agent submission **Best time**: Sept.-Dec. **Response**: 3 months

AMERICAN STANISLAVSKI THEATRE
485 Park Ave. Apt. 6, New York, NY 10022
(212) 755-5120 **Contact**: Sonia Moore, Artistic Director **Theatre**: off off Broadway **Works**: full-length plays, one-acts, translations, adaptations, musicals **Special interests**: "Important messages; plays for actors aged 18-45." **Specifications**: no offensive language; "small cast preferred but will consider larger" **Tours**: some shows **Stage**: proscenium **Policy**: unsolicited script **Best time**: spring **Response**: Sept.-Oct. **Your chances**: 40/1 **Program**: classes year round

AMERICAN THEATRE COMPANY
Box 1265, Tulsa, OK 74101   (918) 747-9494
Contact: Kitty Roberts, Artistic Director **Theatre:** professional not-for-profit **Works:** full-length plays, translations, adaptations, musicals, children's plays **2nd productions:** yes **Special interest:** small-cast comedies **Specifications:** maximum cast: 20, 8 or fewer preferred; single set; low budget **Stage:** proscenium **Policy:** query/synopsis with letter of introduction and dialogue sample **Best time:** late spring **Response:** 2 months

AMERICAN THEATRE OF ACTORS
314 W. 54th St., New York, NY 10019
(212) 581-3044   Contact: James Jennings, Artistic Director **Theatre:** professional not-for-profit **Works:** full-length plays **Special interests:** developing new playwrights; dramas, comedies **Specifications:** no musicals or avant garde plays **Stages:** proscenium, 140 seats; proscenium, 65 seats **Policy:** unsolicited script **Response:** 2 months **Your chances:** 500/25 **Remuneration:** no **Programs:** readings, staged readings, workshop productions

ANGEL'S TOUCH PRODUCTIONS
7962 Hollywood Way, Sun Valley, CA 91352
(818) 768-6369   Contact: Phil Nemy, Director of Development **Theatre:** off off Broadway, professional not-for-profit **Works:** full-length plays, translations, adaptations, musicals, screenplays **2nd productions:** "Occasionally." **Specifications:** "Best bet is to keep it all to a minimum." **Stages:** flexible, 99 seats; flexible, 65 seats **Policies:** unsolicited script; query/synopsis; professional recommendation; agent submission **Response:** 3 weeks query; 5-6 months script **Your chances:** 80-90/ 6-8 (stage 1), 15-20 (stage 2) **Remuneration:** negotiable **Programs:** readings, staged readings, development **Advice:** "Keep in mind production costs--tailor show to fit low costs."

APPLE CORPS THEATRE
336 W. 20th St., New York, NY 10011
(212) 929-2955   Contact: Bob Del Pazzo, Literary Manager **Theatre:** off Broadway, professional not-for-profit **Works:** full-length plays, one-acts **Special interest:**

"American plays for totally integrated, multi-ethnic theatre."
Specifications: some limitations on cast size and sets
Stage: proscenium, 175 seats **Audience:** "Middle-class
urban, wide age range, educated." **Policies:** query/synopsis;
agent submission **Response:** 1-2 weeks query; time varies
script **Your chances:** "many/very few" **Remuneration:**
percentage **Programs:** readings, staged readings, workshop
productions, development **Comment:** "We are currently not
producing and are not sure of our upcoming season."

ARENA PLAYERS REPERTORY COMPANY OF LONG ISLAND
296 Rte. 109, E. Farmingdale, NY 11735
(516) 293-0674 Contact: Audrey Perry, Literary
Manager **Theatre:** professional not-for-profit **Works:**
full-length plays **Maximum cast:** 12 mainstage, 6 2nd stage
Stages: arena, 240 seats; arena, 100 seats **Policy:**
unsolicited script **Response:** 3 months **Your chances:**
130/3-4 **Remuneration:** $600-$1000, a video and
reviews from *New York Times* and *Newsday*

ARENA STAGE
6th and Maine SW, Washington, DC 20024
(202) 554-9066 Contact: Gerard Manning, Literary
Associate **Theatre:** professional not-for-profit **Works:**
full-length plays, one-acts, translations, adaptations, musicals
2nd productions: yes **Tours:** "Occasionally." **Stages:**
end thrust; arena; cabaret **Policies:** query/synopsis with
dialogue sample and resume; professional recommendation;
agent submission; unsolicited script from local playwright only
Best time: summer-fall **Response:** 4 weeks query; 6
weeks script **Your chances:** 600/4 plus 4-5 staged readings
Remuneration: "Yes. Depends." **Programs:** readings,
staged readings, development

ARIZONA THEATRE COMPANY
Box 1631, Tucson, AZ 85702   (602) 884-8210
Contact: Director, New Play Program **Theatre:**
professional not-for-profit **Works:** full-length plays,
translations, adaptations, musicals **Exclusive interests:**
"Plays that are written by playwrights from the
Arizona-Southwest region or deal with subjects directly

connected to this area." **Stages:** proscenium, 526 seats; thrust, 300 seats **Policy:** query/synopsis with 10-page dialogue sample and resume **Best time:** spring-summer **Response:** 3-4 months **Remuneration:** fee, travel, housing for staged readings **Comment:** "Because of the termination of the funding for our New Play Program, we no longer accept unsolicited scripts. Our search for new plays will continue, but only through our collaboration with a few organizations able to provide us with scripts that have already gone through some developmental process."

THE ARKANSAS ARTS CENTER CHILDREN'S THEATRE
Box 2137, Little Rock, AR 72203 (501) 372-4000
Contact: Bradley D. Anderson, Artistic Director **Theatre:** professional not-for-profit **Works:** full-length plays, one-acts, translations, adaptations, children's plays **Special interests:** works suitable for family audiences; adaptations of classics **Tours:** yes **Stage:** proscenium, 389 seats **Policy:** unsolicited script **Response:** 6 months

ARKANSAS REPERTORY THEATRE
712 E. 11th St., Little Rock, AR 72202
(501) 378-0405 Contact: Lynn Frazier, Business Manager **Theatre:** professional not-for-profit **Works:** full-length plays, one-acts, translations, adaptations, musicals **2nd productions:** yes **Tours:** yes **Stage:** flexible **Policies:** unsolicited script; query/synopsis; professional recommendation; agent submission **Response:** 2 weeks query; 3-6 months script **Your chances:** 200/1 **Program:** readings

ARROW ROCK LYCEUM THEATRE
Main St., Arrow Rock, MO 65320 (816) 837-3311
Contact: Michael Bollinger, Artistic Producing Director **Theatre:** professional not-for-profit **Works:** full-length plays, translations, adaptations, musicals **2nd productions:** "Not generally; however, a staged reading or non-professional production is okay." **Special interest:** "Plays dealing with or relating to rural and/or small-town America . . . in theme, values and/or setting." **Specifications:** maximum cast: 12 or fewer preferred; "the fewer sets the better"

Tours: "At times." **Stage:** proscenium-thrust **Audience:** "Diverse; there tend to be more patrons from 45+, basically caucasian, rurally based." **Policies:** unsolicited script with resume; query/synopsis with resume; professional recommendation; agent submission **Best time:** Oct.-Feb. **Response:** 1 month query; 2-5 months script **Your chances:** 300/1 **Remuneration:** "Generally $1000 award, possible production with transportation to final rehearsals and opening." **Programs:** On Themes of Rural America (see Contests); Lyceum Airwaves Theatre (radio theatre; inquire)

ART & WORK ENSEMBLE
870 6th Ave., New York, NY 10009
(212) 213-0231 Contact: Gary Garrison, Literary Manager **Theatre:** off Broadway **Works:** full-length plays, one-acts, translations, adaptations **2nd productions:** if New York premieres **Stage:** flexible, 50-90 seats **Audience:** "Mixed audience of New Yorkers; special appeal to senior citizens." **Policies:** unsolicited script with resume; query/synopsis with resume **Response:** 1 month script **Your chances:** 60-70/4 **Remuneration:** "No. Possibly in the future." **Programs:** staged readings, workshop productions; contest planned for future **Advice:** "Write on topics that are relevant to today's society." **Comment:** "We have two playwrights who write for the theatre, and we commission their works."

ARTISTS UNLIMITED
New York, NY Our 1989 questionnaire was returned as "undeliverable," and no phone number is listed for this theatre.

ARTREACH TOURING THEATRE
3074 Madison Rd., Cincinnati, OH 45209
(513) 871-2300 Contact: Dain Paige, Associate **Theatre:** professional not-for-profit **Works:** children's plays **2nd productions:** yes **Special interests:** "Cultural, historical or contemporary situations." **Specifications:** maximum cast: 3; all sets must tour **Stages:** flexible, school spaces **Audience:** children, K-12 **Policies:** unsolicited script with resume; query/synopsis with resume; professional recommendation **Best time:** Jan. **Response:** 2-3 weeks query; 2-3 months script **Your**

chances: 20/0-1 **Remuneration:** "$10 royalty per performance, approximately 100 performances." **Advice:** "We need plays for children; 3 cast members. No stereotypes or trite stories."

THE ARTS AT ST. ANN'S
157 Montague St., Brooklyn, NY 11201
(718) 834-8794 Contact: Janine Nichols, Production Manager **Theatre:** professional not-for-profit **Works:** full-length plays **2nd productions:** "On occasion." **Special interests:** "Inter-cultural relations; American culture and politics." **Specifications:** "Small, informal loft space; limitations on lighting, sets, seating, cast size." **Tours:** "Not so far." **Stages:** church sanctuary, 650 seats; loft, 120 seats **Audience:** "We do such a variety of work that our audience changes all the time. Mostly residents of Brooklyn or lower Manhattan, college-educated, black and white, all ages." **Policy:** inquire **Best time:** spring **Response:** 3 months **Your chances:** 12/1-2 **Advice:** "Keep it simple!" **Comment:** "We often continue to present the work of an artist we are interested in."

ARVADA CENTER FOR THE ARTS AND HUMANITIES
c/o Anne Soerensen, Director of Education, Young Adults Drama Camp, 6901 Wadsworth Blvd., Arvada, CO 80003 (303) 431-3080 Theatre: community/non-professional, educational **Works:** one-acts, children's plays **2nd productions:** yes **Maximum cast:** 8-10 **Stage:** thrust **Policy:** unsolicited script **Best time:** winter **Remuneration:** $25 **Advice:** "We desperately need material for teen-aged actors--usually more girls than boys." **Comment:** Theatre normally receives 15-20 scripts each year.

ASIAN AMERICAN THEATER COMPANY
Ft. Mason Center Bldg. B, San Francisco, CA 94123 (415) 346-8922 Contact: Dom Magwili, Artistic Director **Theatre:** professional not-for-profit **Works:** full-length plays **Special interest:** "Works by and about Asian Americans." **Stage:** flexible **Policy:** inquire **Best time:** Jun.-Sept. **Program:** staged readings

ASOLO STATE THEATER
Postal Drawer E, Sarasota, FL 33578
(813) 355-7115 Contact: John Gulley, Literary Manager
Theatre: professional not-for-profit, LORT **Works:** full-length plays, children's plays **2nd productions:** "Sometimes." **Tours:** yes **Stages:** black box, 100 seats; proscenium, 317 seats **Audience:** "Very broad range." **Policy:** query/synopsis **Best time:** Aug. **Response:** immediate query; 6-8 weeks script **Your chances:** 500/1-2 **Remuneration:** "Yes. Negotiable." **Program:** Asolo Touring Theatre Commissions (see Special Programs)

ASSOCIATED CHILDREN'S THEATRE OF SCOTTSDALE
Scottsdale, AZ See A Contemporary Theater Southwest.

ATLANTIC & PACIFIC RENAISSANCE THEATRE
1000 Westgate Ave., Los Angeles, CA 90049
(213) 826-8807 Contact: Mitchell Nestor, Literary Manager **Theatre:** off off Broadway, professional not-for-profit **Works:** full-length plays **2nd productions:** no **Special interest:** commercial works **Specifications:** small cast, single set **Stages:** proscenium, 99 seats; thrust, 99 seats **Audience:** general **Policies:** unsolicited script; professional recommendation; agent submission **Response:** 3 months **Your chances:** 296/6 **Remuneration:** "Only if sold as film material." **Programs:** workshop productions, development **Advice:** "Write plays that can be made into films."

ATLANTIC COMMUNITY COLLEGE THEATRE
Walter Edge Hall, Mays Landing, NJ 08330
(609) 343-5040 Contact: John Pekich or Kathie Brown **Theatre:** professional not-for-profit, university/college **Works:** one-acts **2nd productions:** no **Special interest:** "New plays by Southern New Jersey playwrights residing within a 100-mile radius of Atlantic City." **Maximum cast:** 8 **Tours:** "Showcased." **Stage:** proscenium, 444 seats **Policy:** call issued for scripts **Best time:** Sept.-Jan. **Response:** 2 weeks query; 6 month script **Your chances:** 20-40/6 **Remuneration:** "All plays are videotaped; playwright receives a copy." **Programs:** staged

readings, classes, Atlantic Community College Playwrights Weekend (see Contests) **Advice:** "There are no factors or limitations considered when selecting plays. The play, on its own merit, is selected." **Comment:** "1st year, script-in-hand reading; 2nd year, full production."

AT THE FOOT OF THE MOUNTAIN
2000 S. 5th St., Minneapolis, MN 55454
(612) 375-9487 Contact: Rebecca Rice, Co-Artistic Director **Theatre:** professional not-for-profit **Works:** full-length plays, one-acts, musicals **2nd productions:** yes **Special interests:** "Plays by and about women, particularly women of color; experimental works." **Specifications:** small cast, preferably female; simple set **Stage:** black box, 90 seats **Audience:** "Young professionals, artists, educators, feminists, blacks, ages 20-50." **Policies:** query/synopsis; agent submission **Response:** 3 weeks query; 4-6 months script **Your chances:** 200/1 **Remuneration:** "Royalty based on performances." **Programs:** see listing in Special Programs

ATTIC THEATRE
Box 02457, Detroit, MI 48202 (313) 875-8285
Contact: Ron Martell, Associate Artistic Director **Theatre:** professional not-for-profit **Works:** full-length plays, musicals **2nd productions:** yes **Specifications:** simple sets **Tours:** "Possibly." **Stage:** proscenium, 299 seats **Audience:** "Adventurous and demanding . . . expect productions with impact and substance." **Policy:** query/synopsis **Best time:** Jan.-May **Response:** 3 weeks if interested in query; 3-5 months script **Your chances:** 50-60/1-3 **Remuneration:** "Negotiable, usually royalty." **Programs:** staged readings, residencies

BACK ALLEY THEATRE
15231 Burbank Blvd., Van Nuys, CA 91411
(818) 780-2240 Contact: Laura Zucker, Producing Director **Theatre:** professional not-for-profit **Works:** full-length plays, translations, adaptations, musicals **2nd productions:** yes **Special interests:** "Human concerns, emotion." **Tours:** yes **Stage:** proscenium, 93 seats

Policy: agent submission **Response:** 4 months **Your chances:** 400/4 **Remuneration:** "Royalty percentage."

BACKSTAGE THEATRE
Breckenridge, CO This theatre has requested that we discontinue its listing.

BAILIWICK REPERTORY
3212 N. Broadway, Chicago, IL 60657
(312) 883-1090 Contact: David Zak, Executive Director **Theatre:** professional not-for-profit **Works:** full-length plays, adaptations, musicals **2nd productions:** yes **Stage:** thrust **Policies:** unsolicited script; query/synopsis; professional recommendation **Best time:** winter **Response:** 3 months **Remuneration:** "Royalty fee similar to standard leasing fees." **Program:** directors' collective (inquire) **Comment:** Theatre produces 1 new play each season.

BAINBRIDGE PERFORMING ARTS
Box 10554, Bainbridge Island, WA 98110
(206) 842-8569 Contact: Susan Glass Burdick, Artistic Director **Theatre:** community/non-professional **Works:** full-length plays, one-acts, translations, adaptations, musicals, children's plays **2nd productions:** "We haven't yet, but it's not out of the question." **Special interests:** "A wide spectrum: children-teen-family-adult." **Specifications:** maximum cast: 50; "budget limits are large scale" **Tours:** yes **Stage:** flexible, 200+ seats **Audience:** "Varies according to project." **Policies:** unsolicited script with resume; query/synopsis with dialogue sample and resume; professional recommendation; agent submission; commission **Best time:** fall-winter **Your chances:** 10-20/2+ **Remuneration:** "Unless the production is a workshop/staged reading, we try to pay a minimum royalty." **Programs:** readings, staged readings, workshop productions, development, internships, classes, contests (inquire)

BALDWIN THEATRE
336 West End Ave, New York, NY 10023
Contact: Anita Sorel, Artistic Director This theatre is looking for a new home and is not producing in 1989.

THE BARBARA BARONDESS THEATRE LAB
281 Ninth Ave., New York, NY 10001
Contact: Leslie Hoban Blake, Director **Theatre:** professional not-for-profit **Works:** full-length plays **2nd productions:** no **Special interest:** traditional, well-made plays **Maximum cast:** 6 **Policy:** query/synopsis with resume **Response:** 1 month query; 3 months script

BARKSDALE THEATRE
Box 7, Hanover, VA 23064   (703) 537-5333
Contact: Muriel McCauley, Producer **Theatre:** non-Equity dinner **Works:** full-length plays, musicals **2nd productions:** yes **Special interests:** comedies, farces, musicals, dramas **Specifications:** simple set **Policy:** unsolicited script **Comment:** Theatre is separate from dining room.

BARN PLAYERS
Box 713, Shawnee Mission, KS 66201
(913) 381-4004 Contact: Don Ramsey, President, Board of Directors **Theatre:** community/non-professional **Works:** full-length plays, one-acts, musicals **Specifications:** simple production requirements **Tours:** "Senior Acting Troupe tours church groups and nursing homes and other organizations; about 200 performances a year. The Seniors perform one-acts and a musical review. One-acts are generally light comedies or warm dramas." **Stage:** 1/3 arena, 238 seats **Audience:** "35+, upper mid-income, college educated, professional; audience is expanding to include children and young families." **Policy:** unsolicited script **Best time:** before Sept. 15 **Response:** 4-6 weeks **Remuneration:** $500 prize, possible playwriting seminar with stipend during run of show **Your chances:** 30/1 **Program:** Barn Players Playwrighting Contest (see Contests) **Comment:** See Senior Acting Program of the Barn Players listing in this section.

BARTER THEATRE
Box 867, Abingdon, VA 24210   (703) 628-2281
Contact: Rex Partington, Producing Director **Theatre:** professional not-for-profit **Works:** full-length plays, translations, adaptations, children's plays **2nd productions:** yes **Special interests:** social issues, current events **Specifications:** cast of 4-12; single or unit set **Stages:**

proscenium, 394 seats; thrust, 150 seats **Policy:** unsolicited script **Best times:** Mar., Sept. **Response:** 6-9 months

BERKELEY REPERTORY THEATRE
2025 Addison St., Berkeley, CA 94704
(415) 841-6108 Contact: Sharon Ott, Artistic Director **Theatre:** professional not-for-profit **Works:** full-length plays, one-acts, translations, adaptations, children's plays **2nd productions:** yes **Special interest:** "Plays whose imaginary worlds are fully realized, but which have resonance for larger society." **Specifications:** maximum cast: 18; no fly space **Tours:** "Educational shows." **Stage:** thrust, 400 seats, "various capacities and configurations" **Audience:** "Large multi-cultural urban area with broad education and sophistication." **Policies:** professional recommendation; agent submission **Your chances:** 300/1-2 **Remuneration:** varies

BERKELEY SHAKESPEARE FESTIVAL
Box 969, Berkeley, CA 94701   (415) 548-3422
Contact: Michael Addison, Artistic Director **Theatre:** professional **Works:** full-length plays, translations, adaptations **Exclusive interest:** "Shakespeare--in theme, subject, structure." **Stage:** Elizabethan, 350 seats **Policy:** query/synopsis **Response:** 1 month query; 3 months script

BERKSHIRE PUBLIC THEATRE
30 Union St., Box 860, Pittsfield, MA 01202
(413) 445-4631 Contact: Bruce MacDonald, Associate Director **Theatre:** professional not-for-profit **Works:** full-length plays, translations, adaptations, musicals, children's plays, small operas/musicals **2nd productions:** yes **Maximum cast:** 10 plus extras **Tours:** yes **Stage:** proscenium, 300 seats **Policies:** unsolicited script with resume; query/synopsis with resume; professional recommendation; agent submission **Response:** 1 month query; 4 months script **Your chances:** 75/"ususally none; 2 to date" **Remuneration:** "Sometimes." **Program:** development

BERKSHIRE THEATRE FESTIVAL
Box 797, Stockbridge, MA 01262   (413) 298-5536
Contact: Richard Dunlap, Artistic Director **Theatre:** professional not-for-profit **Works:** full-length plays,

musicals **2nd productions:** yes **Specifications:** maximum cast: 12; small orchestra for musical; simple set preferred **Stages:** proscenium, 429 seats; thrust, 99 seats **Policy:** agent submission **Best time:** Nov.–Dec. **Response:** 6 months **Your chances:** 60/1–2 **Remuneration:** yes **Program:** readings

THE BILINGUAL FOUNDATION OF THE ARTS
421 N. Ave. 19, Los Angeles, CA 90031
(213) 225–4044 Contact: Margarita Galban, Artistic Director **Theatre:** professional not-for-profit **Works:** full-length plays, one-acts, translations, adaptations, musicals, children's plays **2nd productions:** no **Exclusive interest:** Hispanic authors or subjects **Specifications:** maximum cast: 15; simple set **Stage:** thrust, 99 seats **Policy:** unsolicited script **Response:** 3 months

BLOOMINGTON PLAYWRIGHTS PROJECT
409 S. Walnut St. #15, Bloomington, IN 47401
(812) 332–0822 Contact: Rita Kniess, Literary Manager **Theatre:** not-for-profit **Works:** full-length plays, one-acts, monologues, "half-acts" **2nd productions:** no **Specifications:** maximum cast: 15; simple sets; small space **Stage:** flexible **Audience:** "Young adults: college students, local community." **Policy:** unsolicited script **Best time:** by Oct. 15, 1989 **Response:** 2 months **Your chances:** 40/12 **Remuneration:** royalty for full-length play **Programs:** readings, staged readings, workshop productions, development, Bloomington Playwrights Project Contest (see Contests) **Comment:** Local playwrights are preferred.

BLOOMSBURG THEATRE ENSEMBLE
Box 66, Bloomsburg, PA 17815   (717) 784–5530
Contact: Rand Whipple, New Scripts Coordinator **Theatre:** professional not-for-profit **Works:** full-length plays, translations, adaptations **2nd productions:** "Not yet. We hope to in future." **Maximum cast:** 6 **Stage:** proscenium, 369 seats **Audience:** "We live and create in a rural, small, university town. Our audience is largely professional and on the conservative side." **Policy:** query/synopsis **Response:** 2 months **Remuneration:** negotiable contract **Comments:**

"In 10 years we've done 5 new plays. When we finally get our new stage going, we hope to improve this ratio." See McGovern, Michael. "Grassroots Actor-Managers: The Bloomsburg Theater Ensemble" (*Theater Week*, Oct. 17, 1988), 34-39.

BLUE ISLAND PARK DISTRICT SHOWCASE THEATER
12757 South Western, Blue Island, IL 60406
(312) 388-0482 Contact: Dan Flynn, Producer **Theatre:** community/non-professional **Works:** full-length plays, one-acts, translations, adaptations, musicals **2nd productions:** yes **Maximum cast:** 12 **Tours:** some shows **Stages:** thrust—4 staging areas, 2 side stages **Audience:** "Loyal; 300 season subscribers." **Policy:** unsolicited script **Your chances:** 2-3/1 **Remuneration:** no **Programs:** workshop productions, classes

BOARSHEAD: MICHIGAN PUBLIC THEATER
425 S. Grand Ave., Lansing, MI 48933
(517) 484-7800 Contact: John Peakes, Artistic Director **Theatre:** professional not-for-profit **Works:** full-length plays, one-acts, translations, adaptations **2nd productions:** yes **Special interests:** "The Midwest; social issues." **Maximum cast:** 10 **Stage:** thrust, 249 seats **Audience:** "Average America." **Policies:** unsolicited script; query/ synopsis with sas postcard; professional recommendation; agent submission **Response:** 1 month query; 3-9 months script **Your chances:** 300/7-9 **Remuneration:** "It depends upon our budget." **Programs:** readings, staged readings **Adivce:** "A full page or two of synopsis and 3 or 4 pages of dialogue."

BODY POLITIC THEATRE
2261 N. Lincoln Ave., Chicago, IL 60614
(312) 348-7901 Contact: Pauline Brailsford, Artistic Director **Theatre:** professional not-for-profit **Works:** full-length plays, one-acts **Special interest:** works suitable for ensemble company **Specifications:** maximum cast: 10, fewer than 8 preferred; single set **Stage:** 3/4 thrust, 192 seats **Policy:** query/synopsis **Response:** 6

months query; 1 year script **Program:** staged readings of new works by authors not known to the Chicago area

BOND STREET THEATRE
2 Bond St., New York, NY 10012   (212) 254-4614
Contact: Joanna M. Sherman, Artistic Director **Theatre:** off off Broadway, professional not-for-profit, touring **Works:** full-length plays, adaptations **Special interest:** "Material of political/social significance, satirical but not didactic." **Specifications:** no "sit-coms" **Tours:** yes **Stages:** "Vary." **Audience:** "Varies considerably; for touring, often non-English speaking." **Policies:** query/synopsis with "artistic point of view"; professional recommendation **Best time:** Oct.-Apr. **Response:** 2 months **Your chances:** 12/1 **Remuneration:** varies **Programs:** staged readings, workshop productions, Palenville Interarts Colony (see Special Programs) **Comment:** "We are a 12-year-old ensemble of 7 highly physically trained actors. Our work is always provocative, stylized to present a heightened reality."

BOSTON POST ROAD STAGE COMPANY
Box 38, Fairfield, CT 06430 (203) 255-4122
Contact: Douglas Moser, Artistic Director **Theatre:** professional not-for-profit **Works:** full-length plays **Maximum cast:** 10 **Stage:** thrust, 100 seats **Policy:** query/synopsis **Best time:** Jun.-Aug. **Response:** 3 weeks query; 1-3 months script

BOSTON SHAKESPEARE COMPANY
17 Harcourt St., Boston, MA 02116
(617) 267-5600 Contact: Stanley Richardson, Literary Manager **Theatre:** professional not-for-profit **Works:** full-length plays, one-acts, translations, adaptations **2nd productions:** yes **Special interests:** "Politics, history, ideas, the social contract." **Stages:** thrust, arena, flexible--99-200 and 399-699 seats **Policies:** query/synopsis; professional recommendation; agent submission **Best time:** Sept.-Jun. **Response:** 1 month query; 5 months script **Remuneration:** varies **Programs:** staged readings, workshop productions, development, internships **Advice:** "Focus on ideas, language. Forget

psychological motivations. Care." **Comment:** Theatre produces 6 plays "of various sorts" each season.

BRIDGE ARTS THEATRE COMPANY
113 Prince St., New York, NY 10012 Contact: Gibson Glass, Artistic Director This theatre is not accepting submissions in 1989.

BRIGHAM YOUNG THEATRE & FILM DEPARTMENT
BYU, D-581 HFAC, Provo, UT 84602
(801) 378-4574 Contact: Max Golightly, Professor, Theatre/Film **Theatre:** university/college **Works:** full-length plays, one-acts, translations, adaptations, musicals, children's plays **2nd productions:** yes **Specifications:** "Depends on theatre and space requirements." **Tours:** yes **Stages:** proscenium; arena; flexible **Audience:** "50% students, faculty and staff; 50% townspeople; conservative, primarily white middle class." **Policy:** unsolicited script **Best time:** fall **Response:** "Depends on time script is received." **Your chances:** 15/3 **Remuneration:** "Depends on production, record and theatre used." **Programs:** development, classes **Advice:** "Plays should be suitable for family audiences."

BRISTOL RIVERSIDE THEATRE
Box 1250, Bristol, PA 19007 (215) 785-6664
Contact: Robert K. O'Neill, Managing Director **Theatre:** professional not-for-profit **Works:** full-length plays, one-acts, translations, adaptations, musicals **2nd productions:** yes **Special interests:** "Topical, biographical, historical and socially relevant plays." **Specifications:** maximum cast: 7-10; single set; "no dead baby, abortion or excessively sexual themes; no excessive foul language" **Tours:** yes **Stages:** proscenium, 302 seats; black box, 60 seats **Audience:** "Broad cross-section from affluent to blue collar." **Policies:** query/synopsis with dialogue sample and resume preferred; unsolicited script; professional recommendation; agent submission **Response:** 1 month query; 3-4 months script **Your chances:** 250/5 on main stage, 4 in black box, 20-25 staged readings **Remuneration:** "Percentage and consideration for future production."

Programs: readings, staged readings, workshop productions, development, classes, internships **Comment:** "The Bristol Riverside Theatre was founded on the principle of developing new American plays and playwrights, and freshly interpreting often overlooked plays which seem appropriate for our cooperative artistry."

BROADWAY TOMORROW MUSICAL THEATRE
191 Claremont Ave. Suite 53, New York, NY 10027
(212) 864-4736 Contact: Elyse Curtis, Artistic Director
Theatre: off off Broadway, professional not-for-profit
Works: musicals, musical adaptations **Exclusive interest:** "Wholesome material." **Specifications:** "Writers must be residents of Metropolitan New York area or able to spend time in the city." **Stage:** proscenium, 99 seats **Audience:** general **Policy:** unsolicited script with synopsis, resume and cassette of music **Response:** 6 months **Your chances:** 50/8 **Remuneration:** "Standard Dramatists Guild Off Broadway contract if first-class production." **Programs:** readings, staged readings, workshop productions, marketing and producing seminars **Advice:** "Submit uplifting material."

BROKEN ARROW COMMUNITY PLAYHOUSE
Box 452, Broken Arrow, OK 74013
(918) 258-0077 Contact: Joyce Polkinghorne, Board of Operations **Theatre:** community non/professional **Works:** full-length plays, musicals, children's plays **2nd productions:** no **Maximum cast:** 35 **Stage:** thrust **Audience:** "White collar, family." **Policy:** unsolicited script **Response:** time varies **Advice:** "We work with guest directors--we are weak in tech, would hope to have as many ideas on set, costuming and lighting as possible." **Comment:** Theatre hopes to produce 1 new play each year.

BROOKLYN PLAYWORKS
295 Douglass St., Brooklyn, NY 11217
(718) 875-4408 Contact: David Ravel, Literary Manager **Theatre:** off off Broadway **Works:** full-length plays **2nd productions:** "Rarely." **Special interests:** "Plays that fully exploit the values unique to live performance. Don't send plays that could just as easily be done for movies or television. Don't send plays that are about any sort of therapy

or have couches in them." **Specifications:** maximum cast: 10, character age range 20-40 preferred; unit or single set preferred; "we like to create environmental sets" **Tours:** "Rarely." **Stage:** black box, 75 seats **Audience:** "New York City; sophisticated culturally, politically." **Policies:** unsolicited script preferred; query/synopsis; professional recommendation **Best time:** Mar.-Apr. **Response:** 2 months query; 4-6 months script **Your chances:** 500/4-5 plus 12-16 staged readings **Remuneration:** $100 advance against 5% of box office." **Programs:** readings, staged readings, development **Advice:** "If you are in the Tri-State (NY, NJ, CT) area, come to a production and see if our work is compatible with yours before sending a script."

BROOKLYN THEATRE ENSEMBLE
c/o Matthew Paris, Director, 850 E. 31st St. Apt. C-6, Brooklyn, NY 11210 (718) 258-5367 Theatre: community/non-professional **Works:** one-acts **2nd productions:** yes **Special interest:** "Brooklyn material." **Specifications:** maximum cast: 5; single set **Stage:** flexible **Audience:** "All kinds." **Policy:** unsolicited script **Response:** 3 months **Your chances:** 10/2 **Remuneration:** no **Advice:** "Make it related to Brooklyn."

BROWN GRAND THEATRE
310 W. 6th St., Concordia, KS 66901 (913) 243-2553 Contact: Susan L. Sutton, President **Theatre:** community/non-professional **Works:** full-length plays, translations, adaptations, musicals, children's plays **2nd productions:** "Possibly." **Special interest:** "Works relevant to the audience and region." **Specifications:** "Cast size and sets within reason." **Tours:** yes **Stage:** proscenium **Audience:** "Midwestern, rural." **Policies:** unsolicited script; query/synopsis **Best time:** fall-winter **Response:** 6 weeks **Remuneration:** "Possibly." **Advice:** "Submit scripts. Just because our in-house performing group has not produced original scripts, that doesn't mean it won't."

BURBAGE THEATRE ENSEMBLE
10508 W. Pico Blvd., Los Angeles, CA 90064
(213) 478-0897 Contact: Ivan Spiegel, Artistic Director
Theatre: professional not-for-profit **Works:** full-length plays, one-acts, musicals **2nd productions:** yes **Special interests:** social issues; avant garde, stylized work for ensemble company **Specifications:** minimal set preferred **Stages:** thrust, 99 seats; flexible, 49 seats **Audience:** "People who like well-written plays." **Policies:** query/ synopsis; professional recommendation; agent submission **Response:** 1 month query; 6 months script **Your chances:** 200/2 **Remuneration:** negotiable **Program:** readings

THE CABARET THEATRE
Mason Gross School of the Arts,
Rutgers University, New Brunswick, NJ 08903
(201) 246-0341 Contact: Ruth K. Zielinski, Producer
Theatre: university/college **Works:** full-length plays, one-acts, adaptations, musicals **2nd productions:** yes **Special interest:** comedies **Specifications:** maximum cast: 15, 8-10 co-ed, preferred; relatively simple, single set preferred; "manageable number of props" **Stage:** flexible, 90 seats **Audience:** "Mainly university students, co-ed, some members of surrounding community; basically open minded, like to be entertained." **Policy:** query/synopsis with dialogue sample **Best times:** Oct.-Nov., Mar.-Apr. **Response:** 21 days query; 30 days script **Remuneration:** no **Program:** staged readings

CALDWELL THEATRE COMPANY
Boca Raton, FL This theatre has requested that we discontinue its listing.

CALIFORNIA THEATRE CENTER
Box 2007, Sunnyvale, CA 94087 (408) 245-2979
Contact: Will Huddleston, Resident Director **Theatre:** professional not-for-profit **Works:** children's plays **2nd productions:** yes **Specifications:** cast of 3-7; single set; works must be no more than 1 hour in length and suitable for touring **Tours:** local, national, international **Stage:** proscenium, 200 seats **Audience:** "Children of all ages." **Policy:** unsolicited script **Best time:** Sept.-May

Response: 3-4 months **Your chances:** 75-100/"1 for this coming season" **Remuneration:** yes **Advice:** "Plays which can work in a variety of venues are best. Plays which do not require extensive technical effects are also appreciated."

CAPITAL REPERTORY COMPANY
Box 399, Albany, NY 12201 (518) 462-4531
Contact: Stephen Spoonamore, Literary Manager **Theatre:** professional not-for-profit **Works:** full-length plays, translations, adaptations, chamber musicals **2nd productions:** yes **Special interests:** "Plays studying what man can be, or ought to be. Puzzle plays." **Specifications:** maximum cast: 10-12; small-scale musicals only; no 3-story sets; no fly space **Stage:** thrust, 258 seats **Audience:** "Intelligent, good theatre-goers, willing to listen." **Policy:** query/synopsis with 5-10 page dialogue sample, "include write-ups of any previous productions or readings" **Response:** 3-4 months **Your chances:** 400+/2 plus 5-6 readings **Remuneration:** royalty **Programs:** readings, staged readings, internships **Advice:** "We are looking for anything we haven't seen."

CARAVAN THEATRE COMPANY, INC.
377 Broome St. Apt. 15, New York, NY 10013
(212) 431-7962 Contact: Peter Hodges, Artistic Director **Theatre:** not-for-profit **Works:** full-length plays **2nd productions:** "If New York premieres." **Specifications:** "No sit-coms." **Stages:** rented spaces **Audience:** "Young." **Policy:** query/synopsis with resume and reviews of previous productions **Response:** 6 months if interested in query **Your chances:** 15/2 **Remuneration:** no **Program:** development **Advice:** "We want to develop a core of actors, playwrights and directors to work within a similar set of ideas."

CARROLL COLLEGE LITTLE THEATRE
Helena, MT 59625 (406) 442-3450 ext. 308
Contact: Jim Bartruff, Director **Theatre:** university/college **Works:** one-acts, musicals, children's plays **2nd productions:** yes **Specifications:** maximum cast: 20; single set **Stage:** proscenium **Audience:** "College students and townspeople." **Policies:** query/synopsis with resume;

professional recommendation **Best time:** early spring **Response:** 6 weeks **Your chances:** 12-15/0-1 **Remuneration:** "Royalty, maximum $50 per performance."

THE CAST THEATRE
804 El Centro Ave., Hollywood, CA 90038
(213) 462-9872 Contact: Diane Gibson, Literary Manager **Theatre:** professional not-for-profit **Works:** full-length plays, musicals, children's plays, cabaret/revues **2nd productions:** no **Special interest:** world premieres **Maximum cast:** 10 **Stages:** proscenium, 99 seats; proscenium, 65 seats **Policy:** unsolicited script **Response:** 3-4 months **Programs:** readings, staged readings

CELEBRATION THEATRE
1765 N. Highland Ave. #536, Hollywood, CA 90028
(213) 876-4257 Contact: Michael McClellan, Dramaturg **Theatre:** professional not-for-profit **Works:** full-length plays, one-acts, translations, adaptations, musicals **Exclusive interest:** "Plays which present gay/lesbian life in a positive way." **Specifications:** maximum cast: 6; simple sets; no complex lighting or sound effects **Tours:** yes **Stages:** arena, 45 seats; flexible **Audience:** "All adults are welcome, but our audience consists mostly of gay and lesbian people." **Your chances:** 50/5 **Programs:** readings, staged readings, workshop productions, development, internships, classes

CENTER FOR PUPPETRY ARTS
1404 Spring St. NW, Atlanta, 6A 30309
(404) 873-3089 Contact: Playreading Committee **Theatre:** professional not-for-profit **Works:** full-length plays, one-acts, translations, adaptations, musicals, children's plays, avant garde, performance art **Tours:** yes **Stages:** proscenium, 223 seats; flexible, 75 seats **Audience:** "Adult puppetry; adventurous." **Policy:** unsolicited script **Response:** 6-8 weeks **Your chances:** 10-12/"none so far, because they have not been suitable to the puppetry meduim" **Remuneration:** royalty **Programs:** workshop productions, internships **Advice:** "Play needs to be suitable for puppets or a combination of puppets and live actors."

CENTER STAGE
700 N. Calvert St., Baltimore, MD 21202
(301) 685-3200 Contact: Rick Davis, Resident Dramaturg **Theatre:** professional not-for-profit **Works:** full-length plays, one-acts, translations, adaptations **2nd productions:** yes **Stage:** modified thrust, 541 seats **Audience:** "Approximately 13,000 subscribers of diverse tastes and interests." **Policies:** query/synopsis with dialogue sample and resume; professional recommendation; agent submission **Response:** 2-4 weeks query; 2-4 months script **Remuneration:** negotiable **Your chances:** 300/varying number **Programs:** readings, staged readings **Advice:** "Please think carefully before considering Center Stage as a venue for your work; take a moment to review our recent production history and our various statements of artistic policy that are on public record."

CENTER THEATER
1346 W. Devon, Chicago, IL 60660 (312) 508-0200
Contact: Hilary Hammond, Literary Manager **Theatre:** professional not-for-profit **Works:** full-length plays, one-acts, adaptations **Special interests:** comedy; heightened reality; language **Specifications:** maximum cast: 15; equal number of male/female roles preferred; limited wing space; no fly space **Stages:** modified thrust, 75 seats; black box, 35 seats **Policy:** professional recommendation **Best time:** summer **Response:** 1-2 months **Programs:** Center Theater Youtheatre Program: workshop productions (see Special Programs); Playreading Project: staged readings of 6 plays (inquire)

CHAGRIN VALLEY LITTLE THEATRE
40 River St., Chagrin Falls, OH 44022
(216) 247-8955 Contact: Rollin DeVere, Literary Manager **Theatre:** community/non-professional **Works:** full-length plays, one-acts, translations, adaptations, musicals, children's plays **2nd productions:** no **Specifications:** maximum cast: 10; single or unit set **Stage:** proscenium, 66 seats **Policies:** unsolicited script; query/synopsis **Response:** 1 month query; 2-3 months script **Your chances:** 20/1-2 **Remuneration:** no **Advice:** "Good character development, sharp dialogue."

THE CHANGING SCENE
1527 1/2 Champa St., Denver, CO 80202
(303) 893-5775 **Contact:** Alfred Brooks, President
Theatre: professional not-for-profit **Works:** full-length plays, one-acts **2nd productions:** no **Special interest:** unconventional works **Specifications:** small cast, simple set **Stage:** flexible, 76 seats **Policy:** unsolicited script **Response:** 6 weeks-6 months **Your chances:** 100/6 in Theatre Workshop **Remuneration:** "We share box office receipts with participants." **Advice:** "We try to avoid naturalistic plays."

CHECK PLEASE PRODUCTIONS
Box 480093, Los Angeles, CA 90048
Contact: April Janow, Producer **Production company:** off off Broadway **Works:** full-length plays, one-acts, improv **2nd productions:** no **Special interest:** comedy **Stages:** "Theatres vary." **Policies:** unsolicited script; query/synopsis; professional recommendation **Response:** 1-3 weeks **Your chances:** 10-75/varying number **Remuneration:** "Possible." **Advice:** "Be flexible with the written word."

CHEYENNE LITTLE THEATRE PLAYERS
Box 1086, Cheyenne, WY 82003 (307) 638-6543
Contact: Linda McVey, Managing Director **Theatre:** community/non-professional **Works:** one-acts **2nd productions:** no **Special interests:** "Every summer CLTP produces a melodrama with an 'Old West' flavor. Generally, these are written locally, but original scripts are welcome from other sources; audience inter-active material." **Specifications:** maximum cast: 15; 1 hour maximum playing time **Stage:** proscenium, 256 seats **Audience:** "Tourists out for a good time." **Policy:** unsolicited script **Best time:** Aug.-Dec. **Your chances:** 3-4/0-1 **Remuneration:** negotiable

CHICAGO MEDIEVAL PLAYERS
International House, 1414 E. 59th St.,
Chicago, IL 60637 (312) 491-9516
Contact: Ann Faulkner, General Director **Theatre:** professional not-for-profit **Works:** translations, adaptations,

children's plays **2nd productions:** yes **Special interests:** "Medieval and Renaissance material; new renderings of old tales." **Tours:** "Occasionally." **Stages:** arena, flexible—"generally about 100 seats" **Audience:** "Extremely diverse." **Policy:** query/synopsis with dialogue sample **Response:** 1-2 weeks **Remuneration:** negotiable **Advice:** "We are especially looking for 3 things: folk-type and other plays on the early American explorers and colonists to be produced in 1992; an adaptation of *Beowulf*; a pre-1650 Purim play, translation or adaptation." **Comment:** Theatre produces 2 secular and 2 liturgical plays each season.

THE CHICAGO THEATRE COMPANY
Parkway Playhouse, 500 E . 67th St.,
Chicago, IL 60637   (312) 493-1305
Contact: Michael A. Perkins, Artistic Director **Theatre:** professional not-for-profit **Works:** full-length plays, musicals **2nd productions:** yes **Special interests:** African-American plays; experimental plays **Specifications:** maximum cast: 10; single set **Tours:** yes **Stage:** thrust, 100 seats **Audience:** "Mixed ages and races." **Policy:** unsolicited script with synopsis **Best time:** summer **Response:** 1 month **Your chances:** 20-30/2 **Remuneration:** no **Program:** staged readings **Advice:** "Get to know our work." **Comment:** Company has a resident playwright.

THE CHILDREN'S THEATRE COMPANY
2400 Third Ave. S, Minneapolis, MN 55404
(612) 874-0500 Contact: Thomas W. Olson, Literary Editor **Theatre:** professional not-for-profit **Works:** full-length plays, one-acts, translations, adaptations, musicals, children's plays **2nd productions:** yes **Special interests:** "Adaptations of popular classic and contemporary works for young people and families." **Specifications:** maximum cast: 50; no more than 8 sets **Tours:** "Touring productions are drawn from the mainstage productions." **Stages:** proscenium, 745 seats; studio, 80-100 seats **Audience:** "Public performances: 65% adult. 1987-88 Mainstage total: 240,000." **Policy:** unsolicited script **Best time:** Oct.-Apr. **Response:** 5 months **Your chances:** 125/0 **Remuneration:** "Playwrights commissioned receive

fee and percentage." **Program:** workshop productions **Comment:** "Scripts are read for purposes of referrals and familiarization."

CHIMERA THEATRE COMPANY
St. Paul, MN   This theatre is permanently closed.

CHOCOLATE BAYOU THEATER COMPANY
Box 270363, Houston, TX 77277   (713) 528-0070
Contact: Jo Marks, Artistic Director **Theatre:** professional not-for-profit **Works:** full-length plays, one-acts, translations, adaptations, children's plays **2nd productions:** yes **Maximum cast:** 8 **Stage:** modified thrust, 149 seats **Policy:** unsolicited script **Best time:** fall-spring **Response:** 2-6 months **Your chances:** 150/1 **Remuneration:** "Varies." **Programs:** readings, staged readings, workshop productions, development

CINCINNATI PLAYHOUSE IN THE PARK
Box 6537, Cincinnati, OH 45206   (513) 421-5440
Contact: Ara Watson, Playwright-in-Residence/Literary Manager **Theatre:** professional not-for-profit **Works:** full-length plays, translations, adaptations **2nd productions:** yes **Special interests:** "Theatricality, excellent writing." **Stages:** thrust; arena **Audience:** "Every group." **Policies:** unsolicited script with resume and available reviews; professional recommendation; agent submission **Best time:** summer-fall **Response:** 6-9 months **Your chances:** 600/2-3 **Remuneration:** royalty **Program:** Lois and Richard Rosenthal New Play Prize (see Contests) **Advice:** "Absence of the trivial; intelligent, authentic dialogue; characters of substance; compelling situations; language that engages in action."

CIRCA '21 DINNER PLAYHOUSE
Box 784, 1828, Third Ave., Rock Island, IL 61201 (309) 786-2667   Contact: Jennie May Donnell, Director of Children's Theatre **Theatre:** professional not-for-profit **Works:** musicals, children's plays **2nd productions:** yes **Specifications:** maximum cast: 10; 2-act plays must have intermission **Tours:** yes **Stage:** proscenium/thrust, 344 seats **Audience:** conservative, Midwestern **Policies:**

unsolicited script; query/synopsis; professional recommendation **Response:** 6 months **Remuneration:** $500, residency with transportation **Your chances:** 60/"none yet, but we are constantly looking for shows that meet our needs" **Comment:** Theatre holds rights for 2 years.

CIRCLE IN THE SQUARE
1633 Broadway, New York, NY 10019
(212) 307-2700 Contact: Seth Goldman, Literary Advisor **Theatre:** professional not-for-profit **Works:** full-length plays, translations, adaptations **2nd productions:** yes **Stage:** arena, 600 seats **Policies:** agent submission preferred; query/synopsis with dialogue sample and resume; professional recommendation **Response:** 1-2 months query; 9 months script **Comment:** Theatre produces mostly revivals but is open to new plays and receives approximately 200 new scripts each year.

CIRCLE REPERTORY
161 Avenue of the Americas, New York, NY 10013
(212) 691-3210 Contact: B. Rodney Marriott, Associate Artistic Director **Theatre:** professional not-for-profit **Works:** full-length plays **2nd productions:** yes **Special interest:** American authors **Stage:** thrust, 177 seats **Policy:** query/synopsis **Response:** 1 week query; 3 months script **Your chances:** 2000/4-5 **Programs:** staged readings

CITY THEATRE COMPANY
B39 CL, University of Pittsburgh,
Pittsburgh, PA 15260 (412) 624-1357
Contact: Lynne Conner, Literary Manager **Theatre:** professional not-for-profit **Works:** full-length plays, adaptations, small chamber musicals, children's plays **2nd productions:** yes **Special interests:** "New or recent work; socially relevant plays." **Specifications:** maximum cast: 10; no fly space; 20th-century American plays only; "no frivolous comedies or plays that want to be TV pilots" **Tours:** "Only children's plays, which are normally commissioned." **Stage:** thrust, 120 seats **Audience:** "Sophisticated, urban, professional, educated, ages 25-75." **Policies:** query/synopsis with dialogue sample and resume; professional

recommendation; agent submission **Best time:** Sept.-Apr. **Response:** 1 week query; 3 months script **Your chances:** 500/1-2 plus 6-8 staged readings **Remuneration:** percentage **Program:** (TNT) Tuesday Night Theatre (inquire)

THE CLARENCE BROWN COMPANY
UT Box 8450, Knoxville, TN 37996
(615) 974-3447 Contact: Thomas P. Cooke, Producing Director **Theatre:** professional not-for-profit **Works:** translations, adaptations **2nd productions:** yes **Special interests:** classical source material; new Eastern European and Latin American works **Tours:** yes **Stages:** proscenium, 600 seats; arena, 500 seats **Audience:** "From university and community, representing area's demographics." **Policy:** query/synopsis with dialogue sample and resume **Best time:** fall **Response:** 6-8 weeks **Remuneration:** negotiable **Comment:** Theatre receives approximately 30 new scripts each year.

CLAVIS THEATRE
Box 93158, Milwaukee, WI 53203 (414) 272-3043
Contact: Ted Altschuler, Program Director **Theatre:** professional not-for-profit **Works:** full-length plays, one-acts **Special interests:** "Provocative, innovative, fun approaches to contemporary issues"; one-acts for Milwaukee Annual One-Act Festival only (see information below) **Specifications:** for one-acts: maximum cast: 7, maximum playing time: 1 hour **Stage:** flexible, 99 seats **Policies:** query/synopsis preferred for full-length play; unsolicited script for one-act **Best times:** Feb.-Oct. for full-length play; Oct. 1-Dec. 31 only for one-act **Response:** 2 months query; 4 months script **Your chances:** 275/varying number **Remuneration:** "Negotiated on a per-play basis." **Programs:** Milwaukee Annual One-Act Festival: previously unproduced one-acts; readings of full-length plays; residency for collaborative work with company (inquire)

THE CLEVELAND PLAY HOUSE
Box 1989, Cleveland, OH 44106 (216) 795-7010
Contact: Roger T. Danforth, Literary Manager **Theatre:** professional not-for-profit **Works:** full-length plays, translations, adaptations, musicals, children's plays **2nd**

productions: yes **Tours**: pre-Broadway productions and tours; 1 1988-89 show will move to Pasadena Playhouse (see listing in this section) **Stages**: flexible proscenium, 625 seats; proscenium, 499 seats; proscenium, 160 seats; flexible, 80-100 seats **Policy**: agent submission **Response**: 6 months **Your chances**: 500/"1988-89: 6 new plays and/or American premieres" **Programs**: Playwrights Lab Company (inquire)

COCONUT GROVE PLAYHOUSE
3500 Main Hwy., Miami, FL 33133 (305) 442-2662
Contact: Arnold Mittelman, Producing Artistic Director **Theatre**: professional not-for-profit **Works**: full-length plays, musicals **2nd productions**: yes **Special interests**: "Musicals, comedies, mysteries, entertainment value, commercial appeal." **Stages**: proscenium, 1100 seats; second stage, 120 seats **Policy**: agent submission **Best time**: fall-spring **Response**: 2 months

COLDWATER COMMUNITY THEATER
89 Division, Coldwater, MI 49036
(517) 278-2389, -2380 Contact: J. Richard Colbeck, Chairman, Play Selection **Theatre**: community/non-professional **Works**: full-length plays, children's plays **2nd productions**: no **Special interest**: works of interest to Midwesterners **Stage**: proscenium, 500 seats **Policy**: call issued for unsolicited script **Best time**: fall-Nov. 15 **Response**: 2 weeks query; mid-Jan. script **Your chances**: 125/1 **Remuneration**: "Cash prize of $200, housing." **Program**: Robert J. Pickering Award (see Contests)

THE COLONY THEATRE COMPANY/ STUDIO THEATRE PLAYHOUSE
1944 Riverside Dr., Los Angeles, CA 90039
Contact: John Banach, Literary Manager **Theatre**: professional not-for-profit **Works**: full-length plays **2nd productions**: yes **Specifications**: maximum cast: 10; minimal set **Stage**: thrust, 99 seats **Audience**: "Subscriber based, broad range of ages and ethnic backgrounds." **Policy**: request submission guidelines **Response**: 2 weeks query; 6-9 months script **Your chances**: 300/3 **Remuneration**: royalty **Programs**: staged readings, workshop productions

COMMUNITY CHILDREN'S THEATRE

8021 E. 129th Terrace, Grandview, MO 64030
(816) 761-5775   Contact: Mrs. M. E. Sellens, Chairman, Playwriting Award   **Theatre:**   elementary schools/non-professional   **Works:** children's plays, adaptations and musicals   **Specifications:** some limitations on sets   **Tours:** yes   **Stages:** flexible, 300-600 seats   **Audience:** "Grades K-6."   **Policies:** unsolicited script; query/synopsis   **Best time:** Sept.-Dec.   **Response:** Nov. query; Dec. script   **Your chances:** 20-50/1   **Remuneration:** $500 award   **Program:** Margaret Bartle Annual Playwriting Award (see Contests)

THE COMMUNITY THEATRE OF LITTLE ROCK

Little Rock, AR   This theatre did not respond to our 1989 questionnaire, and its phone has been disconnected.

COMPANY OF ANGELS

Hollywood, CA   Our 1989 questionnaire was returned as "undeliverable," and no phone number is listed for this theatre.

COMPANY THEATRE

Box 1324, Cambridge, Ontario, Canada N1R 766
Contact: Linda   Scadron-Wattles,   Literary   Manager **Theatre:** professional not-for-profit   **Works:** full-length plays, one-acts, translations, adaptations, musicals   **2nd productions:** yes   **Exclusive interest:** "Contemporary plays expressing biblical world view."   **Specifications:** maximum cast: 12; no large-scale proscenium productions; "we rarely produce Bible stories"   **Tours:** yes   **Stage:** flexible   **Audience:** "Highly educated; college area: Christians and non-Christians."   **Policies:** query/synopsis; professional recommendation   **Best time:** late spring-early summer **Response:** 1 month query   **Your chances:** 20/2   **Program:** staged readings

CONEY ISLAND, USA

Boardwalk at W. 12th St., Coney Island, NY 11224
(718) 372-5159   Contact: Dick D. Zigun, Artistic Director **Theatre:** professional not-for-profit   **Works:** existing productions of plays and performance-art works   **Special interests:** new and traditional vaudeville; grassroots political works; street theatre   **Stages:** arena, 150 seats; cabaret, 200

seats; open-air spaces (streets, beach, boardwalk) **Policy**: inquire **Response**: 1 month letter; 6 months script

CONKLIN PLAYERS DINNER THEATRE
Box 301 Timberline, Goodfield, IL 61742
(800) 322-2304   Contact: Chaunce Conklin, Producer **Theatre**:   non-Equity dinner   **Works**: full-length plays, musicals, children's plays **2nd productions**: yes   **Stage**: 260 seats **Policy**: unsolicited script **Comment**: Inquire about Madison Theatre (professional not-for-profit) in Peoria, IL.

CONTEMPORARY ARTS CENTER
900 Camp St., New Orleans, LA 70130
(504) 523-1216   Contact: Elena Ronquillo, Performing Arts Coordinator   **Theatre**:   professional not-for-profit **Works**:   full-length plays, one-acts, musicals   **Special interests**:   political and contemporary issues, experimental or multi-media works, ethnic plays   **Policy**:   query/ synopsis **Best time**: Sept.-Jan. **Response**: 6 weeks query; 6-12 months script **Programs**: readings, staged readings, workshop productions, development, Playwrights' Unit (inquire), CAC New Play Competition (see Contests) **Comment**:   CAC's building is currently being renovated; spaces may be rented for productions.

CONTEMPORARY THEATRE OF SYRACUSE
119 Ferris Ave., Syracuse, NY 13224
(315) 446-5154   Contact: David Feldman, New Plays Program Director **Theatre**:   semi-professional/community **Works**: full-length plays, one-acts **2nd productions**: yes **Special interests**: "Plays by Syracuse area playwrights; plays set in this area." **Tours**: yes **Stage**: flexible, 150 seats **Audience**: "We look to develop a sophisticated audience."   **Policies**:   query/synopsis;   professional recommendation; "reference by local theatre people" **Response**: 1 month query; 1-6 months script   **Your chances**: 30-40/7 readings **Remuneration**: "Depends on funding."   **Programs**:   readings,   staged   readings, development (all programs for area writers)   **Comments**: "The only new plays we do are products of our staged reading program."

CONTRACT PLAYERS THEATRE
7239 Wales NW, North Canton, OH 44720
(216) 494-8311 Contact: Carla Derr, Executive Producer
Works: full-length plays **Special interests:** drama, comedy, new plays **Specifications:** small cast; simple set and costume demands; no period plays **Stage:** 45 seats **Policy:** unsolicited script **Best time:** before May 31 for following season **Response:** 2 months

COOPERSTOWN THEATER FESTIVAL
Box 851, Cooperstown, NY 13326
Contact: Raphael Chenier, Dramaturg **Theatre:** professional not-for-profit **Works:** full-length plays, adaptations, musicals **2nd productions:** no **Special interest:** "Good stories with good roles." **Specifications:** maximum cast: 20; "no political or sexual themes" **Stage:** proscenium, 150-200 seats **Audience:** "All types, but mainly of British, French and American descent." **Policies:** unsolicited script; query/synopsis; professional recommendation; agent submission **Best time:** Sept.-May **Response:** 2-8 weeks **Your chances:** 25/1 **Remuneration:** "Small fee, expenses." **Programs:** readings, staged readings

CORDEL PRODUCTIONS
1 Beaufort Pl. #E3, New Rochelle, NY 10801
(914) 636-1676 Theatre: off Broadway **Works:** full-length plays **Specifications:** simple sets **Policy:** unsolicited script with production history

THE COTERIE, INC.
2450 Grand, Kansas City, MO 64108
(816) 476-6785 Contact: Pam Sterling, Artistic Director **Theatre:** professional not-for-profit **Works:** children's plays: one-acts, translations, adaptations, musicals **2nd productions:** yes **Specifications:** maximum cast: 4-9; simple staging requirements; no fairy tales **Tours:** "Limited touring." **Stage:** flexible **Policy:** query/synopsis with resume **Best time:** Jun. **Response:** 2-3 weeks **Your chances:** 20/7; "most writing is done in-house" **Remuneration:** negotiable **Advice:** "Quality theatre that educates as well as entertains; honest and serious writing."

COUNTRY DINNER PLAYHOUSE
6875 S. Clinton, Englewood, CO 80112
(303) 790-9311 Contact: Bill McHale, Producer
Theatre: Equity **Works:** full-length plays, musicals **2nd productions:** yes **Special interests:** musicals, comedies, farces **Maximum cast:** 18 **Stage:** arena, 470 seats **Policy:** query/synopsis

CREATION PRODUCTION COMPANY
127 Greene St., New York, NY 10012
(212) 674-5593 Contact: Anne Hemenway, Managing Director **Theatre:** professional not-for-profit **Works:** experimental pieces **Stage:** no permanent facility **Policy:** solicited script

CREATIVE ARTS TEAM
NYU, 715 Broadway 5th Floor, New York, NY 10003
(212) 598-2360 Contact: Miriam Flaherty, Associate Executive Director **Theatre:** professional not-for-profit, university/college **Works:** young people's plays **Special interest:** "Concerns of youth: teen pregnancy, child abuse, substance abuse, employment, literary." **Specifications:** works must be suitable for touring **Stages:** school auditoriums, fewer than 300 seats **Audience:** teenagers **Policy:** query/synopsis of proposed project to be created in collaboration with company **Best time:** spring **Response:** 1 month

CREATIVE THEATRE
102 Witherspoon St., Princeton, NJ 08540
(609) 924-3489 Contact: Laurie Huntsman, Artistic Director **Theatre:** professional not-for-profit **Works:** children's full-length plays, translations, adaptations and musicals **2nd productions:** yes **Specifications:** maximum cast: 6; simple sets and costumes; audience participation **Tours:** yes **Stages:** proscenium, arena, flexible—150-200 seats; "we utilize all stages on tour" **Audience:** "Grades K-12." **Policies:** unsolicited script; query/synopsis; commission **Best time:** Dec.-Mar. **Response:** 1 week **Your chances:** 20-25/2-3 **Remuneration:** royalty or commission **Program:**

development **Advice:** "Must be children's theatre K-6, 7-9, 9-12; must be suitable for production in open space, with audience participation; must be musical, or suitable for musical adaptation by our composers." **Comment:** Formerly Creative Theatre Unlimited.

THE CRICKET THEATRE
9 14th St. W, Minneapolis, MN 55403
(612) 871-3763 Contact: William Partlan, Artistic Director **Theatre:** professional not-for-profit **Works:** full-length plays, one-acts **2nd productions:** yes **Special interests:** the Midwest; Midwestern issues **Maximum cast:** 8 preferred **Stage:** proscenium, 215 seats **Audience:** "Adults and students." **Policies:** query/ synopsis preferred; unsolicited script; professional recommendation **Best time:** Sept.-Mar. **Response:** 3-4 weeks query; 6 months script **Your chances:** "305 for 1987-88/0; 5-play season was made up of solicited scripts." **Programs:** readings, development, residencies

CROSSROADS THEATRE COMPANY
320 Memorial Pkwy., New Brunswick, NJ 08901
(201) 249-5625 Contact: Sydné Mahone, Literary Manager **Theatre:** professional not-for-profit **Works:** full-length plays, one-acts, translations, adaptations, musicals, children's plays, cabaret/revues **2nd productions:** yes **Special interests:** Afro-American, African and West Indian plays **Specifications:** cast of 4-7; single set **Stage:** thrust, 150 seats **Policy:** query/synopsis **Best time:** spring-summer **Response:** 1-4 months

CSC: CLASSIC STAGE COMPANY
136 E. 13th St., New York, NY 10003
(212) 677-4210 Contact: Suzanne Collins, Literary Assistant **Theatre:** off Broadway, professional not-for-profit **Works:** translations, adaptations of classics **2nd productions:** yes **Special interests:** adaptations of major works from other genres; translations and adaptations of classical European plays **Maximum cast:** 10-12 **Stage:** flexible, 180 seats **Policies:** query/synopsis with dialogue sample; professional recommendation; agent submission **Response:** 3 months **Your chances:** 200/3 plus 6 readings

Remuneration: varies **Programs**: readings, development **Advice**: "Submit only plays of classic scope or translations/ adaptations of classics."

CUMBERLAND COUNTY PLAYHOUSE
Box 484, Crossville, TN 38555
(615) 484-2300, -4324 Contact: James Crabtree, Producing Director **Theatre**: professional not-for-profit **Works**: full-length plays, adaptations, musicals, children's plays **Special interests**: Tennessee history and culture, Southern or rural settings and themes, plays suitable for family audiences **Stages**: proscenium, 485 seats; thrust, 165 seats; outdoor arena, 200 seats **Policy**: query/synopsis **Best time**: Aug.-Dec. **Response**: 2 weeks if interested in query; 6-12 months script

DALLAS THEATRE CENTER
3636 Turtle Creek Blvd., Dallas, TX 75219
(214) 526-8210 Contact: Kimberly Cole, Assistant to Artistic Director **Theatre**: professional not-for-profit **Works**: full-length plays, translations, adaptations **2nd productions**: yes **Special interest**: "Subject matter that is relevant and challenging to our company and our audience." **Stages**: thrust, 466 seats; flexible, 410 seats; flexible, 150 seats **Policies**: unsolicited script; query/synopsis; professional recommendation; agent submission **Best time**: anytime **Response**: 3-4 months **Your chances**: 500/2

DAYTONA PLAYHOUSE
100 Jessamine Blvd., Daytona Beach, FL 32018
(904) 255-2431 Contact: Dale Jordan, President, Board of Directors **Theatre**: community/non-professional **Works**: full-length plays, adaptations, musicals, children's plays **2nd productions**: no **Special interests**: "We are dedicated to doing scripts of literary merit as well as those farcical bits of froth that are dominant in community theatre circles. We attempt to provide our audiences with a balance of choices." **Maximum cast**: 40 **Stage**: proscenium **Audience**: "Many retired people from northern U.S.; family-oriented; preferences in order: comedy/farce, musicals, mysteries, historical dramas." **Policies**: unsolicited script; query/synopsis; professional recommendation **Best time**:

Aug.–Dec. **Response:** 5 months **Your chances:** 15/1
Remuneration: negotiable **Advice:** "Submit scripts that are
well composed, workable for a cast of 8-15 members; omit
excessive profanity and write for an intelligent audience—to
entertain, not shock."

DELAWARE THEATRE COMPANY
Box 516, Wilmington, DE 19899 (302) 594-1104
Contact: Cleveland Morris, Artistic Director **Theatre:**
professional not-for-profit **Works:** full-length plays,
translations, adaptations, musicals **2nd productions:** yes
Tours: yes **Stage:** thrust **Audience:** "Educated,
professional, middle-aged." **Policies:** unsolicited script;
query/synopsis; professional recommendation; agent
submission **Response:** 6 weeks query; 6 months script
Your chances: 300/0-1 **Remuneration:** negotiable
royalty

DELL'ARTE PLAYERS COMPANY
Box 816, Blue Lake, CA 95525 (707) 668-5411
Contact: Michael Fields, Managing Director **Theatre:**
professional not-for-profit **Works:** full-length plays,
translations, adaptations, children's plays **Special
interests:** comedies, works in commedia dell'arte style,
Christmas plays for young people, issue-oriented plays
Specifications: works must be suitable for touring **Stage:**
flexible, 100 seats **Policy:** query/synopsis **Best time:**
Jan.– Mar. **Response:** 3 weeks query; 6 weeks script

THE DELRAY BEACH PLAYHOUSE
950 NW 19th St., Box 1056,
Delray Beach, FL 33444 (305) 272-1281
Contact: Randolph DelLago, Director **Theatre:** community/
non-professional **Works:** full-length plays, adaptations,
children's plays **2nd productions:** no **Special interests:**
"Mysteries, musicals, comedies, dramas." **Specifications:**
maximum cast: 12; simple sets; little capacity for special
effects **Stage:** proscenium **Audience:** "Older, conservative,
middle to upper middle class." **Policies:** query/synopsis;
professional recommendation **Best time:** winter **Your
chances:** 6/3 in 4 years **Program:** workshop productions
for children **Advice:** "We are always looking for good new

mysteries and children's plays that deal intelligently with serious issues; classical farces and melodramas for audiences of children."

DENVER CENTER THEATRE COMPANY
1050 13th St., Denver, CO 80204
(303) 893-4200 ext. 235 Contact: Barbara Sellers, Producing Director **Theatre:** professional not-for-profit **Works:** full-length plays **2nd productions:** no **Special interest:** the West, particularly Colorado **Maximum cast:** 12 **Stages:** thrust, 642 seats; thrust, 155 seats; flexible, 450 seats **Policy:** unsolicited script **Best time:** Jun.-Nov. **Response:** 10-12 weeks **Your chances:** 800+/4 **Program:** PrimaFacie (see Special Programs) **Comment:** "We accept only 1 script per playwright."

DERBY DINNER THEATRE
525 Marriott Dr., Clarksville, IN 47130
(812) 288-2632 Contact: Producer **Theatre:** non-Equity **Works:** full-length plays, musicals **Special interests:** comedies, musicals **Maximum cast:** 19 **Stage:** arena **Policy:** unsolicited script **Comment:** Theatre produces 1 new play each year.

DETROIT CENTER FOR THE PERFORMING ARTS
615 Griswold Suite 420, Detroit, MI 48226
(313) 925-7925 Contact: Gary Steward-Jones, Artistic Director **Theatre:** professional not-for-profit **Works:** full-length plays, one-acts, musicals, children's plays, cabaret/revues **2nd productions:** yes **Exclusive interest:** American playwrights, particularly MI playwrights **Specifications:** maximum cast: 10 preferred; simple set **Stages:** proscenium, 2000; flexible, 150 seats **Policies:** query/synopsis preferred; unsolicited script **Response:** 3 months query; 6 months script **Your chances:** 60/2 **Remuneration:** negotiable **Program:** Playwrights Development Series: staged readings leading to mainstage production of 1 new play each season (inquire)

DETROIT REPERTORY THEATRE
13103 Woodrow Wilson, Detroit, MI 48238
(313) 868-1347 **Contact:** Barbara Busby, Literary Manager **Theatre:** professional not-for-profit **Works:** full-length plays, musicals **2nd productions:** yes **Special interest:** "We are an affirmative action theatre and cast without regard to color." **Maximum cast:** 12 **Stage:** proscenium **Audience:** "70% black, lower middle class to professional." **Policies:** unsolicited script; query/synopsis with dialogue sample; professional recommendation; agent submission **Best time:** Oct.-Mar. **Response:** 2 weeks query; 6 months script **Your chances:** 100-200/1-3 **Remuneration:** royalty **Comment:** "We produce 4 plays each year."

DINNER PLAYHOUSE, INC.--NEW PLAYS
6922 Hollywood Blvd., Fries Bldg. 11th Floor,
Los Angeles, CA 90028 **(213) 466-2266**
Contact: Donn G. Miller, Director of New Play Development **Theatre:** 2 Equity dinner theatres in Kansas City **Works:** full-length plays, musicals **2nd productions:** yes **Special interests:** "We actively avoid plays which can be associated with the image of dinner theatre in the past. We seek plays that are funny, but the humor must be reality-based and must come from the characters." **Specifications:** maximum cast: 12; no more than 2 sets **Stages:** 3/4 round, 340 seats; 3/4 round, 380 seats **Audience:** "Very, very conservative, middle-to-upper middle class, from Kansas City and surrounding area." **Policies:** unsolicited script; query/synopsis with dialogue sample; professional recommendation; agent submission **Response:** 3 days query; 2 months script **Your chances:** 150/2 **Remuneration:** negotiable **Advice:** "Please do not send serious works unless they have a very strong comedic background. We must be very careful of the moral and sexual content of the works presented." **Comment:** "Each script is read, and every playwright receives a response."

DIXIE COLLEGE THEATRE & PIONEER PLAYERS
225 S. 700 E. St. George, UT 84770
(801) 628-3121 **Contact:** C. Paul Andersen, Director **Theatre:** professional not-for-profit, community/non-

professional, university/college **Works:** full-length plays, adaptations, musicals, children's plays **2nd productions:** yes **Special interests:** "19th century Pioneer Movement, 19th century and musical melodrama, scripts which appeal to tourists." **Specifications:** maximum cast: 8; no more than 2 sets **Stages:** proscenium; arena **Audience:** "Community and tourist patrons interested in either a good time or a moving experience." **Policy:** query/synopsis with resume **Best time:** Jan.–Mar. **Response:** 1 month **Remuneration:** "Reasonable royalty." **Advice:** "Family-oriented plays are needed." **Comments:** Theatre produces 1–2 new plays each season. "Regular theatre season is educational theatre; summer theatre is pre-professional."

DIXON PLACE
37 E. 1st St., New York, NY 10003
(212) 673-6752 Contact: Ellie Covan, Producer **Theatre:** not-for-profit laboratory **Works:** performance pieces **Exclusive Interest:** "Works in progress: experimental works, visually oriented works, collaborations." **Specifications:** no more than 4 performers; pieces should be 20–45 minutes in length and suitable for a very small space (10' x 10') **Stage:** living room proscenium, 50 seats **Audience:** "People from the arts community and friends of the performers." **Policy:** short proposal with video tape of past work; solicited work **Response:** 2–4 weeks **Remuneration:** "Guaranteed minimum fee of $70 per performance piece." **Comments:** "We are famous for our informal ambiance conducive to creative and social interaction." **Advice:** "Take risks."

DOBAMA THEATRE
1846 Coventry Rd., Cleveland Heights, OH 44118
(216) 932-6838   Contact: Jean Cummins, Literary Manager **Theatre:** community/non-professional **Works:** full-length plays, one-acts, translations, adaptations **2nd productions:** "Previously unproduced plays are preferred." **Special interest:** "Paired one-acts are preferred over single one-acts." **Specifications:** low ceilings; limited backstage area **Stage:** 3/4 arena **Policy:** unsolicited script with resume **Best time:** May–Sept. **Response:** 6–9

months **Your chances:** 40/3-4 **Remuneration:** "Standard fee (about $35 per performance)." **Program:** readings

DORDT COLLEGE THEATRE
Sioux Center, IA 51250 (712) 722-3771
Contact: Verne Meyer, Theatre Arts Deptartment Chair **Theatre:** university/college **Works:** full-length plays, one-acts, adaptations, musicals **2nd productions:** yes **Special interest:** "Current social or moral questions." **Tours:** yes **Stages:** thrust; arena; flexible **Audience:** "Conservative residents; college crowd." **Policies:** unsolicited script; query/synopsis **Best time:** fall **Your chances:** 3/1 **Remuneration:** 1-2 week residency, honorarium **Programs:** readings, staged readings, workshop productions, development, residencies, classes **Advice:** "Write the story. Develop the characters clearly. Don't try to be funny; let the humor as well as the drama evolve from the character and the story."

DORSET THEATRE FESTIVAL
Box 519, Dorset, VT 05251 (802) 867-2223
Contact: Jill Charles, Artistic Director **Theatre:** professional not-for-profit **Works:** full-length plays, adaptations, musicals **2nd productions:** "Yes, but prefer unencumbered plays." **Special interests:** "General audience appeal; depth, whether comedy or drama." **Specifications:** maximum cast: 8; unit set preferred **Stage:** proscenium, 218 seats **Audience:** "Sophisticated; conservative in terms of language." **Policies:** professional recommendation; agent submission; workshop in New York City **Best time:** Sept.-Feb. **Response:** 3-4 months **Your chances:** 150/1 **Remuneration:** negotiable royalty, transportation, expenses **Program:** Dorset Colony House (see Special Programs) **Advice:** "Have an agent or artistic director of a theatre where the play has been produced send us a query, or inform us of a reading or workshop in New York City."

DOWNTOWN CABARET THEATRE
263 Golden Hill St., Bridgeport, CT 06604
(203) 576-1634 Contact: Richard C. Hallinan, Executive Producer **Theatre:** professional not-for-profit **Works:** musicals, children's plays, cabaret/revues **Specifications:**

maximum cast: 6-18; simple sets; no fly space **Stage:** proscenium, 294 seats **Policy:** query/synopsis **Response:** 2 weeks-1 month

DRAMA COMMITTEE REPERTORY THEATRE
118 W. 79th St., New York, NY 10024
Contact: Arthur Reel, Artistic Director **Theatre:** professional not-for-profit **Works:** full-length plays, one-acts, adaptations **2nd productions:** no **Special interest:** adaptations of classics originallly written in prose **Specifications:** maximum cast: 10; moveable sets **Policy:** query/synopsis with 1st act of script **Response:** 2 months

DRAMA DUCK, INC.
New York, NY Our 1989 questionnaire was returned as "undeliverable," and no phone number is listed for this theatre.

THE DRAMA GROUP
330 W. 202nd St., Chicago Heights, IL 60411
(312) 755-3444 **Contact:** Charles Barnett, Business Manager **Theatre:** community/non-professional **Works:** full-length plays, musicals **2nd productions:** "Under consideration." **Maximum cast:** 20 **Stages:** proscenium, thrust, arena, flexible--150-1304 seats **Audience:** "Blue collar; education level tops generally with B.A.; ethnic melting pot; average age 40-60." **Policy:** unsolicited script **Best time:** fall-winter **Remuneration:** "Subject to grant funding." **Program:** contests (inquire) **Comment:** "Production of new plays is currently under consideration by the board."

DREISKE PERFORMANCE COMPANY
1517 W. Fullerton Ave., Chicago, IL 60614
(312) 281-9075 **Contact:** Nicole Dreiske, Artistic Director **Theatre:** professional not-for-profit **Works:** full-length plays, one-acts **2nd productions:** no **Special interests:** "Non-naturalistic, poetic texts that can be staged with movement by the actors; tech-oriented and visual elements." **Maximum cast:** 15 **Tours:** all shows **Stages:** proscenium; thrust; arena; black box **Audience:** "European festivals, American universities, theatre and art

festivals." **Policies:** query/synopsis with dialogue sample; professional recommendation **Response:** 4-6 weeks **Advice:** "Familiarize yourself with the work of Grotowski, Peter Brook and Eugenio Barba. Be patient."

DUO THEATRE
Box 1200 Cooper Station, New York, NY 10276
(212) 598-4320 Contact: Michael Alasa, Managing Director **Theatre:** off off Broadway **Works:** musicals **Exclusive interest:** Hispanic American playwrights writing in English **Maximum cast:** 10 **Tours:** "A few." **Audience:** "We are a theatre for 2nd generation Hispanics. We try to interest all groups of people; we give tickets to people to allow them to experience Hispanic theatre." **Policies:** unsolicited script with resume; query/synopsis with resume; commission **Best time:** early fall **Response:** 3 months script **Your chances:** 50-60/"8 in this season series" **Remuneration:** "A fee and a piece of the house." **Programs:** readings, staged readings, playwrights' unit for authors who write only in Spanish **Advice:** "A place for playwrights to tell about living in America. Also universal themes, not 'kitchen sink' drama." **Comments:** "This is essentially a showcase theatre, a place for Hispanics to try out their work. In our experience, staged readings are an entree to production." See Shirakawa, Sam H. "Beyond the Ghetto Mentality" (*Theater Week,* May 16, 1988), 32-37.

EAST WEST PLAYERS
4424 Santa Monica Blvd., Los Angeles, CA 90029
(213) 660-0366 Contact: Literary Manager **Theatre:** professional not-for-profit **Works:** full-length plays, one-acts, adaptations, musicals **Special interests:** "New works dealing with the Asian-American experience in the U.S., contemporary American works." **Specifications:** works must be suitable for Asian actors **Stage:** flexible **Audience:** "Middle-class, college-educated, 60% Asian American, 40% Anglo." **Policy:** unsolicited script **Response:** 6 months **Your chances:** 100/2-3 **Remuneration:** negotiable royalty

ECCENTRIC CIRCLES THEATRE
400 W. 43rd St. #4N, New York, NY 10036
(212) 564-3798 Contact: Rosemary Hopkins, Artistic Director **Theatre:** off off Broadway **Works:** full-length plays, one-acts, musicals **2nd productions:** no **Specifications:** maximum cast: 10; simple set **Stage:** proscenium, 99 seats **Audience:** general **Policies:** unsolicited script; query/synopsis with dialogue sample **Response:** 2 weeks query; 6 weeks script **Your chances:** 150/1 **Remuneration:** no **Program:** readings

EMMY GIFFORD CHILDREN'S THEATER
3504 Center St., Omaha, NE 68105
(402) 345-4852 Contact: James Larson, Artistic Director **Theatre:** professional not-for-profit **Works:** children's plays, adaptations and musicals **2nd productions:** yes **Exclusive interest:** "Works suitable for a family audience." **Specifications:** some limitations on sets; no fly space **Tours:** "Small-cast shows." **Stage:** proscenium, thrust—500 seats **Policies:** query/synopsis; professional recommendation **Best time:** summer **Your chances:** 12/2 **Remuneration:** negotiable **Program:** Susie Barker Playwriting Commission (selection by committee)

EMPIRE STATE INSTITUTE
FOR THE PERFORMING ARTS
Empire State Plaza, Albany, NY 12223
(518) 443-5222 Contact: James Farrell, Literary Manager **Theatre:** professional not-for-profit **Works:** full-length plays, adaptations, musicals, children's plays **2nd productions:** "Possibly." **Tours:** yes **Stages:** flexible thrust, 883 seats; thrust, 450 seats **Audience:** "Families." **Policies:** query/synopsis; professional recommendation; agent submission **Response:** 3 weeks query; 4 months script **Your chances:** 350/1-2 **Remuneration:** varies

THE EMPTY SPACE THEATRE
95 S. Jackson St., Seattle, WA 98104
(206) 587-3737 Contact: Kurt Beattie, Artistic Associate **Theatre:** professional not-for-profit **Works:** full-length plays, one-acts, translations, adaptations, musicals **2nd**

productions: yes Special interests: "Political plays; broad humor; translations of contemporary European plays." Tours: "Not usually." Stage: flexible, 250-300 seats Audience: "Well educated, middle class, intellectually alive." Policies: query/synopsis with resume; professional recommendation; agent submission Best time: fall-winter Response: 2 weeks query; 3-4 months script Remuneration: royalty; commission Advice: "We avoid excessively derivative or obviously commercial scripts."

ENCORE THEATRE
991 North Shore Dr., Lima, OH 45801
(419) 223-8866 Contact: Allyn Barnes, President **Theatre:** community/non-professional **Works:** full-length plays, musicals **2nd productions:** yes **Specifications:** maximum cast: 25; easy set changes; no fly gallery **Stage:** thrust, 309 seats **Audience:** "Upper income, educated, ages 20-70." **Policies:** unsolicited script; query/synopsis **Best time:** fall **Response:** 6-9 months **Advice:** "Complete working script; we would need the presence of the playwright during early rehearsals." **Comment:** Theatre normally receives 2-3 scripts each year.

ENSEMBLE STUDIO THEATRE
549 W. 52nd St., New York, NY 10019
(212) 581-9603 Contact: Sari Bodi, Literary Manager **Theatre:** professional not-for-profit **Works:** full-length plays, one-acts **Stages:** proscenium, 45 seats; flexible, 98 seats **Policy:** unsolicited script **Best time:** Sept.-Apr. **Response:** 3-4 months **Programs:** readings, staged readings, One-Act Marathon (inquire) **Advice:** Do not send query/synopsis. **Comment:** See Myers, Larry. "Curt Dempster: Running a Theatrical Marathon" (*Theater Week*, Jul. 4, 1988), 52-57.

ENSEMBLE THEATRE OF CINCINNATI
1127 Vine St., Cincinnati, OH 45210
(513) 421-3556, 751-3307 Contact: David A. White III, Artistic Director **Theatre:** professional not-for-profit **Works:** full-length plays **2nd productions:** yes **Special interests:** "Ritualistic devices, stretched boundaries, emotional risks." **Specifications:** maximum cast: 7; unit set

Tours: "Possibly." **Stage:** thrust, 136 seats **Audience:** "Marketing toward yuppies whom we want to shake up." **Policies:** unsolicited script; professional recommendation; agent submission **Best time:** Apr.–Jun. **Response:** 2 months **Your chances:** 300+/5 **Remuneration:** "Fees are based on the playwright's background and the number of performances." **Program:** staged readings

ENSEMBLE THEATRE OF FLORIDA
Box 1103, Melbourne, FL 32902 (407) 727-1901
Contact: Rodney Fairbanks, Assistant Artistic Director **Theatre:** professional not-for-profit **Works:** full-length plays, translations, adaptations, musicals, children's plays **2nd productions:** yes **Stage:** proscenium-thrust, 100 seats **Audience:** "Educated." **Policy:** query/synopsis with resume **Your chances:** "not many/1-2" **Remuneration:** negotiable

ENSEMBLE THEATRE OF SANTA BARBARA
Box 2307, Santa Barbara, CA 93120
(805) 965-6252 Contact: Robert Weiss, Artistic Director **Theatre:** professional not-for-profit **Works:** full-length plays, one-acts, translations, adaptations **Specifications:** small cast; simple production requirements **Stage:** proscenium, 140 seats **Policy:** unsolicited script **Best time:** Sept. 1–Mar. 1 **Response:** 3 months **Program:** 2 Nights Studio Program: staged readings/discussions

EUREKA THEATRE COMPANY
2730 16th St., San Francisco, CA 94103
(415) 558-9811 Contact: Oskar Eustis, Artistic Director **Theatre:** professional not-for-profit **Works:** full-length plays, translations, adaptations **2nd productions:** yes **Special interest:** contemporary social/political issues **Stage:** flexible, 200 seats **Policies:** query/synopsis; professional recommendation; agent submission **Best time:** Oct.–Mar. **Response:** 3 months query; 6 months script **Remuneration:** negotiable **Program:** readings

EXPERIMENTAL THEATRE
OF THE PUERTORICAN ATHENEUM
Box 1180, San Juan, Puerto Rico 00902
(209) 722-4839 Contact: Roberto Ramos-Perea, Executive Director **Theatre:** professional not-for-profit **Works:** full-length plays, one-acts, translations, adaptations **2nd productions:** no **Special interests:** "Puertorican subjects; Hispanics' relations with U.S." **Specifications:** maximum cast: 6; single set **Tours:** yes **Stage:** proscenium, 365 seats **Audience:** "Mainly Puertoricans, high and middle education, students, teachers and artists." **Policy:** unsolicited script **Best time:** summer **Response:** 6 months **Your chances:** 15/3-4 "not necessarily chosen from those submitted" **Remuneration:** royalty **Programs:** readings, staged readings, contests (inquire) **Advice:** "Seriousness in the treatment of political and social issues. Well-written comedies, fresh ideas."

FAIRBANKS DRAMA ASSOCIATION
& FAIRBANKS CHILDREN'S THEATRE, INC.
Box 81327, Fairbanks, AK 99708 (907) 456-PLAY
Contact: Cynthia Steiner, Executive Director **Theatre:** community/non-professional **Works:** full-length plays, one-acts, children's plays **Specifications:** maximum cast: 8; minimal set; "no drops" **Tours:** children's plays **Stage:** flexible, 90 seats **Policies:** unsolicited script; query/synopsis **Best time:** fall **Remuneration:** no

FAIRBANKS LIGHT OPERA THEATRE
Box 2787, Fairbanks, AK 99707 (907) 456-5631
Contact: Linda Aronow-Brown, Administrative Assistant **Theatre:** community/non-professional **Works:** musicals **2nd productions:** no **Special interest:** "Family-type material." **Specifications:** simple sets **Tours:** yes **Stage:** proscenium, 900 seats **Audience:** "Family folks in and around Fairbanks—rural and urban." **Policies:** query/synopsis **Response:** 2 months **Remuneration:** "We're small and non-profit, so we'd have to talk about it." **Advice:** "Musical theater only; very professional; large chorus, more women than men." **Comment:** "We've only produced 1 new show in our 15-year history, RIVERSONG, an Alaskan musical."

FAIRMOUNT THEATRE OF THE DEAF

8500 Euclid Ave., Cleveland, OH 44106
(216) 229-2838 Contact: Miles Barnes, Artistic Director
Theatre: professional not-for-profit **Works**: full-length plays, one-acts, translations, adaptations, musicals, children's plays **Specifications**: maximum cast: 8; sets must tour **Tours**: mainstage shows **Stages**: proscenium; thrust; flexible **Audience**: "All audiences; our productions use sign language and voicemusic." **Policies**: unsolicited script with resume; query/synopsis with dialogue sample and resume; professional recommendation; agent submission **Best time**: Jan-Aug. **Your chances**: 12-25/0-1 **Remuneration**: negotiable **Advice**: "Do not assume anything about deaf theatre."

FERNDALE REPERTORY THEATRE

Box 892, Ferndale, CA 95536 (707) 725-2378
Contact: Peter Buckley, Artistic Director **Theatre**: semi-professional/community **Works**: full-length plays, musicals **2nd productions**: "Rarely." **Special interests**: "Contemporary themes; imagination." **Specifications**: maximum cast: 10; no domestic comedies, no "bedroom dramas" **Tours**: yes **Stage**: proscenium, 267 seats; thrust, 267 seats **Audience**: "Well educated, 35-65." **Policies**: query/synopsis; professional recommendation **Best time**: spring-summer **Response**: 1 month query; 6 months script **Your chances**: 125/1-2 **Remuneration**: "Royalty and performance rights, $50/$25." **Program**: Ferndale Repertory New Works Competition (see Contests) **Advice**: "Simple, small-cast shows, intriguing formats."

FIJI THEATRE COMPANY

New York, NY See Ping Chong & Company.

FIREHOUSE DINNER THEATRE

514 S. 11th St., Omaha, NE 68102
(402) 346-6009 Contact: Richard Mueller, Artistic Director **Theatre**: Equity **Works**: full-length plays, musicals **Special interests**: comedies, farces, musicals **Policy**: unsolicited script

FIRELITE DINNER THEATRE
4350 Transport St. #104, Ventura, CA 93003
(805) 642-8515 Contact: Executive Producer **Theatre:** non-Equity **Works:** full-length plays, musicals **2nd productions:** yes **Exclusive interests:** comedies, musicals **Maximum cast:** 25 **Stage:** proscenium **Audience:** "Middle class, average age 45." **Policy:** unsolicited script **Best times:** Oct.-Nov., Mar.-Apr.

FLORIDA STUDIO THEATRE
124 N. Palm Ave., Sarasota, FL 34236
(813) 366-9017 Contact: Jack Fournier, New Play Coordinator **Theatre:** professional not-for-profit **Works:** full-length plays, one-acts, translations, adaptations, musicals **2nd productions:** yes **Specifications:** cast size: 4-8; some technical limitations **Tours:** yes **Stage:** proscenium, 163 seats **Audience:** "Older community. The theatre tries to educate, enlighten and expand its audience's taste." **Policies:** query/synopsis; professional recommendation; agent submission **Best time:** Sept.-Jun. **Response:** 1 month query; 6-9 months script **Your chances:** 750/2-3 **Remuneration:** negotiable **Programs:** readings, staged readings, workshop productions, Florida Studio Theatre Artists Colony (see Special Programs)

FMT
Box 92127, Milwaukee, WI 53202 (414) 271-8484
Contact: M. Moynihan, Co-Founder/Director **Theatre:** professional not-for-profit **Works:** full-length plays, adaptations, musicals, children's plays **2nd productions:** "Not usually." **Special interest:** "Writers interested in working with the company to develop a work." **Tours:** yes **Stages:** flexible; outdoor **Audience:** "General, young to old." **Policy:** query/synopsis **Best time:** Sept. **Response:** 4 months query; 6 months script **Your chances:** 50/0-1 **Remuneration:** "Flat fee or royalty." **Advice:** "Know our company's work; work with us on a short-term project."

FOLKSBEINE THEATER
123 E. 55th St., New York, NY 10022
(212) 755-2231 Contact: Ben Schechter, Managing Director **Theatre:** off off Broadway **Works:** full-length

plays **2nd productions:**   yes **Exclusive interest:**
Jewish content **Maximum cast:** 10 **Stage:** proscenium,
445 seats **Audience:** "Jewish, Yiddish-speaking audiences."
Policy: query/synopsis with resume **Response:** 3 months
Advice: "Plays may be literary but must also entertain.
Interesting subject matter; may have a message but should not
be too philosophical." **Comments:** Plays written in English
will be translated and performed in Yiddish.   Theatre has a
16-week season from Oct.-Jan. and produces 1 play each year.

FORD'S THEATRE
511 Tenth St. NW, Washington, DC 20004
(202) 638-2941 Contact: David H. Bell, Artistic Director
Theatre: professional not-for-profit **Works:**   full-length
plays, musicals **2nd productions:** "Possibly." **Special
interests:**   small-scale   musicals,   American   authors
Maximum cast: 15 **Stage:** proscenium-thrust, 699 seats
Audience: "Articulate, intelligent,   upwardly   mobile."
Policies: query/synopsis;   professional recommendation;
agent submission **Best times:** late fall, late spring
Response: 3 weeks query; 3 months script **Your chances:**
200/1-2   **Remuneration:** "Standard   Dramatists   Guild
contract." **Programs:** staged readings, workshop productions

45TH STREET THEATRE
584 9th Ave., New York, NY 10018
(212) 582-7862, 333-7471 Contact: Casey Childs,
Artistic Director **Theatre:** off off Broadway **Works:**
full-length plays, one-acts **2nd productions:** if New York
premieres **Special interest:** "American plays by American
playwrights."   **Specifications:** maximum cast: 10; single
set or minimal stage requirements **Stages:** proscenium, 99
seats; proscenium-thrust, 60 seats **Policy:**   unsolicited
script with resume **Best time:** Mar.-Jul. **Response:** 2-6
months **Your chances:** 500/4-5 **Remuneration:** $200
Programs: readings, staged readings, workshop productions
Advice: "Off-beat material, Black Comedy, the kind of thing
you do not see on TV." **Comments:** "We are a development
organization and do 3-4 readings each month."   "Primary
Stages Company (see Special Programs) is the producing
organization."

FOUNTAIN SQUARE PLAYERS
416 E. Main St., Bowling Green, KY 42101
(502) 842-8844 Contact: Pat Sprouse
Theatre: community/non-professional **Works:** full-length plays, musicals, children's plays **2nd productions:** yes **Specifications:** "6 free battens to fly set pieces." **Stage:** proscenium, 860 seats **Audience :** "Middle American; 1/3 university, 1/3 agriculture, 1/3 manufacturing." **Policies:** unsolicited script; query/synopsis **Best time:** spring **Response:** 1 month **Your chances:** 2-3/"3 in 10 years existence" **Remuneration:** $200

FREE STREET THEATER
411 W. North Ave., Chicago, IL 60610
(312) 642-1234 Contact: Patrick Henry, Producer Artistic Director **Theatre:** professional not-for-profit **Works:** full-length plays, musicals **Special interests:** inter-racial or inter-generational issues; documentary projects based on oral histories and experiences of local residents; urban issues **Tours:** all shows **Stage:** mobile outdoor **Policy:** solicited script

THE FULLER YOUNG PEOPLE'S THEATRE
3046 Aldrich Ave. S, Minneapolis, MN 55408
(612) 824-9576 Contact: Melanie Spewock, Director of Education **Theatre:** non-profit youth theatre **Works:** children's plays and musicals **2nd productions:** "Possibly." **Special interests:** "Non-stereotypical children's theatre, adaptations, cross-cultural and unusual fairy tales and plays around which a teaching unit can be structured. For older audiences, issues current in young people's lives." **Specifications:** maximum cast: 12, 10-20 age range; all sets must tour; minimal lighting and special effects **Stages:** schools, 100-800 seats **Audience:** "Young people and their families: age groups 4-11 and 12-18." **Policies:** unsolicited script; personal contact **Best time:** Dec.-Mar. **Response:** 4 weeks **Your chances:** 6-12/2-3 **Remuneration:** "$500-$1000, sometimes with percentages." **Programs:** readings, staged readings, workshop productions of scripts by playwrights under age 22 **Advice:** "Plays should fit into a class period of 45-60 minutes, include more girls than boys and allow for gender-free casting."

FULTON OPERA HOUSE
**Box 1865, N. Prince St., Lancaster, PA 17603
(717) 394-7133 Contact:** Kathleen Collins, Artistic Director **Theatre:** professional not-for-profit **Works:** full-length plays, musicals, children's plays **Special interest:** contemporary issues **Specifications:** maximum cast: 10; unit set **Tours:** children's shows **Stage:** proscenium, 900 seats **Policy:** query/synopsis **Response:** 2-3 weeks query; 2-3 months script **Your chances:** 100-200/1 **Remuneration:** negotiable **Program:** staged readings

THE GALLERY PLAYERS OF PARK SLOPE
**Box 150705, Brooklyn, NY 11215 (718) 638-5725
Contact:** Jack Kaplan, President **Theatre:** off off Broadway, semi-professional/community **Works:** full-length plays, one-acts, adaptations, musicals, children's plays **2nd productions:** no **Exclusive interest:** Brooklyn playwrights only **Specifications:** small cast, simple sets **Stage:** proscenium, 100 seats **Audience:** "All ages; our subscribers tend to be 35-60, but we want to attract younger audiences, too." **Policy:** query/synopsis **Best time:** May-Aug. **Response:** 2 weeks query; 6 months script **Your chances:** 10-30/1-3 **Remuneration:** no **Programs:** workshop productions, Playwright Focus (see Contests)

GARY YOUNG MIME THEATRE
Rockville, MD This theatre did not respond to our 1989 questionnaire, and no phone number is listed.

THE GASLAMP QUARTER THEATRE COMPANY
**547 4th Ave., San Diego, CA 92101
(619) 232-9608 Contact:** Jean Hauser, Company Manager **Theatre:** professional not-for-profit **Works:** full-length plays, musicals **2nd productions:** yes **Specifications:** maximum cast: 8; no more than 2 sets **Stages:** proscenium; thrust **Audience:** "Median age 45, college educated." **Policies:** query/synopsis with dialogue sample and resume; agent submission **Best time:** spring **Response:** 9 months **Your chances:** 40/1 **Remuneration:** "Depends on agent." **Program:** California Young Playwrights Project (see Contests)

GENE FRANKEL THEATRE
24 Bond St., New York, NY 10012 (212) 777-1710
Contact: Gene Frankel, Artistic Director **Theatre:** off off
Broadway **Works:** full-length plays, one-acts **2nd
productions:** yes **Specifications:** maximum cast: 100;
some limitations on sets; no fly space, "but creative space"
Tours: yes **Stage:** flexible **Audience:** "Varied--from
agents and critics to first-time theatre-goers." **Policy:**
unsolicited script **Best time:** "Now." **Response:** 1-4
months **Your chances:** 100/"variable number"
Remuneration: varies **Advice:** "Write excellent plays, full
of truth. Attend our playwrights' workshop."

GEORGE STREET PLAYHOUSE
9 Livingston Ave., New Brunswick, NJ 08901
(201) 846-2895 Contact: Wendy Liscow, Artistic
Director **Theatre:** professional not-for-profit **Works:**
full-length plays, musicals **2nd productions:** yes
Specifications: maximum cast: 8, 12 for musicals; single
set, "can have multiple locales" **Tours:** "High school
outreach program. Tour 2 shows, 2 actors." **Stages:**
proscenium-thrust, 367 seats; 3/4 round, 99 seats
Audience: "Broad-based." **Policies:** query/synopis with
dialogue sample; professional recommendation **Response:** 3-6
months **Your chances:** 300/1 play and 1 musical plus 6
staged readings **Programs:** readings, staged readings
Advice: "Plays that have universal scope and explore unique
situations, world views, characters and relationships."

GERMINAL STAGE DENVER
2450 W. 44th Ave., Denver, CO 80211-1508
(303) 455-7108 Contact: Edward Baierlein, Director/
Manager **Theatre:** professional not-for-profit **Works:**
full-length plays, translations, adaptations **Specifications:**
maximum cast: 8; minimal production requirements **Stage:**
3/4 thrust, 100 seats **Audience:** general **Policy:** solicited
script

GEVA THEATRE
75 Woodbury Blvd., Rochester, NY 14607
(716) 232-1366 Contact: Ann Patrice Carrigan, Literary
Director **Theatre:** professional not-for-profit **Works:** full-

length plays, adaptations, musicals **2nd productions**: "Not yet; probably in 2 years." **Maximum cast**: 20 for classics; "new plays tend to have small casts" **Stage**: thrust, 537 seats **Audience**: "12,500 subscribers, highly educated." **Policies**: query synopsis; agent submission **Response**: 2 weeks query; 6 months script **Your chances**: 500/1 plus 6 in workshop **Remuneration**: negotiable advance on percentage **Programs**: readings, staged readings

THE GLINES
240 W. 44th St., New York, NY 10036
(212) 354-8899 Contact: John Glines, Artistic Director **Theatre**: professional not-for-profit **Works**: full-length plays, one-acts, translations, adaptations **2nd productions**: yes **Exclusive interest**: "The gay experience." **Stages**: "Various." **Policies**: professional recommendation; agent submission **Response**: 3 months **Your chances**: 100/1-2 **Program**: staged readings **Advice**: "Write something that I won't see on television."

GLOUCESTER STAGE COMPANY
267 E. Main St., Gloucester, MA 01930
(617) 281-4099 Contact: Israel Horovitz, Artistic Director **Theatre**: professional not-for-profit **Works**: full-length plays **2nd productions**: yes **Special interest**: "New American plays about working-class people." **Stages**: flexible warehouse, 120 seats; 3/4, 40 seats **Audience**: "From Boston theatre-goers to local people." **Policy**: agent submission **Best time**: summer **Response**: 3 months **Your chances**: 400/6-8 plus 8-12 staged readings **Remuneration**: "Favored nation payment, $100 per week." **Programs**: staged readings, workshop productions, development, internships

GNU THEATRE
10426 Magnolia Blvd., North Hollywood, CA 91601
(818) 508-5344 Contact: Jeff Seymour, Artistic Director **Theatre**: professional not-for-profit **Works**: full-length plays, one-acts, translations, adaptations, musicals **2nd productions**: yes **Special interest**: "Contemporary themes." **Specifications**: maximum cast: 15; "simple sets, but we are interested in sets" **Stage**: proscenium, 50

seats **Audience:** "Mixed." **Policy:** query/synopsis with resume and dialogue sample **Response:** 3 weeks **Your chances:** 100/3 **Remuneration:** royalty **Program:** staged readings **Advice:** "Ideal would be a full-length play of 2 acts, with 5-9 characters and simple but interesting sets."

THE GOLD COAST REPERTORY COMPANY
575 Surfside Dr., Pt. Hueneme, CA 93041
(805) 488-3625 Contact: Joseph Bertucci, Producer **Theatre:** professional **Works:** full-length plays, one-acts, translations, adaptations, musicals, children's plays **2nd productions:** yes **Maximum cast:** 7 **Audience:** "Very middle of the road." **Policies:** unsolicited script; dialogue sample with resume; professional recommendation **Best time:** Feb.–May **Response:** 2-3 weeks query; 3 months script **Your chances:** 300/1 **Remuneration:** $50 or $10 **Programs:** staged readings, workshop productions, development, internships, summer festival of 5 staged readings (inquire) **Advice:** "Don't make it heavy!"

THE GOODMAN THEATRE
200 S. Columbus Dr., Chicago, IL 60603
(312) 443-3811 Contact: Tom Creamer, Dramaturg **Theatre:** professional not-for-profit **Works:** full-length plays **2nd productions:** yes **Special interest:** "Large-scale, highly theatrical works dealing with big ideas." **Stage:** proscenium, 683 seats **Audience:** "Wide age range, white collar, mostly white." **Policies:** query/synopsis with resume; agent submission **Response:** 1 month query; 6-7 months script **Your chances:** 400/"perhaps 1 every 2 seasons" **Remuneration:** standard royalty **Advice:** "Most of the new work we produce is generated in-house, through a commission to a playwright we have a long-standing relationship with, or through a special project originating with one of our directors. Playwrights who have established their careers with productions at other recognized theatres stand the best chance of being produced at the Goodman."

GOODSPEED OPERA HOUSE
East Haddam, CT 06423 (203) 873-8664
Contact: Michael Price, Executive Director **Theatre:** professional not-for-profit **Works:** musicals, "usually

revivals" **2nd productions**: "New musicals--readings/ workshops." **Stages**: proscenium, 400 seats; flexible proscenium, 200 seats **Policies**: query/synopsis; agent submission **Best time**: Jan.-Mar. **Response**: 1 month query; 9 months script **Your chances**: 300/3 **Remuneration**: no **Programs**: readings, staged readings, workshop productions

THE GREAT-AMERICAN THEATRE COMPANY
Box 92123, Milwaukee, WI 53202 (414) 276-4230
Contact: Amanda Barrickman, General Manager **Theatre**: professional not-for-profit **Works**: children's plays and adaptations **2nd productions**: no **Special interests**: "New children's plays; adaptations of classic tales and stories." **Specifications**: maximum cast: 12; no more than 2 sets **Tours**: yes **Stages**: proscenium, 2260 seats; proscenium, 1500 seats; proscenium, 1420 seats **Audience**: ages 5-18 **Policies**: unsolicited script; professional recommendation; showcase **Best time**: Jan. **Response**: 2-3 weeks **Your chances**: 3-5/fewer than half of these **Remuneration**: salary or negotiable fee

GREAT LAKES THEATER FESTIVAL
1502 Euclid Ave. Suite 250, Cleveland, OH 44115 (216) 241-5490 Contact: Victoria Bussert, Associate Artistic Director **Theatre**: professional not-for-profit **Works**: full-length plays **2nd productions**: "Yes and no; depends upon the year." **Specifications**: 2nd stage: maximum cast 8, minimal sets, simple costumes **Stages**: proscenium, 600-1000 seats; modified thrust, 300 seats **Policies**: professional recommendation **Best time**: Oct.-Apr. **Response**: 6 months **Your chances**: "hundreds/none to date"

GREAT NORTH AMERICAN HISTORY THEATRE
Landmark Center 327, St. Paul, MN 55102 (612) 292-4323 Contact: Lance Belville, Literary Manager **Theatre**: professional not-for-profit **Works**: full-length plays, translations, adaptations, musicals **2nd productions**: yes **Exclusive interest**: history **Specifications**: maximum cast: 8; few and simple sets **Tours**: "Yes, very important." **Stages**: proscenium, 230

seats; arena; flexible **Audience:** "Wide range of ages, economic levels and educational backgrounds." **Policies:** query/synopsis; professional recommendation; agent submission **Response:** 1 month query; 3 months script **Remuneration:** "Yes. Most of our scripts we commission." **Programs:** readings, staged readings, development, internships **Advice:** "Plays must bear some relationship to historical people, places or events—preferably but not exclusively in the Northwest U.S." **Comments:** Theatre receives approximately 150 new scripts each year. "We read scripts to find authors we are interested in; then, we commission scripts from them."

THE GROUP THEATRE COMPANY
Seattle, WA   See The Seattle Group Theatre

GROVE SHAKESPEARE FESTIVAL
12852 Main St., Garden Grove, CA 92640
(714) 636-7213, 638-6747   Contact: Thomas F. Bradac, Producing Artistic Director **Theatre:** professional not-for-profit **Works:** full-length plays, translations, adaptations **Specifications:** maximum cast: 10 preferred; single set **Stages:** proscenium, 172 seats; ampitheatre, 550 seats **Policy:** professional recommendation **Best time:** Aug.-Dec. **Response:** 4-6 weeks

THE GUTHRIE THEATER
725 Vineland Pl., Minneapolis, MN 55403
(612) 347-1100 Contact: Mark Bly, Literary Manager/ Dramaturg **Theatre:** professional not-for-profit **Works:** full-length plays, translations, adaptations **2nd productions:** yes **Stage:** thrust, 1441 seats **Policies:** query/synopsis with 10-page dialogue sample; agent submission **Response:** 1-2 weeks query; 1-2 months script **Comment:** See Stelling, Lucille Johnsen. "The Guthrie Theater: A Dream Turns 25" (*Theater Week*, Aug. 22, 1988), 44-49.

HARRISBURG COMMUNITY THEATRE
513 Hurlock St., Harrisburg, PA 17110
(717) 238-7382 Contact: Thomas G. Hostetter, Artistic Director **Theatre:** community/non-professional **Works:**

full-length plays, adaptations, musicals **2nd productions:** no
Specifications: maximum cast: 25; no fly space **Stage:**
proscenium, 450 seats **Audience:** "Moderate outlook, middle
to upper class, largely 40-55 age range, not wildly
experimental in taste." **Policies:** query/synopsis;
professional recommendation **Best time:** Aug.-Oct.
Response: 6 months **Your chances:** 12-15/"none
recently" **Remuneration:** negotiable

HARTFORD STAGE COMPANY
50 Church St., Hartford, CT 06103
(203) 525-5601 Contact: Nadia Zonis, Literary Associate
Theatre: professional not-for-profit **Works:** full-length
plays, translations, adaptations **2nd productions:** yes
Stage: thrust, 489 seats **Policies:** query/synopsis;
professional recommendation; agent submission **Response:**
7-10 days query; 3 months script **Remuneration:** standard
contract

THE HARTMAN THEATRE
Stamford, CT This theatre is permanently closed.

HAVURAT YISRAEL THEATRE GROUP
Havurat Yisrael Synagogue, 106-20 70th Ave.,
Forest Hills, NY 11375 (718) 997-1899
Contact: Alan Magill, Artistic Director **Theatre:**
community/non-professional **Works:** full-length plays, one-
acts, children's plays, cabaret/revues **2nd productions:**
yes **Special interest:** "Works relating to the trials and
triumphs of deepening one's Jewish commitment."
Specifications: maximum cast: 6-8; simple sets **Stage:**
100 seats **Audience:** "Mostly from Forest Hills area."
Policy: unsolicited script **Response:** 1-4 months
Programs: readings, staged readings **Comment:** "We are
a new theatre group."

HEDGEROW THEATRE
Rose Valley Rd., Rose Valley, PA 19086
(215) 565-4211 Contact: David zum Brunnen, Managing
Director **Theatre:** professional not-for-profit **Works:**
full-length plays, children's plays **2nd productions:** yes
Stages: flexible, 150 seats; studio, 30 seats **Policy:**

query/synopsis **Best time:** spring **Response:** 1 month
query; 2 months script **Remuneration:** negotiable
Comments: Inquire for detailed information. Theatre burned
in 1985 and was under construction when *The Playwright's
Companion* went to press.

HERITAGE ARTISTS, LTD.
Box 586, Cohoes, NY 12047 (518) 235-7969
Contact: Robert W. Tolan, Producing Director **Theatre:**
professional not-for-profit **Works:** musicals, cabaret/
revues, plays with music **2nd productions:** yes
Specifications: small cast, no chorus **Stage:** thrust,
250-350 seats **Policies:** unsolicited script; query/synopsis;
professional recommendation; agent submission **Response:**
1-2 months **Your chances:** 60-80/1-2 **Remuneration:**
travel, housing for readings; royalty for production
Program: readings

THE HIGHWAY ENSEMBLE
2126 The Highway, Wilmington, DE 19810
(302) 475-9805 Contact: Alicia Ann Chomo, President
Theatre: community/non-professional **Works:** full-length
plays, one-acts, adaptations **2nd productions:** yes
Specifications: maximum cast: 10; limited lighting **Stages:**
proscenium; thrust; arena; flexible **Audience:** "Small but
dedicated, with 15-60 people attending each performance."
Policies: unsolicited script; query/synopsis; professional
recommendation **Response:** 1-2 months **Remuneration:** no
Programs: readings, staged readings

HILBERRY THEATRE
Wayne State University, Detroit, MI 48202
(313) 577-2972 Contact: Robert Hazzard, Chairman
Theatre: college/university, graduate repertory company
Works: full-length plays, one-acts, translations, adaptations,
children's plays **2nd productions:** yes **Specifications:**
maximum cast: 19; no avant garde, no nudity or profanity
Stages: proscenium; modified thrust, 530 seats **Audience:**
"Mixed, city and university." **Policy:** unsolicited script with
resume **Best time:** late fall-early winter **Response:** 3
months **Your chances:** 5-10/0-2 **Remuneration:**
negotiable **Advice:** "Open to all styles and approaches."

HIP POCKET THEATRE
1627 Fairmount, Ft. Worth, TX 76104
(817) 927-2833 Contact: Johnny Simons, Artistic Director **Theatre:** professional not-for-profit **Works:** full-length plays, translations, adaptations, musicals **Special interest:** "Plays that have elements of fantasy and do not take place in a New York apartment." **Maximum cast:** 15 (flexible) **Tours:** yes **Stages:** flexible outdoor ampitheatre, 200 seats; flexible, 112 seats **Audience:** "Wide variety of ages and backgrounds from highly educated professionals to working-class folks." **Policy:** unsolicited script **Best time:** summer **Response:** 2-3 weeks **Your chances:** 150/5 **Remuneration:** negotiable **Advice:** "Make your work fresh, exciting, challenging, demanding imagination and creativity to produce."

THE HIPPODROME STATE THEATRE
25 SE 2nd Pl., Gainesville, FL 32601
(904) 373-5968 Contact: Mary Hausch, Producing Director **Theatre:** professional not-for-profit **Works:** full-length plays, translations, adaptations, musicals **2nd productions:** yes **Specifications:** small cast, unit set preferred **Stages:** thrust, 266 seats; flexible, 87 seats **Policies:** query/synopsis; agent submission **Response:** 2 weeks query; 4 months script

HOLLYWOOD ACTORS THEATRE, INC.
Box 5618, Santa Rosa, CA 95402 (707) 542-7422
Contact: Ron Bastone, President/Artistic Director **Theatre:** professional not-for-profit **Works:** full-length plays, one-acts **2nd productions:** yes **Special interests:** "Contemporary, fantasy, futuristic works." **Specifications:** maximum cast: 8; single set **Stage:** proscenium **Audience:** "Diverse, median age 30-40." **Policies:** unsolicited script with resume for one-act; query/synopsis with resume for full-length play **Response:** 3 weeks query; 3 months script **Your chances:** 15-30/1-3 **Remuneration:** "10% of box office." **Comment:** "Most successful of one-acts is videotaped for local cable broadcast."

HONOLULU COMMUNITY THEATRE
529 Makapuu Ave., **Honolulu, HI 96816**
(808) 734-8763 Contact: Jim Hutchison Artistic Director
Theatre: community/non-professional **Works:** full-length plays, one-acts, adaptations, children's plays **2nd productions:** "Sometimes." **Specifications:** 20' x 30' stage **Stage:** proscenium **Audience:** "Middle to upper class, all races, ages 25-85." **Policy:** inquire **Your chances:** "few/1 every other year" **Remuneration:** "Equivalent to royalty." **Programs:** readings, workshop productions, development; "staged reading or production during a dark night of a regular season production"

HONOLULU THEATRE FOR YOUTH
Box 3257, Honolulu, HI 96801 (808) 521-3487
Contact: John Kauffman, Artistic Director **Theatre:** professional not-for-profit **Works:** children's full-length plays, one-acts and adaptations **2nd productions:** yes **Special interests:** "Concerns of contemporary young people; Pacific Rim cultures." **Stages:** proscenium, thrust, flexible—500-670 seats **Audience:** "Target audience is youth (K-high school) and their families." **Policies:** unsolicited script; query/synopsis **Response:** 1 month query; 6 months script **Your chances:** 75/1-2 **Remuneration:** royalty; commission **Programs:** readings, staged readings

HORIZONS:
THEATRE FROM A WOMAN'S PERSPECTIVE
1041 Wisconsin Ave. NW, Washington, DC 20007
(202) 342-5503 Contact: Carole Myers, Associate Artistic Director **Theatre:** professional not-for-profit **Works:** full-length plays, one-acts, translations, adaptations **Exclusive interest:** women playwrights **Specifications:** single set; no fly space **Stage:** flexible, 75-100 seats **Policies:** query/synopsis preferred; unsolicited script **Response:** 3 months query; 6 months script

HORIZON THEATRE COMPANY
Box 5376, Station E, Atlanta, GA 30307
(404) 584-7450 Contact: Lisa Adler, Co-Artistic Director **Theatre:** Small Professional Theatre Contract **Works:** full-length plays **2nd productions:** yes **Special**

interests: "Atlanta, Southeastern and world premieres; strong female roles and roles for ensemble of 3-10 actors." **Maximum cast:** 14 **Stage:** flexible, 105-150 seats **Policies:** query/synopsis with resume preferred; unsolicited script **Best times:** Jun.-Aug., Nov.-Jan. **Response:** 1 month if interested in query; 6-12 months script **Remuneration:** "Percentage of box office plus rehearsal stipend." **Programs:** readings, staged readings **Advice:** "We are particularly interested in satire and comedy of an off-beat nature and dramas with socio-political significance." **Comment:** Theatre normally produces 1-3 new plays each season.

HORSE CAVE THEATRE
Box 215, Horse Cave, KY 42749 (502) 786-1200
Contact: Warren Hammack, Director **Theatre:** professional not-for-profit **Works:** full-length plays, translations, adaptations **2nd productions:** "Possibly." **Exclusive interests:** Kentucky playwrights; "Kentucky life--past, present or future." **Specifications:** maximum cast: 10; single or unit set preferred **Tours:** yes **Stage:** thrust, 355 seats **Audience:** "All ages, attitudes, interests, levels of education, ethnic composition." **Policy:** professional or personal recommendation **Best time:** fall **Your chances:** 30-50/1-2 **Remuneration:** percentage **Programs:** readings, staged readings, internships

HUDSON GUILD THEATRE
441 W. 26th St., New York, NY 10001
(212) 760-9836 Contact: Steven Ramay, Literary Manager **Theatre:** off Broadway **Works:** full-length plays, translations, adaptations, musicals **2nd productions:** no **Special interests:** "Social and political significance." **Maximum cast:** 10 **Stage:** proscenium, 135 seats **Audience:** "Various groups; large subscriber base." **Policy:** inquire **Response:** 3-4 months **Your chances:** 1200/5+ **Remuneration:** $1000 **Programs:** readings, staged readings, workshop productions, development, internships **Comment:** See Raymond, Gerard. "A Neighborhood Theater" (*Theater Week,* Jun. 27, 1988), 22-28.

HUNTINGTON THEATRE COMPANY
Boston University Theatre, 264 Huntington Ave., Boston, MA 02115 (617) 353-3320
Contact: Peter Altman, Producing Director **Theatre:** professional not-for-profit **Works:** full-length plays, translations, adaptations **2nd productions:** yes **Special interests:** New England authors, regional themes **Stage:** proscenium, 850 seats **Policy:** query/synopsis **Response:** 3-4 months

IDAHO SHAKESPEARE FESTIVAL
Box 9365, Boise, ID 84707
Contact: Rod Ceballos, Artistic Director This theatre is not currently accepting query/synopses or unsolicited scripts.

ILLINOIS THEATRE CENTER
400A Lakewood Blvd., Park Forest, IL 60466 (312) 481-3510 **Contact:** Steve S. Billig, Artistic Director **Theatre:** professional not-for-profit **Works:** full-length plays, musicals **Special interest:** small-cast plays **Maximum cast:** 9 for play, 14 for musical **Stage:** proscenium-thrust, 200 seats **Policy:** unsolicited script **Response:** 1 month

ILLUSION THEATER
528 Hennepin Ave. Suite 704, Minneapolis, MN 55403 (612) 339-4944
Contact: Michael Robins, Producing Director **Theatre:** professional not-for-profit **Works:** full-length plays, one-acts, translations, adaptations, musicals **2nd productions:** no **Special interest:** "Collaboration between writer and company to create new works." **Maximum cast:** 12 **Tours:** "Irregular transfer production to touring production." **Stage:** semi-thrust, 220 seats **Audience:** "Educated, adventuresome, thoughtful." **Policy:** professional recommendation **Best time:** May-Jun. **Response:** 6-8 months **Remuneration:** yes **Programs:** readings, workshop productions, development, internships **Advice:** "Send resume with cover letter explaining why you are interested in collaborating with the company."

ILLUSTRATED STAGE COMPANY
25 Van Ness Ave., San Francisco, CA 94102
(415) 861-6655 Contact: Barbara Malinowski, Artistic Director **Theatre:** professional not-for-profit **Works:** full-length plays, one-acts, adaptations, musicals **2nd productions:** "Yes, but not a priority." **Tours:** yes **Stages:** proscenium; thrust; black box **Audience:** "Mixed--wide range." **Policies:** introductory letter followed by unsolicited script; query/synopsis **Response:** 4 months **Your chances:** 400/2 **Programs:** staged readings, development, classes

THE IMMEDIATE THEATRE
1146 W. Pratt Ave., Chicago, IL 60626
(312) 465-3107 Contact: Jeff Ginsberg, Co-Artistic Director **Theatre:** professional not-for-profit **Works:** full-length plays, one-acts, translations, adaptations **Special interests:** "Contemporary American social and political issues, language, unique voices, women writers." **Specifications:** maximum cast: 8-10, doubling possible; limited fly space **Stages:** proscenium, 55 seats; black box, 100 seats **Audience:** "Ethnically diverse; large Hispanic and senior citizen populations." **Policies:** query/synopsis preferred; unsolicited script; professional recommendation; agent submission **Response:** 3 weeks query; 2 months script **Your chances:** 20/2 in 4 years **Remuneration:** "Something equitable." **Advice:** "Company is all white, late 20's-early 30's. Our spaces are very intimate."

INDEPENDENCE THEATER COMPANY
Box 112, Ft. Lee, NJ 07024 (201) 592-6060
Contact: Michelle Ortlip, Producing Artistic Director **Theatre:** professional not-for-profit **Works:** full-length plays, translations, musicals, children's plays **2nd productions:** yes **Special interest:** "Life affirming works." **Specifications:** maximum cast: 8; single or simple set; limitations on lighting; musicals must be simple; "no experimental work" **Tours:** "Yes, children's plays without sets." **Stage:** thrust, 200 seats **Audience:** middle to upper class **Policy:** query/synopsis with resume and dialogue sample **Best time:** Oct.-Mar. **Response:** 2 months script **Remuneration:** no **Advice:** "Simple and

honest, humorous if possible; issues and concepts for a contemporary audience." **Comment:** This is a new theatre company which produces 1 new play plus workshop productions each season.

THE INDEPENDENT EYE
208 E. King St., Lancaster, PA 17602
(717) 393-9088 Contact: Conrad Bishop, Producing Director **Theatre:** professional not-for-profit **Works:** full-length plays, related one-acts, musicals **2nd productions:** yes **Specifications:** small cast, maximum 4 for musicals; unit set **Stage:** open end, 100 seats **Policy:** query/synopsis with 5-page dialogue sample **Best time:** Nov.-Dec. **Response:** 1 month query; 3 months script **Your chances:** 100+/1 **Remuneration:** "Royalty against percentage of receipts." **Advice:** "Casting is local; few minorities are available."

INDIANA REPERTORY THEATRE
140 W. Washington, Indianapolis, IN 46204
(317) 635-5277 Contact: Janet Allen, Artistic Associate **Theatre:** professional not-for-profit **Works:** full-length plays, adaptations, cabaret/revues **2nd productions:** yes **Specifications:** some limitations on cast size and sets; "cabaret musicals must be small-scale: 4 performers, piano only" **Stages:** modified proscenium, 600 seats; proscenium, 250 seats; cabaret, 150 seats **Audience:** "Average age about 45; mostly white collar professionals." **Policies:** query/synopsis; professional recommendation; agent submission; commission **Best times:** Jan., May **Response:** 2-3 months query; 5-6 months script **Remuneration:** "Approximately 6%." **Program:** readings **Comment:** Theatre receives approximately 200 new scripts each year but rarely produces new plays.

INTAR HISPANIC AMERICAN THEATRE
Box 788, New York, NY 10109
(212) 695-6134, -6135 Contact: Max Ferrá, Artistic Director **Theatre:** professional not-for-profit **Works:** full-length plays, one-acts, translations, adaptations, musicals **Exclusive interests:** Hispanic-American writers; translations and adaptations of Hispanic works

Specifications: maximum cast: 8 preferred; no wing space **Stages:** proscenium, 99 seats; proscenium, 75 seats **Audience:** "Mixed cultural." **Policy:** unsolicited script **Best time:** spring-late summer **Response:** 3 months **Your chances:** 200/3 plus readings **Remuneration:** varies **Programs:** workshop productions; INTAR Hispanic Playwrights-in-Residence Laboratory and INTAR Hispanic American Music Theatre Laboratory (see Special Programs)

INTERMOUNTAIN ACTORS ENSEMBLE, INC.
1735 S. 1300 E, Salt Lake City, UT 84105
(801) 485-7249   Contact: Ron Burnett, Producing Director **Theatre:** professional not-for-profit **Works:** full-length plays, one-acts, musicals, children's plays **2nd productions:** "Sometimes." **Special interests:** "American drama, plays of topical interest, historical plays of this region." **Specifications:** maximum cast: 8 preferred; no wing space **Tours:** Shakespearean Festival **Stages:** proscenium; thrust; arena **Audience:** "Upwardly mobile who come here to ski in winter and relax in summer." **Policy:** query/synopsis **Best time:** summer **Response:** 3 weeks **Your chances:** 30/3 **Remuneration:** "Depends upon grant situation and audience." **Program:** workshop productions **Advice:** "Present the play in playscript format."

INTIMAN THEATRE COMPANY
Box 19645, Seattle, WA 98109 (206) 626-0775
Contact: Susan Fenichell, Artistic Associate **Theatre:** professional not-for-profit **Works:** adaptations **Special interest:** new adaptations and translations of classics **Maximum cast:** 10 **Stage:** thrust, 410 seats **Policy:** query/synopsis **Response:** "Undetermined." **Program:** staged readings

INVISIBLE THEATRE
1400 N. First Ave., Tucson, AZ 85719
(602) 882-9721   Contact: Susan Claassen, Artistic Director **Theatre:** off off Broadway **Works:** full-length plays, one-acts, translations, adaptations, musicals **Special interest:** contemporary issues **2nd productions:** yes **Specifications:** maximum cast: 8; simple sets **Stage:** flexible, 78 seats **Audience:** "Middle to upper middle class,

generally liberal." **Policy:** query/synopsis **Best time:** Jun.-Jul. **Response:** 1-6 months **Your chances:** 25/1 **Remuneration:** percentage **Program:** staged readings

IRONBOUND THEATRE
179 Van Buren St., Newark, NJ 07105
(201) 792-3524, 351-6685 Contact: Steve Gravatt, Artistic Director **Theatre:** community/non-professional **Works:** full-length plays, one-acts, musicals **2nd productions:** yes **Special interests:** "Contemporary American themes; urban settings." **Specifications:** some limitations on sets **Stage:** thrust, 80 seats **Audience:** "Well educated, middle to upper middle class; broad ethnic spectrum and sampling of occupations." **Policies:** unsolicited script with synopsis; query/synopsis **Best time:** fall-winter **Response:** 3-4 weeks query; 3-4 months script **Your chances:** 100+/1-2 plus 7-10 staged readings **Remuneration:** "Small honorarium ($50-$100)." **Advice:** "Send plays that are at least ready for a staged reading. Be willing to participate in reading/development process." **Comment:** "We are committed to producing at least 2 original American plays per season."

IRONDALE ENSEMBLE PROJECT
782 West End Ave., New York, NY 10025
(212) 633-1292 Contact: Steven Osgood, Dramaturg **Theatre:** professional not-for-profit **Works:** full-length plays, one-acts, translations, adaptations, musicals, children's plays **Special interest:** works with political/social relevance **Specifications:** maximum cast: 8-9; unit set **Stage:** black box, 50 seats **Policies:** query/synopsis preferred; unsolicited script **Response:** 2-4 weeks query; 6 months script

IUPUI UNIVERSITY THEATRE
525 N. Blackford St., Indianapolis, IN 46202
(317) 274-0556 Contact: J. Edgar Webb, Director, Theatre Programs **Theatre:** university/college **Works:** full-length plays, one-acts, children's plays **2nd productions:** "Rarely." **Special interests:** "Characters of college age; uplifting subjects; dramatic action is a must." **Specifications:** budget limitations **Stage:** flexible

Audience: "On site audience is mature. Tour audiences are generally school children, parents and teachers." **Policies:** query/synopsis; "our playwriting class" **Best time:** spring for next school year **Response:** 1 week query; time varies script **Your chances:** adult plays:12–15/1 **Remuneration:** standard royalty **Programs:** classes, Indiana University-Purdue University at Indianapolis Children's Theatre Playwriting Competition (see Contests)

JACKSONVILLE UNIVERSITY
DEPARTMENT OF THEATRE ARTS
Jacksonville, FL 32211 (904) 744–3950
Contact: Davis Sikes, Professor of Theatre **Theatre:** university/college **Works:** full-length plays, one-acts **2nd productions:** no **Special interest:** "Off-beat, experimental scripts." **Specifications:** maximum cast: 20; "reasonable technical requirements" **Tours:** yes **Stage:** proscenium **Audience:** community and college **Policies:** unsolicited script with resume; professional recommenation; agent submission; contest entry **Best time:** fall **Your chances:** 400/1 **Program:** Jacksonville University Playwriting Contest (see Contests)

JANUS THEATRE COMPANY, INC.
Box 65, Phoenix, AZ 85001–0065   (602) 258–9773
Contact: Charles W. Hunt, Artistic Director **Theatre:** community/non-professional **Works:** full-length plays, one-acts **2nd productions:** "Remounts, if available or popular." **Special interests:** "Alternate lifestyles; topical issues." **Tours:** "Rarely." **Stage:** flexible, 200–250 seats **Audience:** "Large cross-section of the community." **Policies:** unsolicited script with resume; query/synopsis with resume **Best time:** late spring-summer **Response:** immediate query; 2 weeks script **Your chances:** 12/2–3 **Remuneration:** "The Board votes on this issue; the cost of a piece could be a factor in its selection." **Comments:** "We invite guest directors to produce either published works or their own material. We have received grants from the Arizona Commission on the Arts for having produced educational or topical material for the benefit of the community."

JCC CENTER STAGE
1200 Edgewood Ave., Rochester, NY 14618
(716) 461-2000 Contact: Herb Katz, Arts Director
Theatre: community/non-professional **Works:** full-length plays, one-acts, translations, adaptations, musicals **Special interest:** "Jewish subject matter." **Maximum cast:** 10 **Stage:** thrust **Audience:** "Sophisticated, affluent, all ages." **Policy:** query/synopsis **Response:** immediate query; 1 month script **Your chances:** 25/variable number **Program:** staged readings **Comment:** "At this time in our readers theatre we do not do full productions, but we are not closed to the idea."

JEWISH REPERTORY THEATRE
344 E. 14th St., New York, NY 10003
(212) 674-7200 Contact: Ran Avni, Artistic Director
Theatre: off Broadway, Equity mini-contract **Works:** full-length plays **2nd productions:** if not previously produced off off Broadway **Exclusive interest:** Jewish themes **Maximum cast:** 8 **Stage:** proscenium, 100 seats **Policy:** unsolicited script **Best time:** Sept.-May **Response:** 4-6 weeks **Remuneration:** "6% of gross." **Programs:** staged readings, residencies **Comment:** See Siegel, Fern. "Defining a Jewish Voice" (*Theater Week*, Jun. 13, 1988), 50-54.

JIM SCHULTZ PRODUCTIONS
1939 N. Kenmore Ave. #108,
Los Angeles, CA 90027 (213) 660-3643
Contact: Jim Schultz, Producer **Theatre:** professional not-for-profit **Works:** full-length plays, one-acts, translations, adaptations **2nd productions:** yes **Maximum cast:** 8 **Stages:** rented spaces **Audience:** "Youthful--20's-30's." **Policies:** unsolicited script with resume; query/synopsis with resume; commission **Response:** 3 weeks **Remuneration:** negotiable **Programs:** readings, staged readings **Advice:** "Emotional, heightened reality along the line of Sam Shepard, Christopher Durang." **Comment:** Theatre produces 3-4 new plays each year.

JOHN DREW THEATRE
158 Main St., East Hampton, NY 11937
Contact: Laura Lyons, Business Manager
This theatre is not accepting submissions in 1989.

THE JULIAN THEATRE
777 Valencia, San Francisco, CA 94110
(415) 626-8986   Contact: Richard Reineccius, Artistic Director **Theatre:** professional not-for-profit **Works:** full-length plays, one-acts, translations **2nd productions:** yes **Special interests:** "Thought, wit, social/political significance." **Tours:** yes **Stages:** flexible, 150 seats **Audience:** "Multi-cultural." **Policy:** query/synopsis with dialogue sample **Response:** 3 months **Your chances:** 50-250/2-4 **Remuneration:** "5% of gross." **Programs:** classes, internships; "Voices of our Time: A Series of New Play Readings" is currently "on hold" **Advice:** "West Coast playwrights; collaboration with playwrights."

JUST US THEATER COMPANY
710 Peachtree St. NE Suite 225, Box 7,
Atlanta, GA 30308   (404) 876-2350
Contact: Byron Saunders, Artistic Director **Theatre:** professional not-for-profit **Works:** full-length plays, one-acts, translations, musicals, children's plays **2nd productions:** yes **Special interests:** "Love stories; stories about black Americans; avant garde." **Specifications:** maximum cast: 10-15; set limitations depend upon the show **Stage:** proscenium **Audience:** 51% subscribers **Policies:** query/synopsis with resume; professional recommendation **Response:** 1 year **Your chances:** 20/2 **Remuneration:** royalty **Advice:** "Be patient and keep in touch with the theatre."

KALAMAZOO CIVIC PLAYERS
329 S. Park, Kalamazoo, MI 49007
(616) 343-1313   Contact: David Grapes, Associate Director **Theatre:** community/non-professional **Works:** full-length plays, musicals, children's plays **Special interests:** musicals; plays for or about women **2nd productions:** yes **Stages:** proscenium, 536 seats; arena, 200 seats; flexible **Audience:** "Sophisticated, well-educated, somewhat

conservative but open to new work." **Policies:** unsolicited script; professional recommendation; agent submission **Best time:** Oct.-Nov. **Response:** 6 months query; 1 year script **Your chances:** 40/1-3 **Remuneration:** "Royalty fee, possible transportation." **Programs:** staged readings, workshop productions **Advice:** "Directors at Civic also work in other non-profit theatres and in the commercial theatre and are always on the lookout for exciting new works."

KILGORE COLLEGE THEATRE
TEXAS SHAKESPEARE FESTIVAL
1100 Broadway, Kilgore, TX 75662
(214) 983-8118 Contact: Raymond Caldwell, Director of Fine Arts **Theatre:** university/college **Works:** full-length plays, one-acts, translations, adaptations, children's plays **2nd productions:** yes **Maximum cast:** 12 **Stages:** flexible--238 seats and 1600 seats in 2 theatres **Audience:** "College students and community citizens of all ages, predominantly conservative." **Policy:** query/synopsis with dialogue sample **Best time:** Aug.-Oct. **Response:** 8 weeks query; 3 months script **Your chances:** 12/"sometimes none" **Programs:** "Anything is possible."

LACE PRODUCTIONS
23 W. 73rd St., New York, NY 10023
(212) 496-0251 Contact: Francine Mancini, Executive Artistic Director **Theatre:** off off Broadway, professional not-for-profit **Works:** full-length plays, one-acts, children's plays **2nd productions:** "Sometimes." **Special interests:** "Women; social issues." **Specifications:** single set **Stage:** flexible **Policies:** unsolicited script; professional recommendation **Response:** 6 months-1 year **Your chances:** 100's/3-5 **Remuneration:** no **Programs:** staged readings, readings, workshop productions, development, classes

L.A. DESIGNERS' THEATRE
Box 1883, Studio City, CA 91604 (818) 769-9000
Contact: Richard Niederberg, Artistic Director **Theatre:** professional not-for-profit **Works:** full-length plays, translations, adaptations, musicals **2nd productions:** "Occasionally, if the show needs a second interpretation." **Specifications:** "Sets within reason; quick change-over

time between acts and between productions is crucial; 80-minute shows are ideal." **Stages:** proscenium; flexible **Audience:** "People who work in the TV/motion picture business and are 'jaded.'" **Policies:** unsolicited script; query/synopsis; professional recommendation; agent submission **Response:** 10 days query; 120 days script **Your chances:** 500-1000+/20+ **Remuneration:** negotiable **Programs:** workshop productions, occasional internships **Advice:** "Make it unusual, commercial and easy to promote. There is no censorship whatsoever in terms of language, nudity, social themes, religious themes, political themes."

LA JOLLA PLAYHOUSE
Box 12039, La Jolla, CA 92037 (619) 534-6760
Contact: Robert Blacker, Associate Director/Dramaturg **Works:** full-length plays, translations, adaptations **2nd productions:** no **Stages:** proscenium, 500 seats; thrust, 300 seats **Policy:** professional recommendation **Best time:** Jul.-Nov. **Response:** 4 months

LAKE CHARLES LITTLE THEATRE
813 Enterprise Blvd., Lake Charles, LA 70601
(318) 433-7988 Contact: A. J. Cormier, Board of Directors **Theatre:** community/non-professional **Works:** full-length plays, one-acts, translations, musicals **2nd productions:** yes **Special interest:** "Universal plays that are marketable and not too avant garde." **Specifications:** no complicated technical requirements **Tours:** yes **Stages:** proscenium, 840 seats; proscenium, 134 seats; thrust, 60 seats; flexible, 80 seats **Audience:** "Mixed ages, occupations, ethnic background; generally conservative; some regional interest." **Policies:** query/synopsis preferred; unsolicited script **Best time:** Jan.-Apr. **Response:** 1 month **Your chances:** 8/1-3 **Remuneration:** standard royalty **Advice:** "Scripts need to be relatively complete unless the author is local (300-500 miles)."

LAKE GEORGE DINNER THEATRE
Holiday Inn, Box 266, Lake George, NY 12845
(518) 668-5781 Contact: David Eastwood, Producer **Theatre:** Equity dinner **Works:** full-length plays, musicals **Exclusive interests:** comedies, farces, musicals

Specifications: maximum cast: 5; single set **Stage:** arena, 165 seats **Audience:** "Tourists/senior citizens." **Policy:** unsolicited script **Response:** 6 months **Your chances:** 50/1 **Comment:** Theatre produces 1 new play each year.

LAKEWOOD LITTLE THEATRE
Beck Center, 17801 Detroit Ave., Lakewood, OH 44107 (216) 521-2540
Contact: LaVerne Lugibihl, Chairman, Selection Committee **Theatre:** community/non-professional **Works:** full-length plays, musicals **2nd productions:** yes **Special interests:** American comedies and mysteries **Specifications:** maximum cast: 20-25, 40 for musical **Policy:** unsolicited script **Best time:** Nov.-Dec. **Response:** 8 weeks **Your chances:** 50/1 in studio theatre

LA MAMA EXPERIMENTAL THEATRE
74A E. 4th St., New York, NY 10003
(212) 254-6468 Contact: Ellen Stewart, Founder and Producer **Theatre:** off off Broadway **Works:** full-length plays, one-acts, translations, adaptations, musicals **2nd productions:** no **Special interest:** experimental works **Tours:** yes **Stages:** flexible, 90 seats; flexible, 299 seats **Audience:** "Interested in experimental theatre." **Policies:** query/synopsis with resume; commission **Response:** 6 months **Your chances:** 50/0-1 **Program:** workshop productions **Advice:** "We must become interested in the playwright's work."

LAMB'S PLAYERS THEATRE
Box 26, National City, CA 92050 (619) 474-3385
Contact: Kerry Cederberg, Associate Director/Literary Manager **Theatre:** professional not-for-profit **Works:** full-length plays, translations, adaptations, musicals **Special interest:** "Plays which challenge an audience's cultural thinking through a Christian World View." **Stage:** arena, 180 seats **Policy:** professional recommendation **Response:** 3 months **Program:** internships

THE LAMB'S THEATRE COMPANY

130 W. 44th St., New York, NY 10036
(212) 575-0300, 221-1031 Contact: Sonya Baehr, Literary Manager **Theatre:** off Broadway, professional not-for-profit **Works:** full-length plays, musicals **2nd productions:** yes **Special interest:** "Theatre that deals with the problems of our time and inspires us to come up with solutions, that makes palpable the brotherhood of man, that can delight and amaze the entire family." **Specifications:** maximum cast: 9; small spaces, intimate shows **Tours:** "We have negotiated both national and international tours." **Stages:** flexible, 85 seats; proscenium, 360 seats **Audience:** "Off Broadway; group sales to high schools and colleges." **Policies:** query/synopsis with dialogue sample; professional recommendation; agent submission **Best time:** Sept.-Jun. **Response:** 2 weeks query; 3-6 months script **Your chances:** 500/3 **Remuneration:** negotiable **Programs:** readings, staged readings, workshop productions **Advice:** "No nudity or excessive profanity." **Comment:** "We submit scripts to the New Harmony Writer's Project developmental workshops."

LAS CRUCES COMMUNITY THEATRE

Box 1281, Las Cruces, NM 88001 (505) 523-1200
Contact: Ken Byers, President **Theatre:** community/non-professional **Works:** full-length plays, adaptations, children's plays **Specifications:** simple or unit set **Stage:** proscenium **Audience:** varied **Policy:** query/synopsis **Best time:** early spring **Response:** 2 weeks query; 2 months script **Remuneration:** "Equivalent royalty." **Advice:** "Submit family-oriented shows untypical of sit-coms."

LATIN AMERICAN THEATRE ENSEMBLE

Box 1259 Radio City Station, New York, NY 10019
(212) 410-4582 Contact: Margaret Toirac, Administrator **Theatre:** off off Broadway, professional not-for-profit, university/college **Works:** full-length plays, translations, children's plays **Tours:** yes **Stage:** flexible **Audience:** "College students; Spanish and English speaking communities; young, old, every kind." **Policies:** unsolicited script with resume; professional recommendation **Your chances:** 6/3 **Programs:** readings, staged readings, workshop productions,

classes **Advice:** "Mail us a copy of the play; we'll read it and keep in touch."

LAWRENCE WELK RESORT THEATRE
8975 Lawrence Welk Dr., Escondido, CA 92026
(619) 749-3448 Contact: Frank Wayne, Artistic Director **Theatre:** Equity dinner **Works:** full-length plays, musicals **Special interests:** "New musicals with good scores, comedies with merit." **Specifications:** maximum cast: 15; no "off color" language **Audience:** "Senior citizens." **Policy:** unsolicited script **Comment:** Formerly Lawrence Welk Dinner Theatre.

LE PETIT THEATRE DE VIEUX CARRE
616 St. Peter St., New Orleans, LA 70116
(504) 522-9958 Contact: Donald K. Marshall, Executive Director **Theatre:** community/non-professional **Works:** full-length plays, children's plays **2nd productions:** no **Stages:** proscenium; arena **Audience:** 3300 subscribers **Policies:** unsolicited script; professional recommendation **Best time:** summer **Response:** 12 months **Your chances:** 30/"very few" **Remuneration:** no **Program:** Louisiana Playwrights' Project (inquire) **Advice:** "Get productions of other works done in small spaces; send reviews."

LIGHT OPERA OF MANHATTAN
316 E. 91st St., New York, NY 10128
(212) 831-2001 Contact: Steven Levy, Executive Director **Theatre:** off Broadway **Works:** musicals **2nd productions:** yes **Special interest:** "Light fun." **Specifications:** maximum cast: 22; unit set or no more than 2 sets; no avant garde works **Stage:** 299 seats **Audience:** family **Policies:** query/synopsis with tape; commission **Best time:** before Jan. **Response:** 1 month **Remuneration:** negotiable **Program:** development **Advice:** "Something new and different, relevant to contemporary society."

LINCOLN CENTER THEATER
150 W. 65th St., New York, NY 10023
(212) 362-7600 Contact: Anne Cattaneo, Dramaturg **Theatre:** professional not-for-profit **Works:** full-length

87 THEATRES

plays, one-acts, translations, adaptations, musicals **Stage:** thrust, 300 seats **Policy:** agent submission **Response:** 2-4 months

LION THEATRE COMPANY
422 W. 42nd St., New York, NY 10036
(212) 736-7930 Contact: Gene Nye, Artistic Director **Theatre:** off off Broadway **Works:** full-length plays, musicals **2nd productions:** no **Policy:** inquire

LITTLE BROADWAY PRODUCTIONS
Box 15068, North Hollywood, CA 91615
(818) 509-0963 Contact: Jill Shawn Adereth, Producer **Theatre:** professional theatre for young audiences **Works:** children's musicals **2nd productions:** yes **Special interest:** "Musical versions of fairy tale classics." **Specifications:** maximum cast: 8-10; all sets must tour **Stage:** proscenium **Audience:** "Family, ages 4-104." **Policy:** unsolicited script **Response:** 2 months **Your chances:** 25/4 **Remuneration:** negotiable royalty

LITTLE MIAMI THEATER WORKS
West Liberty, OH See Mad River Theater Works.

LONG ISLAND STAGE
Box 9001, Rockville Center, NY 11570-9001
(516) 546-4608 Contact: Clinton J. Atkinson, Artistic Director **Theatre:** professional not-for-profit **Works:** full-length plays, translations, adaptations **2nd productions:** yes **Specifications:** maximum cast: 10; single set **Stage:** proscenium, 297 seats **Audience:** "Mostly over 50, upper middle class, college educated." **Policies:** query/synopsis; professional recommendation; agent submission **Best time:** late spring **Response:** 2 weeks query; 4 months script **Your chances:** 150/1-2 **Remuneration:** negotiable **Advice:** "One set, small cast, contemporary costumes."

LONG WHARF THEATRE
222 Sargent Dr., New Haven, CT 06511
(203) 787-4284 Contact: John Tillinger, Literary Consultant **Theatre:** professional not-for-profit **Works:** full-

length plays, translations, adaptations **2nd productions:**
"Sometimes." **Special interests:** "Social problems, political
awareness, morals, ethics." **Specifications:** maximum cast:
15, 9 for workshop **Tours:** "Occasionally." **Stages:** thrust,
484 seats; flexible, 200 seats **Audience:** "White, majority
40–65, upper middle class." **Policies:** agent submission with
resume preferred; query/synopsis with resume; professional
recommendation **Best time:** summer **Response:** 2 months
query; 6 months script **Your chances:** 300/possibly 1 full
production, 4 workshops, 4–5 readings **Remuneration:** yes
Programs: readings, staged readings, Stage II Workshops
(see Special Programs)

LOOKING GLASS THEATRE
175 Mathewson St., Providence, RI 02903
(401) 331–9080 Contact: Linda D'Ambra, Producing
Director **Theatre:** professional not-for-profit **Works:**
children's plays **Special interest:** social issues, with
audience participation, for grades K–8 **Specifications:** cast
of 3–5; all sets must tour **Stages:** various spaces
Audience: grades K–8 **Policy:** unsolicited script **Best
time:** Mar.–May **Response:** 1 month

LORRAINE HANSBERRY THEATRE
25 Taylor St., San Francisco, CA 94102
(415) 474–8842 Contact: Stanley Williams, Artistic
Director **Theatre:** professional not-for-profit **Works:**
full-length plays, translations, adaptations, musicals **2nd
productions:** yes **Stage:** flexible, 300 seats **Policies:**
unsolicited script with resume; query/synopsis with dialogue
sample and resume; professional recommendation; agent
submission **Response:** 2 months **Your chances:** 20/1
Remuneration: yes **Programs:** readings, staged readings,
workshop productions, development, classes

LOS ALTOS CONSERVATORY THEATRE
Box 151, Los Altos, CA 94022 (415) 941–5228
Contact: Doyne Mraz, Artistic Director **Theatre:**
professional not-for-profit **Works:** full-length plays,
one-acts, musicals **2nd productions:** yes **Specifications:**
maximum cast: 10–12; no more than 2 sets; simple technical
requirements **Policies:** query/synopsis with dialogue sample

preferred; unsolicited script **Best time:** Aug.-Sept. **Response:** 1 year

LOS ANGELES PUBLIC THEATRE
Los Angeles, CA This theatre is permanently closed.

LOS ANGELES THEATRE CENTER
514 S. Spring St., Los Angeles, CA 90013
(213) 627-6500 **Contact:** Dramaturgy Dept. **Theatre:** professional not-for-profit **Works:** full-length plays, translations, adaptations, musicals **2nd productions:** yes **Special interests:** contemporary social/political issues; women and minority authors **Tours:** "Occasionally." **Stages:** modified thrust, 503 seats; proscenium, 296 seats; thrust, 323 seats; flexible, 99 seats **Policies:** query/synopsis with 10-page dialogue sample; professional recommendation; agent submission **Response:** 21 days query; 3-6 months script **Your chances:** 2500/7-8 **Remuneration:** "Royalty varies from 5%." **Programs:** The Women's Project, Young Playwrights Lab, Latino Theatre Lab, Playwrights' Unit, Asian American Theatre Project, Black Theatre Artists Workshop, Music Theatre Lab (see Los Angeles Theatre Center Programs listing in Special Programs) **Advice:** Request information regarding script submission and critiquing program.

LOS ANGELES THEATRE WORKS
681 Venice Blvd., Venice, CA 90291
(213) 827-0808 **Contact:** Diane Sherry, Literary Manager **Theatre:** professional not-for-profit **Works:** full-length plays, one-acts, translations **2nd productions:** yes **Stage:** flexible **Policies:** query/synopsis with dialogue sample and resume; professional recommendation; agent submission **Response:** 6 months **Your chances:** 200+/1-2 **Remuneration:** yes

MABOU MINES
150 First Ave., New York, NY 10009
(212) 473-0559 **Contact:** Ann Eakland, Company Manager **Theatre:** professional not-for-profit **Works:** full-length plays, one-acts, translations, adaptations **Special interests:** "Contemporary works, contemporary issues."

Tours: yes **Stage:** no permanent facility **Policies:** professional recommendation preferred; query/synopsis **Response:** 4-10 weeks

MADISON REPERTORY THEATRE
211 State St., Madison, WI 53703
(608) 256-0029 Contact: Joseph Hanreddy, Artistic Director **Theatre:** professional not-for-profit **Works:** full-length plays, translations, adaptations **Stage:** 3/4 thrust, 355 seats **Policy:** query/synopsis **Response:** 2-3 months **Programs:** readings, workshop productions

MADISON THEATRE GUILD
2410 Monroe St., Madison, WI 53711
(608) 238-9322 Contact: Board of Directors **Theatre:** community/non-professional **Works:** full-length plays **2nd productions:** no **Specifications:** maximum cast: 20; $1000 set budget **Stage:** proscenium, 205 seats **Audience:** "Older, middle class." **Policy:** unsolicited script **Best time:** summer **Response:** 1 month query; 3 months script **Remuneration:** no **Programs:** "None yet; hopefully someday soon." **Advice:** "Send scripts to us, and we'll read them and pass them on to others in town." **Comment:** Theatre has not yet produced a new script but will consider doing so.

MAD RIVER THEATER WORKS
Box 238, West Liberty, OH 43357 (513) 465-6751
Contact: Jeffrey Hooper, Producing Director **Theatre:** professional not-for-profit **Works:** full-length plays, one-acts, musicals **2nd productions:** yes **Special interest:** "Rural issues or themes." **Maximum cast:** 5-6 **Tours:** yes **Stage:** flexible, 325 seats **Audience:** "Intended audience: multi-generational, rural, Mid- western." **Policies:** query/synopsis; professional recommendation **Response:** 1 month **Your chances:** 10-12/0-1 **Remuneration:** "Royalty; sometimes stipends." **Comment:** Formerly Little Miami Theater Works.

MAGIC THEATRE
Ft. Mason Center, Bldg. D, San Francisco, CA 94133
(415) 441-8001 Contact: Eugenie Chan, Literary Manager **Theatre:** professional not-for-profit **Works:** full-

length plays **2nd productions:** "Usually West Coast premieres." **Specifications:** small cast; some limitations on sets **Tours:** "Rarely." **Stages:** proscenium, 150 seats; thrust, 175 seats **Audience:** "Well educated and adventurous." **Policies:** query/synopsis with 3-5 page dialogue sample and resume; professional recommendation; agent submission **Best time:** Sept.-Apr. **Response:** 1 month query; 6 months script **Your chances:** 600/3 **Remuneration:** "Generally 5% of gross with guarantee." **Programs:** staged readings, workshop productions

MAIN STREET THEATER
2540 Times Blvd., Houston, TX 77005
(713) 524-3622 Contact: Rebecca Green Udden, Artistic Director **Theatre:** non-Equity professional **Works:** full-length plays, one-acts, translations, adaptations, musicals, children's plays **2nd productions:** yes **Special interest:** "We try to present a broad spectrum of points of view. Language is very important." **Specifications:** maximum cast: 25; some limitations on sets **Tours:** yes **Stage:** flexible thrust, 91 seats **Audience:** "College educated, 30's-40's, generally Anglo, urban, hard-core theatre-goers." **Policies:** unsolicited script; query/synopsis; professional recommendation; agent submission **Response:** 2-6 months query; 12-18 months script **Your chances:** 50-100/2 **Remuneration:** "Royalty; sometimes travel and lodging." **Programs:** readings, staged readings, workshop productions **Advice:** "Because our stage is small, some large-scale shows are not appropriate for us."

MAIN STREET THEATRE
Box 232, New York, NY 10044 (212) 371-6140
Contact: Worth Howe, Artistic Director **Theatre:** off off Broadway **Works:** full-length plays, one-acts, translations, adaptations, musicals, children's plays **2nd productions:** yes **Specifications:** maximum cast: 12; no 2-story sets; "we are not interested in 'Irish plays' nor in the 'standard daughter/son coming to terms with mother/father play'" **Stages:** proscenium; flexible **Audience:** "Upscale middle class; broad ethnic base plus professionals in all aspects of the theatre." **Policies:** unsolicited script; query/synopsis with dialogue sample; professional recommendation; agent

submission **Best time:** late summer-spring **Response:** 2 months **Your chances:** 150/3 **Programs:** readings, staged readings, workshop productions

MANHATTAN CLASS COMPANY AT THE NAT HORNE
Box 279 Times Square Station, New York, NY 10108 (212) 239-9033 Contact: Kent Adams, Literary Manager **Theatre:** off off Broadway play development company **Works:** full-length plays, one-acts, musicals **2nd productions:** "Rarely." **Special interest:** "The material should be accessible to the general public." **Maximum cast:** 10 **Stages:** proscenium, 99 seats (at Nat Horne Theatre); black box, 250 seats (on Long Island) **Policies:** unsolicited script; professional recommendation; agent submission **Best time:** by Oct. 1 for one-acts **Response time:** 3 weeks query; 6 months script **Your chances:** 600/4 full-length plays and 6 one-acts **Remuneration:** negotiable **Programs:** annual one-act festival (inquire), workshops, playwrights unit **Comment:** "We rarely produce a play ourselves. Usually we workshop a play to the point of option."

MANHATTAN PUNCH LINE THEATRE, INC.
410 W. 42nd St. 3rd Floor, New York, NY 10036 (212) 239-0827 Contact: Steve Kaplan, Artistic Director **Theatre:** off off Broadway **Works:** full-length plays, one-acts, adaptations **2nd productions:** New York City premieres **Special interest:** one-act and full-length comedies **Stage:** proscenium, 99 seats **Audience:** "All ages; usually the same audience that would go to see a Neil Simon play on Broadway." **Policies:** unsolicited script; professional recommendation; agent submission **Best times:** spring-summer for following season; one-act deadline is Oct. 1 **Response:** 2 weeks query; 6-10 weeks script **Your chances:** 1400+/12-15, "about 1%" **Remuneration:** "One-act $200, full-length play $400-$600." **Programs:** readings, staged readings, workshop productions, development, classes, internships, contests (inquire) **Advice:** "Start with the one-act form; we produce 9-15 one-acts each season."

MANHATTAN THEATRE CLUB
453 W. 16th St., New York, NY 10011
(212) 645-5590 Contact: Tom Szentgyorgyi, Literary Associate **Theatre:** off Broadway **Works:** full-length plays, one-acts, translations, adaptations, musicals **2nd productions:** no **Maximum cast:** 10-12 **Stages:** proscenium, 300 seats; thrust, 150 seats **Policies:** query/ synopsis with dialogue sample and resume; professional recommendation; agent submission **Response:** 1 month query; 6 months script **Your chances:** 1200/9 **Remuneration:** negotiable fee

MARIN THEATRE COMPANY
Box 1439, Mill Valley, CA 94942 (415) 388-5200
Contact: Will Marchetti, Interim Artistic Director **Theatre:** professional not-for-profit **Works:** full-length plays, translations, adaptations, children's plays **2nd productions:** yes **Special interests:** psychological and social issues; new translations of classics **Specifications:** unit set preferred **Stages:** proscenium, 250 seats; black box, 125 seats **Policy:** solicited script **Remuneration:** percentage **Program:** West Coast Playwrights Workshop (contact Michelle Swanson) **Comment:** Theatre produces 2-3 new plays plus staged readings each season.

MARKET HOUSE THEATRE
141 Kentucky Ave., Paducah, KY 42001
(502) 444-6828 Contact: April Cochran, Executive Director **Theatre:** community/non-professional **Works:** full-length plays, one-acts, translations, adaptations, musicals, children's plays **2nd productions:** children's plays **Special interests:** "Full-length, tourable children's plays, 40-50 minutes long; good mysteries for main stage." **Specifications:** small cast; minimal set changes preferred **Tours:** yes **Stage:** proscenium **Audience:** conservative **Policy:** inquire **Your chances:** 10/1 every 3rd year **Remuneration:** negotiable

THE MARK TAPER FORUM
135 N. Grand Ave., Los Angeles, CA 90012
(213) 972-7251 Contact: Jessica Teich, Literary Manager **Theatre:** professional not-for-profit **Works:** full-

length plays, translations, adaptations, plays for young audiences, literary cabaret, performance pieces **2nd productions:** yes **Stages:** proscenium, 80-90 seats; thrust, 724 seats; literary cabaret, 200 seats **Policy:** query/synopsis **Response:** 1-2 weeks query; 8-10 weeks script **Programs:** readings, workshop productions

MARRIOTT LINCOLNSHIRE THEATRE
Lincolnshire, IL 60015   (312) 634-0204
Contact: Dyanne Earley, Artistic Director   **Works:** full-length musicals, children's plays **2nd productions:** yes **Special interest:** "Children's shows for 7-12 year olds." **Specifications:** maximum cast: 25; no fairy tales **Stage:** arena, 900 seats **Audience:** "30-35, upper middle class, traditionalist."   **Policies:** unsolicited script; professional recommendation **Response:** 6 months **Your chances:** varying number/1 **Remuneration:** no **Advice:** "Broad-based appeal, musicals only, cast size 8-25; prefer lighter works; nothing esoteric."

MARY BALDWIN COLLEGE THEATRE
Mary Baldwin College, Staunton, VA 24401
(703) 887-7189   Contact: Virginia R. Francisco, Professor of Theatre **Theatre:** university/college **Works:** full-length plays, one-acts, translations, musicals **2nd productions:** yes **Stages:** thrust, 230 seats; flexible, 130 seats **Audience:** "Students, staff and community of conservative, college educated professionals." **Policy:** query/synopsis **Best time:** May-Jul. **Response:** 1 month query; 1 year script **Your chances:** 35/1-2 **Remuneration:** "$50/$30 per performance." **Advice:** "Cast predominantly women; focus on issues of interest to women, either historical or contemporary."

MAXWELL ANDERSON PLAYWRIGHTS SERIES
6 Sagamore Rd., Stamford, CT 06902
(203) 359-9122   Contact: Philip Devine, President **Theatre:** community/non-professional **Works:** full-length plays, one-acts **2nd productions:** if play has been revised **Maximum cast:** 12 **Stage:** black box, 150 seats **Audience:** "Mature, upwardly mobile, sophisticated, college educated." **Policies:** unsolicited script; professional

recommendation **Response:** 1-2 months **Your chances:** 200-300/6 staged readings **Remuneration:** stipend, travel

McCADDEN THEATRE COMPANY
1157 N. McCadden Pl., Hollywood, CA 90038
(213) 462-9070   Contact: Jay Donohue, Joy Rinaldi, Artistic Directors **Theatre:** professional not-for-profit **Works:** full-length plays, one-acts **2nd productions:** no **Maximum cast:** 10 **Stage:** proscenium, 55 seats **Policy:** query/synopsis with dialogue sample and resume **Your chances:** 150/3 **Remuneration:** no **Programs:** readings, staged readings, workshop productions

McCARTER THEATRE
91 University Pl., Princeton, NJ 08540
(609) 683-9100   Contact: Robert Lanchester, Associate Artistic Director **Theatre:** professional not-for-profit **Works:** full-length plays, one-acts, translations, adaptations **2nd productions:** yes **Stages:** proscenium, 1067 seats; 2nd stage (on stage), 100 seats; basement theatre, 100 seats **Policies:** unsolicited script with resume; query/synopsis with resume; professional recommendation; agent submission **Response:** 1 week query;   2-3 months script   **Your chances:** 600/1-2 plus staged readings **Remuneration:** "Negotiable fee for mainstage and 2nd stage; $500 plus travel for basement theatre play readings." **Programs:** readings, staged readings, workshop productions, development, residencies, classes

MERIDIAN GAY THEATRE
New York, NY   This theatre has requested that we discontinue its listing.

MERRIMACK REPERTORY THEATRE
Box 228, Lowell, MA 01853 (617) 454-6324
Contact: David G. Kent, Literary Manager/Dramaturg
This theatre is accepting submissions only through the Merrimack Repertory Theatre Playwriting Contest (see Contests).

MERRY-GO-ROUND PLAYHOUSE
Box 506, Auburn, NY 13021 (315) 255-1305
Contact: Dennis McCarthy, Literary Manager **Theatre:** professional not-for-profit **Works:** full-length plays, translations, adaptations, musicals, children's plays **Special interest:** audience participation for grades 6-12 **Maximum cast:** 3-4 **Stage:** flexible: 325-seat proscenium or 100-seat thrust **Policy:** unsolicited script **Best time:** Mar.–May **Response:** 1 month

METTAWEE RIVER COMPANY
463 West St. #D405, New York, NY 10014
(212) 929-4777 Contact: Ralph Lee, Artistic Director **Theatre:** professional not-for-profit touring company **Work:** multimedia pieces **Special interests:** collaboration between writer and company; works combining dialogue with storytelling, lyrics, masks, puppetry, music, visual elements; works based on myth and legend **Specifications:** cast size: 6 **Stages:** outdoor (summer) and indoor spaces **Policy:** query/synopsis with dialogue sample **Response:** 4 weeks query; 8 weeks script

MIAMI BEACH COMMUNITY THEATRE
2231 Prairie Ave., Miami Beach, FL 33139
(305) 532-4515 Contact: Jay W. Jensen, Drama Director **Theatre:** community/non-professional **Works:** full-length plays, one-acts, children's plays **2nd productions:** yes **Special interest:** "Plays dealing with AIDS and the teenager." **Stages:** proscenium; flexible **Audience:** "All ages, backgrounds; many with Hispanic backgrounds." **Policy:** inquire **Response:** 2-3 weeks query **Your chances:** 19/1 **Remuneration:** no **Programs:** workshop productions, development, classes

MILL MOUNTAIN THEATRE
Center in the Square, 1 Market Sq., Roanoke, VA 24011 (703) 342-5730 Contact: Jo Weinstein, Literary Manager **Theatre:** professional regional **Works:** full-length plays, one-acts, musicals **2nd productions:** yes **Special interest:** "Mixed casts." **Maximum cast:** 12, 20 for musical **Stages:** proscenium, 462 seats; flexible, 100 seats **Audience:** "A conservative and provincial community."

Policies: unsolicited script with resume; agent submission; no synopsis **Response:** immediate if interested in query; 6-8 months script **Your chances:** 250/2 in Fall Festival, 10 in Centerpieces **Remuneration:** "Each arrangement is individual." **Programs:** staged readings; Mill Mountain Theatre New Play Competition (see Contests); Fall Festival of New Plays; Centerpieces: lunchtime staged readings of one-acts (25-35 minutes in length)

MILWAUKEE CHAMBER THEATRE
Box 92583, Milwaukee, WI 53202 (414) 276-8842
Contact: Montgomery Davis, Artistic Director **Theatre:** professional not-for-profit **Works:** full-length plays, one-acts, translations, adaptations **Special interest:** "Shaw and other somewhat classical writers." **Specifications:** limited budget **Tours:** small productions **Stage:** black box, 216 seats **Audience:** "Usually the older, well-read couple; more and more younger couples." **Policies:** query/synopsis with resume; professional recommendation; agent submission **Best times:** Jul.-Aug., Nov.-Jan. **Response:** 4 months **Your chances:** 200/"theatre considers producing 1 new play each season" **Remuneration:** negotiable **Advice:** "Have invited staged readings." **Comment:** "We produce 6 plays each year, 3 of which are part of our Shaw Festival."

MILWAUKEE REPERTORY THEATRE
108 E. Wells, Milwaukee, WI 53202
(414) 224-1761 Contact: Robert Meiksins, Dramaturg **Theatre:** professional not- for-profit **Works:** full-length plays, translations, adaptations, musicals, cabaret pieces **2nd productions:** yes **Special interest:** cabaret pieces **Stages:** 3/4 thrust, 700 seats; black box, 200 seats **Audience:** "Largely middle class." **Policies:** query/synopsis with 10-page dialogue sample; professional recommendation; agent submission **Response:** 2 months **Remuneration:** "Sometimes a modest royalty."

MIMETIC THEATRE
1536 18th St., San Francisco, CA 94107
(415) 621-6002 Contact: Bert Houle, Veera Wilbaux, Co-Artistic Directors **Theatre:** professional not-for-profit **Works:** full-length plays, one-acts **2nd productions:** no

Tours: "We rent theatres and tour across the country for college and university audiences." **Policies:** unsolicited script with resume, query/synopsis with resume **Response:** 1 month **Remuneration:** negotiable **Advice:** "Visual, mystical, spiritual concepts; could be comic." **Comment:** Theatre produces 1 play and 5-10 "skits" each year.

MIRROR REPERTORY COMPANY
352 E. 50th St., New York, NY 10022
(212) 888-6087 Contact: Sabra Jones, Artistic Director **Theatre:** professional not-for-profit **Works:** full-length plays, one-acts, translations, adaptations **Special interest:** large-cast plays for alternating repertory **Stage:** thrust, 199 seats **Policy:** unsolicited script **Response:** several months **Program:** staged readings

MISSION HILLS DINNER THEATRE
Northridge, CA   This theatre is permanently closed.

MISSOURI REPERTORY THEATRE
4949 Cherry St., Kansas City, MO 64110
(816) 363-4541 Contact: Felicia Londré, Dramaturg **Theatre:** professional not-for-profit **Works:** full-length plays, translations, adaptations **Second productions:** yes **Stage:** modified thrust, 788 seats **Policy:** query/synopsis **Response:** time varies **Your chances:** 30-60/0-1

MONTFORD PARK PLAYERS
Box 2663, Ashville, NC 28802   (704) 254-5146
Contact: Hazel Robinson, Director   **Theatre:** community/ non-professional **Works:** full-length plays, one-acts, translations, adaptations, children's plays **2nd productions:** yes **Specifications:** maximum cast: 22; 1 or 2 simple sets; budget considerations **Stages:** proscenium; thrust; flexible; outdoor **Audience:** community residents and tourists **Policies:** unsolicited script; query/synopsis **Best time:** fall **Response:** 1 month query; 1 year script **Your chances:** 10/1 **Remuneration:** "Usually not; we have commissioned scripts." **Programs:** readings, staged readings, workshop productions **Advice:** "Send request for information with synopsis."

THE MOSAIC THEATRE AT THE 92ND STREET Y

New York, NY "The 92nd Street Y no longer has a theatre company."

MOUNTAIN VIEW HIGH SCHOOL THEATRE

14609 NE 7th St., Vancouver, WA 98684
(206) 254-7318 **Contact:** Paige Dickinson, Theatre Instructor **Theatre:** high school **Works:** full-length plays, translations, children's plays **2nd productions:** yes **Stage:** thrust **Audience:** "Students; parents with moderate education." **Policy:** inquire **Best time:** early Jun. **Response:** 2-3 months **Remuneration:** yes

MUSICAL THEATRE WORKS

440 Lafayette St., New York, NY 10003
(212) 228-1210 Contact: Mark S. Herko, Associate Artistic Director **Theatre:** professional not-for-profit **Works:** musicals **Maximum cast:** 12 **Stages:** flexible, 60 seats; flexible, 150 seats **Policies:** unsolicited script; professional recommendation **Response:** 3 months **Your chances:** 100/4 plus readings, "20 projects altogether" **Remuneration:** no **Programs:** readings, staged readings, workshop productions, development

MUSIC HALL THEATRE

564 Monterey Blvd., San Francisco, CA 94127
(415) 485-4098 Contact: Ann Marie Garvin **Theatre:** off off Broadway **Works:** full-length plays, musicals, cabaret/revues **2nd productions:** exclusively **Maximum cast:** 20 **Stage:** 15'x30', 257 seats plus 30 standing **Audience:** general **Policy:** "We are a rental facility." **Best times:** Sept., Apr. **Response:** 1 week **Your chances:** 20/2 **Remuneration:** $3000 per week or $500 per night **Advice:** available upon request

MUSIC-THEATRE GROUP/LENOX ARTS CENTER
735 Washington St., New York, NY 10014
(212) 924-3108 Contact: John Hart, Project Development
Theatre: professional not-for-profit **Works:** musicals, operas, cabaret/revues **2nd productions:** no **Special interest:** experimental musicals using music-theatre, dance and visual arts **Maximum cast:** 15 including musicians **Stages:** flexible, 99 seats; flexible, 75 seats **Audience:** "Well-educated, middle class, open-minded, 20's-30's." **Policies:** query/synopsis; solicited script **Best time:** Sept.-Dec. **Response:** time varies **Advice:** Phone calls are unwelcome. **Comment:** During Jul.-Aug. the theatre's address is Lenox Arts Center, Box 128, Stockbridge, MA 01262 (413) 298-9463. **Comment:** See Carr, Jan. "O Pioneers! A Portrait of Lyn Austin and the Music-Theatre Group/Lenox Arts Center" (*Theater Week*, Mar. 14-20, 1988), 13-15.

NATIONAL IMPROVISATIONAL THEATER
233 Eighth Ave., New York, NY 10011
(212) 243-7224 Contact: Robert Martin, Director of Production **Theatre:** off off Broadway **Works:** full-length plays, one-acts, translations, adaptations, musicals, children's plays **2nd productions:** if New York City premiere **Special interest:** "Positive theatre in which the audience leaves the theatre feeling better than when they arrived." **Specifications:** maximum cast: 10; single set; "no vile language; no negative concepts about humanity" **Stage:** flexible **Audience:** "An audience that is looking for new experiences." **Policy:** unsolicited script with resume **Best times:** early winter, summer **Response:** 2 weeks **Your chances:** 24+/12 including one-acts **Programs:** staged readings, workshop productions, scholarships **Comment:** Theatre emphasizes full productions.

NATIONAL JEWISH THEATER
5050 W. Church St., Skokie, IL 60077
(312) 675-2200 Contact: Fran Brunlik, Managing Director
Theatre: professional not-for-profit **Works:** full-length plays, one-acts, translations, adaptations, musicals **2nd productions:** no **Special interest:** American Jewish experience, both contemporary and historical **Specifications:** maximum cast: 10-12 preferred; no more than 2 sets; no fly space **Stage:** open, 250 seats **Policy:**

unsolicited script **Response**: 2 months **Programs**: readings, workshop productions, internships

NATIONAL RADIO THEATRE
Chicago, IL (312) 751-1625
Contact: Robin Dale Leivers, General Manager   Our 1989 questionnaire was returned as "undeliverable," and this theatre has not responded to our phone messages.

THE NATIONAL THEATRE OF THE DEAF
The Hazel E. Stark Center, Chester, CT 06412
(203) 526-4971 Contact: David Hays, Artistic Director **Theatre:** professional not-for-profit **Works:** full-length plays, one-acts, translations, adaptations, children's plays **Tours:** yes **Stages:** various spaces **Policy:** unsolicited script **Best time:** Sept.-May **Response:** 3 months **Comment:** Telecommunications device for the deaf is available: (203) 526-4974.

NATIVE AMERICANS IN THE ARTS
American Indian Community House, 842 Broadway, New York, NY 10003 (212) 598-4845
Contact: Muriel Miguel or Gloria Miguel, Theatre Coordinators **Theatre:** off off Broadway, professional not-for-profit **Works:** full-length plays, one-acts **2nd productions:** yes **Exclusive interest:** works by or about native Americans **Maximum cast:** 10 **Tours:** yes **Audience:** "Community and New York theatre-goers." **Policies:** unsolicited script; query/synopsis with dialogue sample and resume; professional recommendation **Best time:** fall **Response:** 2 weeks query; 2 months script **Your chances:** 5-10/1 or more **Remuneration:** "Depends upon grants." **Programs:** readings, staged readings, workshop productions, classes, internships **Comment:** See American Indian Community House in Special Programs.

N.C. BLACK REPERTORY COMPANY
610 Coliseum Dr., Box 2793, Winston-Salem, NC 27102 (919) 723-7907
Contact: Larry Leon Hamlin, Director **Theatre:** professional not-for-profit **Works:** full-length plays, one-acts, translations, adaptations, musicals, children's plays **2nd productions:** yes **Special interests:** "Contemporary

dramas involving African-Americans; historical docudramas; statement comedies." **Specifications:** maximum cast: 8; multiple sets discouraged **Tours:** yes **Stages:** proscenium; thrust **Policies:** unsolicited script with resume; query/synopsis with resume **Best time:** summer-fall **Response:** 8-12 weeks query **Your chances:** 25/4-6 **Remuneration:** negotiable royalty, option, percentage **Programs:** staged readings, workshop productions, development, classes **Comment:** "NCBRC's Playwright's Division is committed to development of new works by produced and unproduced playwrights."

NEBRASKA REPERTORY THEATRE
215 Temple Bldg., 12th and R Sts.,
Lincoln, NE 68588 (402) 472-2072
Contact: Albert Pertalion, Artistic Director **Theatre:** professional not-for-profit **Works:** full-length plays, musicals **Specifications:** simple set for studio theatre **Stages:** proscenium, 380 seats; black box studio, 180 seats **Policy:** query/synopsis **Best time:** Aug.-Apr. **Response:** 2 weeks query; 2 months script **Comment:** Theatre operates only in summer.

NEBRASKA THEATRE CARAVAN
6915 Cass St., Omaha, NE 68132 (402) 553-4890
Contact: Carl Beck, Associate Director **Theatre:** professional not-for-profit **Works:** full-length plays, translations, adaptations, musicals, children's plays **2nd productions:** yes **Special interest:** translations and adaptations of classics **Specifications:** maximum cast: 12; single set **Tours:** yes **Stages:** various spaces **Policies:** unsolicited script; agent submission **Response:** 3 months **Program:** workshops

NEGRO ENSEMBLE COMPANY
424 W. 55th St. #800, New York, NY 10036
(212) 575-5860 Contact: Leon Denmark, Producing Director **Theatre:** professional not-for-profit **Works:** full-length plays, one-acts, translations, adaptations **2nd productions:** no **Exclusive interest:** "The black experience." **Tours:** yes **Stage:** proscenium **Audience:** "Black middle and upper middle class; white middle class." **Policies:** unsolicited script; query/synopsis; professional

recommendation **Response:** 6 months–1 year **Your chances:** 60/4 **Remuneration:** royalty **Programs:** staged readings, development, classes, playwriting workshop, McDonald's Literary Achievement Awards (see Contests)

NEIL'S NEW YORKER/BELL PRODUCTIONS
4-C John St., Morristown, NJ 07960
(201) 335–8950 Contact: Brenda Bell, Associate Producer **Theatre:** dinner **Works:** full-length plays, one-acts, musicals, children's plays, mysteries, comedies **2nd productions:** yes **Special interest:** "Leading edge ideas!" **Stage:** flexible thrust with house ramps, 350 seats **Audience:** "For matinee mostly groups, senior citizens; for evening performance middle to upper class." **Policy:** query/ synopsis **Best times:** summer, winter **Response:** 1 month query **Remuneration:** negotiable

NEW AMERICAN THEATER
118 N. Main St., Rockford, IL 61101
(815) 963–9454 Contact: J. R. Sullivan, Producing Director **Theatre:** professional not-for-profit **Works:** full-length plays, one-acts, translations, adaptations **Stages:** thrust, 282 seats; black box, 90 seats **Policies:** query/synopsis preferred; unsolicited script **Best time:** Sept.–Dec. **Response:** 3 weeks query; 6 months script

NEWBERRY COLLEGE THEATRE
1935 Nance St., Newberry, SC 29108
(803) 276–5010 Contact: Sidney Pitts, Instructor **Theatre:** university/college **Works:** full-length plays, one-acts, translations, adaptations, musicals, children's plays **2nd productions:** yes **Maximum cast:** 15 **Stages:** proscenium; arena **Audience:** middle class, all ages **Policy:** unsolicited script **Best time:** May–Aug. **Response:** 3 months **Remuneration:** no **Comment:** Theatre receives approximately 5 new scripts each year.

NEW CITY THEATER
1634 Eleventh Ave., Seattle, WA 98122
(206) 323–6801 Contact: John Kazanjian, Artistic Director **Theatre:** professional not-for-profit **Works:** full-length plays, translations, adaptations, cabaret/revues **2nd productions:** yes **Special interest:** non-naturalistic

contemporary works **Specifications:** some limitations on production requirements; 11-foot ceiling **Stage:** flexible, 100 seats **Policies:** professional recommendation; agent submission **Response:** 5 months **Program:** New City Theater Director's Festival (see Special Programs)

THE NEW CONSERVATORY
Zephyr Theatre Complex, 25 Van Ness Ave. Lower Level, San Francisco, CA 94102 (415) 861-4914 **Contact:** Ed Decker, Artistic Director **Theatre:** professional not-for-profit **Works:** children's plays and adaptations **2nd productions:** yes **Special interest:** "Plays featuring youth dealing with socially relevant issues." **Maximum cast:** 8-12 **Tours:** yes **Stages:** flexible, 60 seats; flexible, 90 seats; proscenium, 150 seats **Audience:** families **Policy:** query/synopsis with resume **Response:** 2 weeks query; 10 weeks script **Your chances:** 75/2 **Remuneration:** royalty **Programs:** readings, staged readings

NEW FEDERAL THEATRE
466 Grand St., New York, NY 10002 (212) 598-0400 Contact: Woodie King, Jr., Producer **Theatre:** professional not-for-profit **Works:** full-length plays **2nd productions:** "Rarely." **Special interests:** social issues; minorities **Stages:** proscenium, 340 seats; arena, 146 seats; flexible, 99 seats **Audience:** "Tri-state area (NY, NJ, CT)." **Policy:** professional recommendation **Response:** 3 months **Your chances:** 300/6 plus readings and staged readings **Remuneration:** "$250 for 6 months."

THE NEW JERSEY PUBLIC THEATRE
1052-A Plainfield Ave., Berkeley Heights, NJ 07922 (201) 322-3808 **Contact:** Robert Vaccaro, Artistic Director **Works:** full-length plays, one-acts, translations, adaptations, musicals, children's plays **2nd productions:** yes **Specifications:** some limitations on sets **Stage:** flexible **Audience:** "Various backgrounds." **Policy:** unsolicited script with resume **Response:** 3 months **Your chances:** 5-10/1-2 **Remuneration:** percentage **Program:** staged readings **Advice:** "Playwrights should be themselves, tell the truth and make sure this is reflected in their work."

NEW JERSEY SHAKESPEARE FESTIVAL
Route 24, Drew University, Madison, NJ 07940
(201) 377-5330 Contact: Paul Barry, Artistic Director **Theatre:** professional not-for-profit **Works:** full-length plays, translations **2nd productions:** yes **Special interests:** classics; contemporary works of classic standards **Specifications:** minimal sets preferred **Stage:** thrust, 238 seats **Audience:** "General." **Policies:** unsolicited script; professional recommendation **Best time:** Jan.-Feb. **Response:** 3 months **Your chances:** 30/0-1

NEW MEXICO REPERTORY THEATRE
Box 789, Albuquerque, NM 87103-0789
(505) 243-4577 Contact: David Richard Jones, Literary Manager **Theatre:** professional not-for-profit **Works:** full-length plays, translations **2nd productions:** yes **Special interest:** Hispanic life **Tours:** yes **Stage:** proscenium **Audience:** "Professional, well-educated." **Policies:** query/ synopsis; professional recommendation; agent submission **Response:** 3 weeks query; 4-6 months script **Your chances:** 30/2 **Remuneration:** standard royalty

NEW PHOENIX, INC.
110 Bartlett Ave., Pittsfield, MA 01201
(413) 443-5915 Contact: Ralph Hammann, Director **Theatre:** professional not-for-profit **Works:** full-length plays, translations, adaptations **2nd productions** yes **Special interest:** "Thrillers that have some psychological complexity and uniqueness." **Specifications:** maximum cast: 8; small set **Tours:** yes **Stages:** proscenium, 290 seats; flexible, 100 seats **Audience:** "Mixed, mostly college educated." **Policies:** query/synopsis with dialogue sample; professional recommendation **Response:** 3 weeks query; 2 months script **Remuneration:** "May offer small royalty." **Programs:** readings, staged readings

NEW PLAYWRIGHTS' PROGRAM
Department of Theatre and Dance, University of Alabama, Box 870239, Tuscaloosa, AL 35487-0239
(205) 348-5283 Contact: Edward Journey, Acting Director **Theatre:** university/college **Works:** full-length plays, one-acts, translations, adaptations, musicals, children's plays **Stages:** mainstage, 338 seats; studio lab, 100 seats

Policy: unsolicited script **Best time:** Aug.–Apr. **Response:** 60 days if submitted Aug.–Apr. **Program:** staged readings **Comment:** Theatre produces at least 1 new play per season.

NEW PLAYWRIGHTS' THEATRE
Ashland, OR This theatre is permanently closed.

NEW PLAYWRIGHT'S THEATRE
1742 Church St. NW, Washington, DC 20036
(202) 232–4527 Contact: Naomi Jacobson, Assistant to Artistic Director **Theatre:** professional not-for-profit **Works:** full-length plays **2nd productions:** yes **Specifications:** maximum cast: 10; small wing space **Stage:** proscenium **Policy:** query/synopsis with dialogue sample and resume **Best time:** Aug. **Response:** 30–60 days query **Your chances:** 300/4 plus 7 staged readings **Remuneration:** yes **Programs:** readings, staged readings, classes, internships

THE NEW ROSE THEATRE
904 SW Main St., Portland, OR 97205
(503) 222–2495 Contact: Michael Griggs, Artistic Director **Theatre:** professional not-for-profit **Works:** full-length plays, translations, adaptations, children's plays **2nd productions:** yes **Special interests:** multi-cultural casting; adaptations and contemporary translations of classics or classical themes **Stages:** 3/4 thrust, 119 seats; flexible, 292–400 seats **Policy:** query/synopsis with dialogue sample **Best time:** Aug.–Jan. **Response:** 2–4 weeks query; 3–6 months script **Remuneration:** negotiable royalty **Program:** readings

NEW STAGE THEATRE
1100 Carlisle St., Jackson, MS 39202
(601) 948–3533 Contact: Jane Reid-Petty, Producing Artistic Director **Theatre:** professional not-for-profit **Works:** full-length plays, one-acts **Specifications:** small cast **Stages:** proscenium, 365 seats; flexible, 100 seats **Policy:** query/synopsis **Best time:** summer-fall **Response:** 2–4 weeks query; 3–5 months script **Program:** readings **Comment:** See Kolin, Philip. "An Interview with Jane Reid-Petty of the New Stage Theatre" (*Southern Quarterly,* 25 [1987]), 39–46.

THE NEW THEATRE OF BROOKLYN
465 Dean St., Brooklyn, NY 11217
(718) 230-3366 Contact: Janice Paran, Literary Manager **Theatre:** professional not-for-profit **Works:** full-length plays, translations, adaptations **2nd productions:** if previously produced outside the New York area **Special interest:** "Originality of dramatic voice and vision. No clones." **Specifications:** maximum cast: 6; single set; simple requirements **Stage:** black box, 99 seats **Audience:** "Wide cross-section." **Policies:** agent submission preferred; query/synopsis with 5-page dialogue sample; professional recommendation **Response:** 2 months query; 6 months script **Your chances:** varying number/1 **Remuneration:** "Small honorarium--varies with production." **Programs:** readings, internships

NEW TUNERS THEATRE
1225 Belmont Ave., Chicago, IL 60657
(312) 929-7367 Contact: George H. Gorham, Associate Producer **Theatre:** professional not-for-profit **Works:** musicals, musical adaptations **2nd productions:** yes **Special interest:** "Scripts for a younger (35 and under) ensemble." **Specifications:** maximum cast: 15; no children's material **Stage:** thrust, 148 seats **Audience:** "Urban and suburban, fairly sophisticated, regular theatre-goers." **Policies:** unsolicited script; query/synopsis **Response:** 6 months **Your chances:** 200/3, "probably only 1 from unsolicited material" **Remuneration:** "Percentage, possible stipend for residency." **Programs:** readings, staged readings, workshop productions, development, classes

NEW VOICES
511 Tremont St., Boston, MA 02116
(617) 357-5667 Contact: Stanley Richardson, Artistic Director **Theatre:** professional not-for-profit **Works:** full-length plays, one-acts, adaptations **2nd productions:** no **Special interests:** "Politics, history, ideas, the social contract." **Tours:** "Sometimes." **Stages:** "Various spaces, 99-250 seats." **Audience:** "We choose plays on merit and assume we'll find an audience." **Policies:** query/synopsis; professional recommendation; agent submission **Best time:** Sept.-Jun. **Response:** 1 month query; 5 months script **Your chances:** 30/10 **Remuneration:** negotiable **Programs:**

staged readings, workshop productions, development, internships, Clauder Competition for Excellence (see Contests) **Advice:** "Focus on ideas, language. Forget psychological motivations. Care."

NEW YORK SHAKESPEARE FESTIVAL
425 Lafayette St., New York, NY 10003
(212) 598-7100 Contact: Joseph Papp, Producer **Theatre:** professional not-for-profit **Works:** full-length plays, translations, adaptations, musicals **2nd productions:** "Not often." **Special interests:** "Themes of sociological impact; individual and unusual writing talent." **Tours:** "Sometimes." **Stages:** proscenium, 299 seats; proscenium, 200 seats; thrust, 275 seats; flexible, 150 seats; flexible, 100 seats **Audience:** "Totally eclectic." **Policies:** unsolicited script with resume; query/synopsis with dialogue sample and resume; professional recommendation; agent submission **Response:** 2-3 weeks query; 2-3 months script **Your chances:** 3000/15 **Remuneration:** negotiable **Programs:** readings, development

NEW YORK STAGE AND FILM COMPANY
450 W. 42nd St. Suite 21, New York, NY 10036
(212) 967-3130 Contact: Annie Evans, Readings Coordinator **Theatre:** professional not-for-profit **Works:** full-length plays **Special interests:** "New plays; short films." **Policies:** professional recommendation; agent submission **Best time:** fall-winter **Response:** 6 months **Your chances:** 300/2 plus 15 staged readings **Programs:** staged readings, workshop productions, development, internships, residencies, classes

THE NEW YORK THEATRE GROUP
Box 1557, New York, NY 10011 (718) 624-4680
Contact: William Neish, Company Manager **Theatre:** off off Broadway, professional not-for-profit **Works:** full-length plays, one-acts **2nd productions:** yes **Special interests:** "Contemporary social issues; plays that explore the possibilities of language; theatricality." **Audience:** "Eclectic, young, New York; broad social/cultural base." **Policy:** unsolicited script **Your chances:** 60/1 full-length play plus public readings and 6 workshop productions

Remuneration: "For full-length play only: percentage of box office on contract." **Programs:** readings, development; New American Theatre Project: long-term developmental program (see Special Programs)

NEW YORK THEATRE STUDIO
150 E. 35th St., New York, NY 10016
(212) 239-9068 Contact: Ted Snowdon, Literary Manager **Theatre:** off off Broadway, professional not-for-profit **Works:** full-length plays, translations, adaptations **Special interests:** political issues; expressionistic and surrealistic works; New York City premieres **Maximum cast:** 20 **Policy:** query/synopsis **Best time:** Sept. **Response:** 4-10 months **Programs:** staged readings, workshop productions, development

NEW YORK THEATRE WORKSHOP
220 W. 42nd St. 18th Floor, New York, NY 10036
(212) 302-7737 Contact: Tony Kushner, Associate Artistic Director **Theatre:** professional not-for-profit **Works:** full-length plays, one-acts, translations, adaptations, musicals **Special interests:** important issues; innovations in form and language **Stage:** proscenium, 99 seats **Policies:** query/synopsis; proposal; professional recommendation; agent submission; solicited script **Response:** 1-3 weeks query; 2-4 months script **Programs:** staged readings, development

NEXT THEATRE COMPANY
927 Noyes, Evanston, IL 60201 (312) 475-6763
Contact: John Carlile, Associate Artistic Director **Theatre:** professional not-for-profit **Works:** full-length plays, adaptations **2nd productions:** yes **Specifications:** maximum cast: 30; single or flexible set **Stages:** proscenium, 200 seats; arena, flexible seating; proscenium, 50 seats **Audience:** "Mixed." **Policies:** query/synopsis with dialogue sample and resume; professional recommendation; agent submission **Response:** 1 month query; 6 months script **Your chances:** 200/0-2 **Remuneration:** standard royalty **Programs:** staged readings, workshop productions **Advice:** "Well-written, interesting, theatrical plays, preferably about social issues."

NIGGLI, WESTERN CAROLINA UNIVERSITY
Cullowhee, NC 28723   (704) 227-7491
Contact: D. L. Loeffler, Director of Theatre   **Theatre:** university/college   **Works:** full-length plays, one-acts, children's plays   **2nd productions:** no   **Special interest:** plays for college-age actors   **Specifications:** small theatre; limited wing space   **Tours:** children's plays   **Stages:** proscenium, 142 seats; proscenium, 380 seats   **Audience:** university community; senior adults   **Policy:** unsolicited script   **Best time:** Feb.   **Response:** 1 month   **Your chances:** 8/1   **Remuneration:** no   **Program:** workshop productions   **Advice:** "Appeal to university theatre students."

NORTHLIGHT THEATRE
2300 Green Bay Rd., Evanston, IL 60201
(312) 869-7732   Contact: Literary Dept.   **Theatre:** professional not-for-profit   **Works:** full-length plays, translations, adaptations, musicals   **2nd productions:** yes   **Special interests:** "Chicago subjects; broad canvas."   **Specifications:** "No domestic realism."   **Stage:** proscenium-thrust, 298 seats   **Audience:** "Upper middle-class, college/post graduates, 35-60."   **Policies:** query/ synopsis with resume; agent submission   **Response:** 4-8 weeks query; 8-10 weeks script   **Remuneration:** negotiable   **Advice:** "We prefer ambitious plays that acknowledge and utilize the patent theatricality of the medium."

NORTHSIDE THEATRE COMPANY
848 E. William St., San Jose, CA 95116
(408) 288-7820   Contact: Richard T. Orlando, Executive Director   **Theatre:** professional not-for-profit   **Works:** full-length plays, one-acts, adaptations, children's plays   **2nd productions:** yes   **Special interest:** "Small-cast plays dealing with concerns of youth: peer pressure, sexual abuse, drug awareness."   **Maximum cast:** 8   **Tours:** yes   **Stages:** "We have a modular performance space; touring, we've played them all."   **Audience:** "Young and old, rich and poor."   **Policies:** unsolicited script; query/synopsis   **Best time:** after Jan.   **Response:** 4-6 weeks   **Your chances:** 20/3-4   **Remuneration:** "Small royalty."   **Programs:** readings, staged readings, contests (inquire)   **Advice:** "We are looking for touring productions 40-50 minutes in length."   **Comment:** This company is not a children's theatre.

OAKLAND ENSEMBLE THEATRE

1428 Alice St. Suite 289, Oakland, CA 94612
(415) 763-7774 Contact: Benny Sato Ambush, Producing Director **Theatre:** professional not-for-profit **Works:** full-length plays, musicals, cabaret/revues **Special interests:** pluralism in society from the Black American point of view; ethnic diversity **Maximum cast:** 16 **Stage:** flexible, 500+ seats **Policy:** inquire

OAK RIDGE COMMUNITY PLAYHOUSE

Box 3223, Oak Ridge, TN 37831 (615) 482-9999
Contact: Stephen F. Krempasky, Managing Director **Theatre:** community/non-professional **Works:** full-length plays, one-acts, translations, adaptations, musicals, children's plays **2nd productions:** yes **Specifications:** maximum cast: 50; small stage; no fly space **Stage:** proscenium, 340 seats **Audience:** "Middle-aged median, 60% female." **Policy:** unsolicited script **Best time:** fall **Response:** 1-2 months **Your chances:** "only a few/usually none" **Remuneration:** "Very limited." **Program:** "Children's scripts for Jr. Playhouse." **Advice:** "Soliciting scripts for annual community theatre competition AACT Fest" (inquire).

ODYSSEY THEATRE ENSEMBLE

12111 Ohio Ave., Los Angeles, CA 90025
(213) 826-1626 Contact: Jan Lewis, Literary Manager **Theatre:** professional not-for-profit **Works:** full-length plays, translations, adaptations, musicals **2nd productions:** yes **Special interest:** "Provocative subject matter or highly theatrical material." **Tours:** "Sometimes." **Stages:** proscenium, 99 seats; thrust, 95 seats; black box, 85 seats **Audience:** "Upper middle-class, urban, primarily over 30." **Policies:** query/synopsis with dialogue sample and resume; agent submission **Response:** 2 weeks query; 6 months script **Your chances:** 500/3-5 **Remuneration:** negotiable royalty **Program:** readings **Advice:** "Please check up on the kind of work we have done--get to know us before you make submissions."

OFF CENTER THEATRE

436 W. 18th St., New York, NY 10011
(212) 929-8299 Contact: Ken Lipman, Literary Manager **Theatre:** off off Broadway, professional not-for-profit

Works: full-length plays, musicals **2nd productions:** no **Special interest:** "Issue-oriented comedies." **Stage:** black box **Audience:** "New Yorkers." **Policy** unsolicited script **Response:** 1-5 months **Your chances:** 100/5 **Remuneration:** no **Programs:** staged readings, development

OHIO THEATER
66 Wooster St., New York, NY 10013
(212) 255-6001 Contact: Marcy Drogin, Producer **Theatre:** off off Broadway **Works:** full-length plays, one-acts, translations, adaptations, musicals, children's plays **2nd productions:** yes **Special interest:** "Social, political and moral issues." **Stage:** black box, 75 seats **Audience:** "Young audiences—18-30." **Policy:** query/synopsis with resume **Best times:** May, Jan. **Response:** 2-6 weeks **Remuneration:** no **Programs:** staged readings, workshop productions **Advice:** "Thoughtful plays about situations or circumstances that will make us care." **Comment:** This is a new theatre that produces 3 new plays each season.

OLDCASTLE THEATRE COMPANY
Box 1555, Bennington, VT 05201 (802) 447-0564
Contact: Eric Peterson, Producing Director **Theatre:** professional not-for-profit **Works:** full-length plays, musicals **2nd productions:** yes **Special interest:** "New England subjects." **Specifications:** small cast preferred **Tours:** yes **Stage:** modified proscenium **Audience:** "General New England." **Policies:** unsolicited script; query/ synopsis; professional recommendation **Best time:** winter **Response:** 6 months **Your chances:** varying number/1-2 **Remuneration:** standard royalty **Program:** readings

OLD CREAMERY THEATRE COMPANY
Box 160, Garrison, IA 52229 (319) 477-3925
Contact: Thomas Peter Johnson, Artistic and Producing Director **Theatre:** professional not-for-profit **Works:** full-length plays, translations, adaptations, musicals, children's plays **Special interest:** touring plays for young audiences **Specifications:** maximum cast: 12 preferred; cast of 2-6 for flexible space **Stages:** thrust, 265 seats; flexible, 100 seats **Policy:** query/synopsis **Best time:** Oct.-Jan. **Response:** 4-6 weeks

OLD GLOBE THEATRE
Box 2171, San Diego, CA 92112 (619) 231-1941
Contact: Robert Berlinger, Associate Director **Theatre:** professional not-for-profit **Works:** full-length plays, translations, adaptations, musicals **2nd productions:** yes **Stages:** proscenium; thrust; arena **Audience:** "Wide base." **Policies:** query/synopsis with resume; agent submission **Response:** 1 month query; 8 months script **Your chances:** 1000/1-2 **Remuneration:** negotiable **Programs:** readings, staged readings, workshop productions, development, internships **Advice:** "Please adhere to guidelines for submission."

OLD LOG THEATER
Box 250, Excelsior, MN 55331 (612) 474-5951
Contact: Don Stolz **Theatre:** professional year-round stock **Works:** full-length plays, adaptations **2nd productions:** yes **Special interest:** small-cast comedies **Stage:** proscenium **Audience:** young, middle class **Policies:** unsolicited script; query/synopsis **Response:** 1 month query; 6 months script **Remuneration:** negotiable royalty **Program:** "Occasional readings." **Comment:** Theatre receives approximately 200 new scripts each year and "intends to produce original scripts in 'Off Night Series' on Monday and Tuesday evenings when theatre is usually dark."

THE OLD SLOCUM HOUSE THEATRE
605 Esther St., Vancouver, WA 98660
(206) 695-5762 Contact: Hermie Duthie Decker, President **Theatre:** community/non-professional **Works:** full-length plays, translations, adaptations, musicals **2nd productions:** yes **Specifications:** maximum cast: 10; simple set **Stage:** proscenium, 65 seats **Policy:** query/synopsis **Remuneration:** no **Advice:** "Our historic site was presented on the premise that we make the plays living history. All plays must deal with the 19th century or earlier." **Comment:** Theatre receives fewer than 1 script each year.

OMAHA MAGIC THEATRE
1417 Farnam St., Omaha, NE 68102
(402) 342-2821 Contact: Jo Ann Schmidman, Artistic Director **Theatre:** professional not-for-profit **Works:** avant garde musical theatre, experimental youth theatre,

performance pieces **Exclusive interests**: experimental works; avant garde musicals; performance art from musicians, dancers, visual artists **Tours**: "We tour a total avant garde production or performance event. We do not cut down productions for touring." **Stages**: flexible, 100 seats; non-traditional and outdoor spaces **Audience**: "People from all walks of life." **Policy**: unsolicited script with $30 critique fee **Response**: 3 months **Your chances**: 1300+/8-10 **Remuneration**: standard royatly **Advice**: "Astonish us!"

ONE ACT THEATRE COMPANY
430 Mason St., San Francisco, CA 94102
(415) 421-5355 Contact: Michael Duff, Literary Manager **Theatre**: professional not-for-profit **Works**: one-acts **2nd productions**: yes **Special interests**: "Long one-acts (60-100 minutes); third-world playwrights; political themes; strong female roles." **Specifications**: maximum cast: 8-12; single set or open staging **Stage**: thrust, 140-150 seats **Audience**: "Older, white, educated, politically savvy." **Policies**: unsolicited script; query/synopsis; professional recommendation; agent submission **Response**: 3 months query; 6 months script **Your chances**: 300-400/1-2 **Remuneration**: negotiable **Program**: readings **Advice**: "Innovative, challenging plays that avoid the sit-com format."

ON STAGE PRODUCTIONS: ON STAGE, CHILDREN
50 W. 97th St. #8H, New York, NY 10025
(212) 666-1716 Contact: Frank Lee, Artistic Director **Theatre**: off off Broadway, professional not-for-profit **Works**: full-length plays, one-acts, musicals, children's plays **2nd productions**: yes **Special interest**: "Contemporary social concerns." **Specifications**: maximum cast: 8; interracial cast; minimal sets; small budget **Tours**: yes **Stage**: multiuse space **Audience**: "Families; mixed racially and economically; young audiences." **Policy**: query/synopsis **Best time**: Jun. **Remuneration**: $5 per performance **Comment**: Theatre usually produces 4-5 new plays each season.

THE OPEN EYE NEW STAGINGS
270 W. 89th St., New York, NY 10024
(212) 769-4141 Contact: Amie Brockway, Artistic Director **Theatre**: professional not-for-profit **Works**:

full-length plays, one-acts, translations, adaptations, musicals, children's plays **2nd productions:** yes **Special interest:** "Plays which invite us as artists and audience to take a fresh look at ourselves and the world of which we are a part." **Specifications:** maximum cast: 13-14; no fly space **Tours:** yes **Stage:** modified proscenium, 115 seats **Audience:** "A typical urban mix." **Policies:** unsolicited script; professional recommendation; agent submission **Best time:** Apr.-Jul. **Response:** 3-6 months **Your chances:** 400+/1-5+ **Remuneration:** $500-$1500 **Programs:** readings, staged readings, workshop productions, "Eye on Playwrights" festival (inquire)

ORDER BEFORE MIDNIGHT
Box 12836, Philadelphia, PA 19108
(215) 729-5385 Contact: Kate Bornstein, Core Member **Theatre:** professional not-for-profit **Works:** full-length plays, one-acts, translations, adaptations, revues **2nd productions:** yes **Special interest:** "Works of a feminist nature, with a majority of women's roles. We are interested in all women's issues, especially lesbian issues." **Tours:** yes **Stages:** "Spaces chosen for each particular show's requirements." **Audience:** "Chiefly women—feminist and lesbian; working class through middle class, with a racial mix." **Policy:** unsolicited script **Best time:** anytime **Response:** 6-12 weeks **Remuneration:** "Currently, no. This could change, pending grants." **Programs:** readings, staged readings **Advice:** "We encourage collaborative work among women artists. Availability to work in Philadelphia during pre-production will be a plus."

OREGON SHAKESPEAREAN FESTIVAL
Box 158, Ashland, OR 97520 (503) 482-2111
Contact: Cynthia White, Literary Manager **Theatre:** professional not-for-profit **Works:** full-length plays, translations **2nd productions:** yes **Specifications:** small cast preferred for flexible space **Stages:** thrust, 600 seats; outdoor Elizabethan, 1194 seats; black box, 140 seats **Audience:** "90% from 150 miles from Ashland (large cities)." **Policies:** query/synopsis with dialogue sample and resume; professional recommendation **Best time:** anytime **Response:** time varies **Your chances:** 200/0-1 plus 4 staged readings **Remuneration:** negotiable royalty

Programs: readings, "more development and workshop programs are currently being explored" **Advice:** "Don't expect quick responses—I'm very busy. Do keep after me, in a nice way, to read your play. And if I say I'm not interested in your play, believe me. Don't keep banging your head against a wall. And remember, it's sometimes as hard to say 'no' as to hear it."

ORGANIC THEATRE COMPANY
3319 N. Clark St., Chicago, IL 60657
(312) 327-5360 Contact: Lawrence Santoro, Literary Manager **Theatre:** professional not-for-profit **Works:** full-length plays, one-acts, adaptations **2nd productions:** "Sometimes." **Special interests:** "Original and unproduced works." **Tours:** yes **Stages:** 3/4 thrust, 300 seats; lab, 90 seats **Audience:** "Young, intelligent." **Policies:** query/synopsis with dialogue sample; agent submission **Best time:** anytime **Response:** immediate query; 3-5 months script **Your chances:** 300/3 **Programs:** staged readings, development, classes, internships **Advice:** "Please do not call."

PAN ASIAN REPERTORY THEATRE
47 Great Jones St., New York, NY 10012
(212) 505-5655 Contact: Tisa Chang, Artistic/Producing Director **Theatre:** professional not-for-profit **Works:** full-length plays, translations, adaptations, musicals **2nd productions:** "Not usually but possible." **Special interest:** "Works suitable for our company of Asian American artists." **Tours:** yes **Stage:** forestage **Audience:** "Half Asian American." **Policies:** unsolicited script; professional recommendation; commission **Response:** immediate query; 9 months script **Your chances:** 60/3 **Remuneration:** individual contract **Programs:** readings, staged readings, workshop productions, development

PAPER MILL PLAYHOUSE
Brookside Dr., Millburn, NJ 07041 (201) 379-3636
Contact: Maryan F. Stephens, Literary Manager **Theatre:** professional not-for-profit **Works:** full-length plays, translations, adaptations, musicals, operas **2nd productions:** yes **Special interests:** new musicals; musical adaptations of previously produced plays; large-scale

works **Stage:** proscenium, 1192 seats **Policies:** unsolicited script with synopsis; query/synopsis **Response:** 2 weeks query; 6-8 weeks script **Programs:** readings, staged readings, laboratory productions

PASADENA PLAYHOUSE
39 S. El Molino, Pasadena, CA 91101
(818) 792-8672 Contact: Peggy Ebright, Director of Community Relations **Theatre:** professional not-for-profit **Works:** full-length plays, one-acts, translations, adaptations, musicals, children's plays **2nd productions:** possibly (send reviews) **Specifications:** "Limited mainly by finances." **Stage:** proscenium **Audience:** "They expect and deserve the best." **Policies:** query/synopsis with dialogue sample and resume; professional recommendation; agent submission **Response:** 6 months **Remuneration:** negotiable

PAYSON COMMUNITY THEATRE
317 E. 100 S, Payson, UT 85651 (801) 465-3317
Contact: Charles L. Frost, Artistic Director **Theatre:** community/non-professional **Works:** full-length plays, one-acts, children's plays **2nd productions:** no **Tours:** yes **Stages:** proscenium; thrust **Audience:** "Educated, conservative." **Policy:** unsolicited script **Best time:** summer **Response:** 3 months **Your chances:** 6-7/1 **Remuneration:** royalty **Program:** staged readings **Advice:** "Submit--as soon as possible!"

PAYSON PLAYMAKERS
893 S. 880 W, Payson, UT 84651 (801) 465-2752
Contact: Dee Hill, President **Theatre:** community/non-professional **Works:** children's musicals **Tours:** yes **Stages:** high school proscenium; flexible **Audience:** 7-12 year-olds **Policy:** unsolicited script **Comment:** "We have a 4 week summer session for 7-12 year-olds and produce 1 play each summer. All who attend are eligible for acting roles."

PCPA THEATERFEST
Box 1700, Santa Maria, CA 93456 (805) 928-7731
Contact: New Play Department **Theatre:** professional not-for-profit; conservatory training program **Works:** full-length plays, one-acts, translations, adaptations, musicals

2nd productions: yes **Special interests:** new plays, new musicals **Stages:** thrust, 750 seats; thrust, 508 seats; black box, 175 seats **Audience:** "Middle to upper class from central coast of California." **Policies:** query/synopsis with dialogue sample; professional recommendation; agent submission **Response:** 5 weeks query; 3 months script **Comment:** See Stevens, Rob. "A Tale of Two Cities" (*Theater Week*, Oct. 3, 1988), 48-53.

PENGUIN REPERTORY COMPANY
Box 91, Stony Point, NY 10980 (914) 947-3741
Contact: Joe Brancato, Artistic Director **Theatre:** professional not-for-profit **Works:** full-length plays, translations, adaptations **2nd productions:** yes **Special interest:** "New works." **Specifications:** maximum cast: 6-8; single set or suggestive settings **Stage:** proscenium-thrust, 108 seats **Policies:** unsolicited script; commission **Best time:** Dec.-Jan. **Response:** 3-6 months **Programs:** readings, staged readings

PENNSYLVANIA STAGE COMPANY
837 Linden St., Allentown, PA 18101
(215) 434-8570 Contact: Wendy Liscow, Associate Director/Literary Manager **Theatre:** professional not-for-profit **Works:** full-length plays, translations, adaptations, musicals **2nd productions:** yes **Special interest:** "Works that have a passion for being presented now, that are entertaining and meaningful to our community and perpetuate our theatrical and literary heritage." **Specifications:** "No grossly offensive language." **Stage:** proscenium, 273 seats **Audience:** "Most are middle class, anglo, fairly conservative, 20-senior citizen." **Policy:** query/synopsis with dialogue sample **Response:** 3 weeks query; 4 months script **Your chances:** 300/1 play, 1 musical, 6 staged readings **Remuneration:** negotiable **Program:** New Evolving Works (inquire) **Advice:** "We are looking for plays with universal and/or mythical scope. Plays that reach beyond discussions around a kitchen table to touch on larger issues, ask demanding questions and offer possible solutions. We do not produce one-acts on mainstage but would be interested in 2-character one-acts."

PENNYRILE PLAYERS THEATRE
410 S. Main, Hopkinsville, KY 42240
(502) 885-2401 Contact: Nita Peacock, Artistic Director
Theatre: not-for-profit community/non-professional
Works: inquire **2nd productions:** yes **Tours:**
"Occasionally." **Stage:** proscenium, 222 seats **Policy:**
unsolicited script **Response:** 1 month **Your chances:**
0-5/"varying number depending upon quality of scripts"
Remuneration: "Each viewed in its own right." **Advice:**
"Low royalties. Family entertainment or children's shows,
preferably!"

THE PENUMBRA THEATRE COMPANY
270 N. Kent St., St. Paul, MN 55102
(612) 224-4601 Contact: Lou Bellamy, Artistic Director
Theatre: professional not-for-profit **Works:** full-length
plays **2nd productions:** yes **Special interest:** "The
African-American experience." **Tours:** "Yes, one and two
person shows." **Stages:** proscenium, 150 seats; thrust, 150
seats **Policy:** unsolicited script **Best time:** Jan.-Mar.
Response: 3 weeks query; approximately 16 weeks script
Your chances: 60/1 **Program:** Cornerstone (see Contests)

PEOPLE'S LIGHT AND THEATRE COMPANY
39 Conestoga Rd., Malvern, PA 19355
(215) 647-1900 Contact: Alda Cortese, Literary
Manager **Theatre:** professional not-for-profit **Works:** full-
length plays, translations, adaptations **2nd productions:** yes
Specifications: maximum cast: 12; single set preferred
Stages: flexible, 350 seats; flexible, 200 seats **Policies:**
query/synopsis with dialogue sample; agent submission
Response: 3 weeks query; 8 months script **Your chances:**
350/1-2 **Remuneration:** percentage (5%-7%)

THE PERFORMANCE CIRCLE
Box 64, Fox Island, WA 98333 (206) 549-2394
Contact: Kathleen McGilliard, Artistic Director **Theatre:**
community/non-professional **Works:** full-length plays,
one-acts, translations, adaptations, musicals, children's plays
Specifications: small stage, 9' ceiling **Stage:** flexible, 99
seats **Audience:** "Middle aged, conservative, high education."
Policy: unsolicited script **Remuneration:** "Depends on
quality." **Program:** staged readings

PERIWINKLE NATIONAL THEATRE FOR YOUNG AUDIENCES

19 Clinton Ave., Monticello, NY 12701
(914) 794-1666 Contact: Sunna Rasch, Artistic Director
Theatre: professional not-for-profit touring company
Works: plays for young audiences **Special interests:** social issues; problems of youth **Specifications:** works must be 45-60 minutes in length; all shows tour **Stages:** various spaces **Audience:** "Students at various levels." **Policies:** query/synopsis; commission **Best time:** spring **Response:** 2 weeks query; 6-8 months script **Remuneration:** royalty; fee for commission **Advice:** "Contact us to see what theme interests us."

PERMIAN PLAYHOUSE OF ODESSA, INC.

Box 6713, Odessa, TX 79767-6713
(915) 362-2329 Contact: Coy L. Sharp, Director
Theatre: community/non-professional **Works:** full-length plays, one-acts, musicals, children's plays **2nd productions:** yes **Tours:** yes **Stage:** proscenium, 454 seats **Audience:** "Middle-class white, 50% white collar, 35% blue collar; rest ethnic." **Policies:** unsolicited script with resume; query/synopsis with resume; professional recommendation **Best time:** Sept.-Dec. **Response:** 1 week query; 1 month script **Your chances:** 3-5/1 **Remuneration:** "Depends upon the script and its value to the theatre." **Programs:** staged readings, workshop productions **Advice:** "Send background information with submission."

PERSEVERANCE THEATRE

914 3rd St., Douglas, AK 99801 (907) 364-2421
Contact: Jack Cannon, Literary Manager **Theatre:** professional not-for-profit **Works:** full-length plays, one-acts, translations, adaptations **2nd productions:** yes **Maximum cast:** 20 **Tours:** "Occasionally." **Stages:** thrust, 150 seats; flexible, 75 seats **Audience:** "Varied: lawyers to fishermen, fairly young, well educated." **Policies:** unsolicited script from Alaskan writer; query/synopsis with resume from other writer **Response:** 6 months **Remuneration:** $500-$1000 **Programs:** readings, staged readings, workshop productions, development, classes **Comment:** Theatre receives approximately 25 new scripts each year and does not seek plays from outside Alaska.

PETERBOROUGH PLAYERS
Box 1, Peterborough, NH 03458 (603) 924-7585
Contact: Charles Morey, Artistic Director **Theatre:** professional not-for-profit **Works:** full-length plays, one-acts, adaptations **Stage:** flexible, 250 seats **Policy:** query/synopsis **Best time:** Sept.-Jan. **Response:** 2 months query; 6 months script **Program:** staged readings

PHILADELPHIA DRAMA GUILD
112 S. 16th St. Suite 803, Philadelphia, PA 19102
(215) 563-7530 Contact: Charles Conwell, Director, Playwrights' Project **Theatre:** professional not-for-profit **Works:** full-length plays, related one-acts in pairs or trios **Special interest:** "Plays with moral, political, social or economic as well as personal dimensions." **Specifications:** Playwrights must reside within 25 miles of Philadelphia's City Hall. **Stages:** proscenium, 99 seats; thrust, 200 seats **Audience:** "Diverse." **Policy:** inquire **Best time:** Sept. 1-Dec. 1 **Response:** 1 week query; Jun. 1 script **Your chances:** 88/3 **Remuneration:** $100 for reading; $1000 for production **Programs:** staged readings, workshop productions; Philadelphia Drama Guild Playwrights' Project (see Special Programs)

PHILADELPHIA FESTIVAL THEATRE
3900 Chestnut St., Philadelphia, PA 19104
(215) 222-5000 Contact: Richard Wolcott, Literary Manager **Theatre:** professional not-for-profit **Works:** full-length plays, one-acts, translations **2nd productions:** no **Stage:** black box **Audience:** "Urban, educated, liberal." **Policies:** unsolicited script; professional recommendation; agent submission **Response:** 6 months **Your chances:** 1500/6 **Remuneration:** yes **Programs:** staged readings, development

THE PHILADELPHIA THEATRE COMPANY
Bourse Bldg. Suite 735, 21 S. 5th St.,
Philadelphia, PA 19106 (215) 592-8333
Contact: Lynn M. Thompson, Artistic Associate/Literary Manager **Theatre:** professional not-for-profit **Works:** full-length plays, one-acts, translations, adaptations **2nd productions:** yes **Exclusive interests:** "Contemporary American drama. Often, our plays treat contemporary

problems. Always there is substance." **Specifications:** maximum cast: 10; "we shy away from extremely light-weight, so-called 'commercial' pieces" **Stage:** proscenium **Audience:** "Sophisticated, urban, well-educated, age cross-section." **Policies:** unsolicited script with resume; query/synopsis with dialogue sample and resume; professional recommendation; agent submission **Best time:** before Dec. 15 **Response:** 1 month query; 6 months script **Your chances:** 500/1 plus workshops **Remuneration:** honorarium for workshop, royalty for full production **Programs:** staged readings, workshop productions, development, Stages (see Special Programs)

PHOENIX THEATRE, INC.
749 N. Park Ave., Indianapolis, IN 46202
(317) 635-7529 Contact: Brian Fonseca, Artistic Director **Theatre:** semi-professional **Works:** full-length plays, adaptations **2nd productions:** yes **Special interest:** "New ideas." **Maximum cast:** 15-16 **Stage:** small flexible proscenium, 150 seats **Audience:** "Educated, liberal." **Policies:** unsolicited script; query/synopsis **Best time:** Jan.-Feb. **Response:** 3 months **Your chances:** 400/3-4 **Remuneration:** $500 for full-length play **Programs:** staged readings, FEAT Playwriting Festival (see Contests) **Advice:** "We are a small house with a small budget."

PIER ONE THEATRE
Box 894, Homer, AK 99603 (907) 235-7333
Contact: Lance Peterson, Artistic Director **Theatre:** professional not-for-profit (summer); community/non-professional (winter) **Works:** full-length plays, one-acts, translations, adaptations, musicals, children's plays **2nd productions:** yes **Tours:** yes **Stages:** proscenium, thrust, flexible—100 seats summer, 495 seats winter **Policies:** unsolicited script preferred; professional recommendation **Response:** 3 months **Your chances:** 100/1-3 **Remuneration:** percentage

PING CHONG & COMPANY
253 Church St., New York, NY 10013
(212) 346-6009 Contact: Ping Chong, Artistic Director **Theatre:** off off Broadway touring company **Policy:** inquire **Comment:** Formerly The Fiji Theatre Company.

PIONEER THEATRE COMPANY
University of Utah, Salt Lake City, UT 84112
(801) 581-6356 **Contact:** Charles Morey, Artistic Director **Theatre:** professional not-for-profit **Works:** full-length plays, translations, adaptations, musicals **Stage:** proscenium, 1000 seats **Policy:** query/synopsis **Best time:** fall **Response:** 1 month query; 6 months script

PITTSBURGH PUBLIC THEATER
Allegheny Square, Pittsburgh, PA 15212
(412) 323-8200 **Contact:** William T. Gardner, Producing Director **Theatre:** professional not-for-profit **Works:** full-length plays, translations, adaptations, musicals **2nd productions:** no **Stage:** arena or thrust, 449 seats **Policy:** agent submission **Best time:** Apr.-Sept. **Response:** 6 months

PLAYERS GUILD OF CANTON, INC.
1001 Market Ave., Canton, OH 44718
(216) 453-7619 **Contact:** Jerry M. Lowe, Artistic Director **Theatre:** community/non-professional **Works:** full-length plays **2nd productions:** yes **Stages:** proscenium, 496 seats; thrust, 138 seats **Audience:** "Somewhat older, high income, theatrically sophisticated." **Policies:** unsolicited script; query/synopsis with resume; agent submission **Best time:** late spring-summer **Response:** 2 weeks query; 6 months script **Your chances:** 25/3 **Remuneration:** negotiable royalty **Program:** workshop productions **Advice:** "The theatre is committed to the annual production of a new script on the Main Stage. These are large-scale productions. We are not interested in 'situation' or 'dinner theatre' comedy; we cannot use scripts intended for small-scale production or 'bare bones' approaches." **Comment:** "Theatre is very large, professionally staffed, high budget, professional standards; works closely with Ohio Arts Commission in looking for new plays."

PLAYERS THEATRE OF COLUMBUS
549 Franklin Ave., Columbus, OH 43215
(614) 224-5528 **Contact:** Steven C. Anderson, Associate Producing Director **Theatre:** professional not-for-profit **Works:** full-length plays, translations, adaptations, musicals, children's plays **Special interest:** the Midwestern

experience **Stages**: thrust, 750 seats; modified thrust, 250 seats; arena, 100 seats **Policy**: query/synopsis **Response**: 3 weeks query; 3-4 months script

PLAYHOUSE ON THE SQUARE
51 S. Cooper, Memphis, TN 38104 (901) 725-0776
Contact: Jackie Nichols, Executive Director **Theatre**: professional not-for-profit **Works**: full-length plays **2nd productions**: no **Specifications**: maximum cast: 10; single or unit set **Stages**: proscenium, 250 seats; proscenium, 136 seats **Audience**: "25-50 years of age, progressive, open-minded." **Policy**: unsolicited script **Response**: 3 months **Your chances**: 500/1 **Remuneration**: $500 **Program**: Midsouth Playwrights Contest (see Contests)

PLAYHOUSE WEST
4250 Lankershim Blvd., North Hollywood, CA 91602 (818) 349-9190 **Contact**: Christie Lemon, Literary Committee **Theatre**: professional not-for-profit **Works**: full-length plays, one-acts **2nd productions**: yes **Special interest**: "Any theme currently relevant." **Stage**: flexible, 99 seats **Audience**: "Eclectic." **Policies**: unsolicited script with resume; query/synopsis with resume; professional recommendation **Response**: 4 weeks query; 8 weeks script **Your chances**: 200/5-10 **Remuneration**: no **Programs**: readings, staged readings, workshop productions **Advice**: "Realistic writing encompassing a socially relevant theme."

PLAYMAKERS
Box 5745, Tampa, FL 33675 (813) 248-6933
Contact: Kathy Tyrell, Associate Director **Theatre**: professional not-for-profit **Works**: full-length plays, one-acts **2nd productions**: yes **Special interests**: traditional and experimental contemporary works **Specifications**: maximum cast: 8; simple set **Stage**: proscenium, 300 seats **Policy**: query/synopsis **Best time**: Sept.-Jan. **Response**: 4-6 weeks query; 3-4 months script

PLAYMAKERS REPERTORY COMPANY
Chapel Hill, NC This theatre has requested that we discontinue its listing.

THE PLAY WORKS COMPANY
Box 25152, Philadelphia, PA 19147
(215) 236-8488   Contact: Christopher J. Rushton, Director   **Theatre**: art service, new play development organization **Works:** full-length plays, one-acts, adaptations, musicals **2nd productions:** no **Exclusive interest:** "Current material." **Specifications:** maximum cast: 15; some set limitations **Tours:** yes   **Stage:** flexible **Policy:** query/synopsis with resume **Best time:** spring **Response:** 2 months query; 6 months script **Your chances:** 200/20 staged readings **Remuneration:** no

PLAYWRIGHT'S ALLIANCE
8 Tompkins Ave., Babylon, NY 11702
(516) 587-8945   Contact: Robert Mantione, Artistic Director **Theatre:** professional not-for-profit **Works:** full-length plays, one-acts, translations, adaptations, performance art   **2nd productions:** no **Special interests:** "Social, political, psychological, ideological works; avant garde." **Specifications:** maximum cast: 4; simple sets or no set **Stages:**   thrust; arena; flexible **Audience:** "All ages, educated, literate, informed, culturally active." **Policies:** unsolicited script; query/synopsis with dialogue sample; professional recommendation **Response:** immediate query; 8-10 weeks script **Your chances:** 40-50/5 **Remuneration:** no **Programs:** readings, staged readings, workshop productions **Advice:** "Be prepared to be present at auditions and as many rehearsals as possible."

PLAYWRIGHTS HORIZONS
416 W. 42nd St., New York, NY 10036
(212) 564-1235   Contact: Tim Sanford, Literary Manager **Theatre:** professional not-for-profit **Works:** full-length plays, musicals **2nd productions:** "Only if first production was recent and not in New York City." **Specifications:** "We cannot produce hugely expensive plays." **Stages:** proscenium, 160 seats; black box, 75 seats **Audience:** "Intelligent, urban, well-versed, older." **Policies:** unsolicited script with resume; query/synopsis with resume; agent submission **Best time:** "Anytime other than late spring and summer." **Your chances:** 1800/4-10 **Remuneration:** varies **Programs:** readings, classes **Advice:** "We respond to theatrical, adventurous, articulate

work. We are not a theatre for beginning playwrights. Professional recommendation, credits help. Authors with limited professional references and resume would do well to submit query/synopsis first."

PLAYWRIGHTS WORKSHOP
Box 728, Stamford, CT 06904 (203) 348-2787
Contact: Ralph Antonacci, Executive Director **Theatre:** community/non-professional **Works:** full-length plays **Policy:** unsolicited script **Response:** 1 month **Program:** Playwrights Academy for New Plays: 1 play selected annually as "Play of the Year" (inquire) **Comment:** Workshop cooperates with the Stamford Community Arts Council.

PLYMOUTH PLAYHOUSE
Plymouth Place Hotel, 2705 Annapolis Ln.,
Plymouth, MN 55411 (612) 333-3302
Contact: Curt Wollan, Producer/Director **Theatre:** dinner **Works:** full-length plays, musicals **2nd productions:** yes **Special interest:** "Light, fun—nothing heavy." **Specifications:** maximum cast: 6; unit set **Tours:** yes **Stage:** thrust, 211 seats **Audience:** "Aged 25-55, white, business white collar, college or technical school education." **Policy:** query/synopsis with dialogue sample **Best time:** spring **Response:** 6 months query; 1 year script **Your chances:** 300/0-1 **Remuneration:** royalty **Advice:** "Send video tape of previous production."

PONCA PLAYHOUSE
Box 1414, Ponca City, OK 74602 (405) 765-7786
Contact: John A. Robinson, Managing/Artistic Director **Theatre:** community/non-professional **Works:** full-length plays, adaptations, musicals **2nd productions:** yes **Special interest:** "A good, clear dramatic plot and point of view." **Specifications:** maximum cast: 12; single set **Stage:** proscenium, 412 seats **Audience:** "Average age 45, upper middle-class, college-educated; no interest in excessive vulgarity or nudity; prefer comedies 3 to 1 over heavy drama." **Policies:** unsolicited script; query/synopsis, professional recommendation; "I go out and look for them." **Best time:** Sept.-Mar. **Response:** 1-2 weeks **Your chances:** 20-30/varying number **Remuneration:** "Up to $500 plus a 2-week residency." **Programs:** readings, staged

readings, workshop productions, development, residencies **Advice**: "Must be theatrically exciting—a reason to be a play rather than an essay. No vague self-discovery epics, please!"

PORTHOUSE THEATRE FESTIVAL
Kent, OH   See Theatre Kent and Porthouse Theatre Festival.

PORTLAND STAGE COMPANY
Box 1458, Portland, ME 04104   (207) 774-1043
Contact: Lisa DiFranza, Associate Director   **Theatre**: professional not-for-profit   **Works**: full-length plays, translations, adaptations   **2nd productions**: yes **Special interest**: "Our goal is to engage, educate, challenge and entertain our audience."   **Stage**: proscenium, 290 seats **Audience**: "Primarily professionals from early 30's to mid-60's." **Policies**: query/synopsis with dialogue sample; professional recommendation; agent submission **Response**: 6 weeks query; 9 months script   **Your chances**: 130/1 **Remuneration**: royalty **Advice**: "Small cast, neatly typed script, engaging and challenging material."   **Programs**: readings, staged readings, workshop productions

POST THEATRE COMPANY
Greenvale, NY 11548 (516) 299-2353
Contact: David Scanlan, Professor of Theatre   **Theatre**: university/college **Works**: full-length plays, one-acts **2nd productions**: yes **Special interest**: "Just good, serious theatre." **Stages**:   black box;   small studio **Audience**: "College   plus   Long   Island   community." **Policies**: query/synopsis with dialogue sample; professional recommendation **Best time**: Jan. **Response**: 1 year **Remuneration**: "Yes, limited." **Program**: development

POTOMAC THEATRE PROJECT
269 W. 72nd St., New York, NY 10023
Contact: Susan Sharkey, Literary Manager   **Theatre**: professional not-for-profit   **Works**:   full-length plays, translations **2nd productions**: yes **Exclusive interest**: "Hard-core political theatre: current social and political issues." **Maximum cast**:   15 **Stages**:   rented spaces **Audience**:   "Politically oriented." **Policies**:   query/ synopsis; commission **Best time**: autumn **Response**: 6-9 months   **Your chances**:   10-15/2   **Remuneration**:

royalty **Advice:** "Send only a synopsis or treatment description. Never send a script. Write for specific information if you are interested. We have a strict definition of political theatre." **Comment:** "Plays are produced in Washington, DC."

THE POWER THEATRE
c/o Anderson, 311 E. 90th St. #2C, New York, NY 10128
Theatre: off off Broadway showcase producer **Works:** full-length plays **2nd productions:** no **Special interest:** "Contemporary plays in a realistic and naturalistic style." **Specifications:** maximum cast: 15, 5 or fewer preferred; simple sets **Policy:** unsolicited script **Best time:** through Sept. 1989 only **Response:** 12 weeks **Program:** "Possibility of becoming playwright-in-residence." **Advice:** "Although subject matter is wide open, we do love explosive urban plays and dynamic family dramas."

PRAIRIE PLAYERS, INC.
Box 291, Kingman, KS 67068 (316) 532-3321
Theatre: community/non-professional **Works:** full-length plays, one-acts, translations, adaptations, musicals, children's plays **2nd productions:** "Occasionally." **Special interest:** "Comedy-farce." **Specifications:** maximum cast: 8-11; some set limitations **Tours:** "We haven't toured outside of 50 miles." **Stage:** proscenium, 120 seats **Audience:** "Primarily 30-65 age range." **Policy:** professional recommendation **Response:** 30 days **Remuneration:** "Small royalty possible." **Programs:** "By contract and prior arrangement." **Advice:** "Royalty is a problem; we are a very small volunteer group." **Comment:** Theatre has not yet produced new plays but is willing to do so.

PRAIRIE PLAYERS YOUTH THEATRE
656 W. Losey, Galesburg, IL 61401
(309) 343-9097 Contact: Rossann Baker, Youth Theatre Director **Theatre:** community/non-professional **Works:** full-length plays, one-acts, adaptations, children's plays **Special interests:** "Christmas themes; pregnancy prevention; sexual responsibility." **Specifications:** maximum cast: 4 for some touring shows; budget limitations **Tours:** yes **Stages:** arena, flexible; 50-350 seats

Audience: "Young audiences, but the play must also be interesting to the adult." **Policies:** unsolicited script; query/synopsis **Best times:** summer, Dec.–Jan. **Your chances:** 20/4+

PRATHER PRODUCTIONS
1160 Old Eagle Rd., Lancaster, PA 17602
(717) 898-8790
Theatre: non-Equity dinner **Works:** full-length plays **Exclusive interests:** comedies, farces **Specifications:** maximum cast: 8; single set **Policy:** query/synopsis **Comment:** Theatre's most popular authors are Ayckbourn, Gurney and Simon.

PRINCETON REP COMPANY
13 Witherspoon St., Princeton, NJ 08542
(609) 921-3682 Contact: Victoria Liberatori, Artistic Director **Theatre:** professional, Small Professional Theatre Contract **Works:** full-length plays **2nd productions:** yes **Special interests:** "Realistic and non-realistic dramas and comedies with daring and exciting subject matter." **Specifications:** maximum cast: 5-7; single or non-realistic set **Tours:** yes **Stage:** flexible **Audience:** "Eclectic: well-educated and affluent to working class; average age 40." **Policies:** query/synopsis with dialogue sample; professional recommendation; agent submission **Best times:** spring, fall **Response:** 2 months query; 6 months script **Your chances:** 300/2 **Remuneration:** negotiable **Programs:** readings, staged readings, workshop productions **Advice:** "We are not interested in soap opera or standard domestic drama. We like work that takes risks and emphasizes character."

PROCESS STUDIO THEATRE
257 Church St., New York, NY 10019
(212) 226-1124 Contact: Bonnie Loren, Artistic Director **Theatre:** off Broadway, not-for-profit **Works:** full-length plays, one-acts, musicals **2nd productions:** yes **Tours:** yes **Stages:** proscenium; thrust; flexible **Audience:** "Varied, sophisticated." **Policies:** query/ synopsis with dialogue sample; professional recommendation; agent submission **Remuneration:** "Only if the production makes a substantial profit." **Programs:** readings, staged readings, workshop productions, development, internships

PRODUCERS CLUB
358 W. 44th St., New York, NY 10036
(212) 246-9069 Contact: Vincent Gugleotti, Artistic Director **Theatre:** off Broadway **Works:** full-length plays, one-acts **2nd productions:** yes **Specifications:** maximum cast: 6; no more than 2 sets **Stage:** proscenium **Policies:** unsolicited script; professional recommendation; agent submission **Response:** 2-6 weeks **Your chances:** 300/3 **Remuneration:** option; royalty **Programs:** readings, staged readings, workshop productions, development

PROMISED VALLEY PLAYHOUSE
Salt Lake City, UT This theatre has requested that we discontinue its listing.

PS PRODUCTIONS
PS, Inc., 355 Madison Ave. 25th Floor,
New York, NY 10017 Contact: Terry Burnstein **Theatre:** off off Broadway **Works:** full-length plays, one-acts **2nd productions:** yes **Specifications:** maximum cast: 10; simple sets **Stage:** proscenium, 100 seats **Audience:** "Cosmopolitan upward." **Policies:** unsolicited script; query/synposis; agent submission **Response time:** 2 weeks query; 3 months script **Your chances:** 150/3 **Remuneration:** no **Program:** development **Advice:** "Material should be comedic, cosmopolitan in nature."

PUERTO RICAN TRAVELING THEATRE
141 W. 94th St., New York, NY 10025
(212) 354-1293 Contact: Miriam Colon Valle, Executive Director **Theatre:** professional not-for-profit **Works:** full-length plays, translations, adaptations, musicals **Special interest:** social issues relevant to contemporary Hispanic experience **Specifications:** maximum cast: 8; no more than 3 sets **Stage:** proscenium, 196 seats **Policy:** unsolicited script **Response:** 6-9 months **Program:** Puerto Rican Traveling Theatre Playwrights' Workshop (see Special Programs)

PUSHCART PLAYERS
197 Bloomfield Ave., Verona, NJ 07004
(201) 857-1115 Contact: Ruth Fost, Executive Producer **Theatre:** professional not-for-profit **Works:** children's

plays **2nd productions:** yes **Special interest:** "Curriculum or current event orientation." **Specifications:** maximum cast: 4; all shows must tour **Stages:** schools **Audience:** grades K-12 **Policy:** inquire **Programs:** staged readings, workshop productions

QUAIGH THEATRE
205 W. 89th St., New York, NY 10024
(212) 221-9088 Contact: Dennis Rickabee, Literary Manager **Theatre:** professional not-for-profit **Works:** full-length plays, one-acts **Stage:** thrust, 100 seats **Policy:** unsolicited script **Response:** 3-6 months one-act; 6-9 months full-length play **Program:** Lunchtime Series: workshop productions of one-acts (inquire)

THE QUARTZ THEATRE
Box 465, Ashland, OR 97520 (503) 482-8119
Contact: Robert Spira, Artistic Director **Theatre:** community/non-professional **Works:** full-length plays, one-acts, musicals, children's plays **2nd productions:** "If there is rewriting to be done." **Stage:** flexible, 30 seats **Audience:** "General." **Policy:** query/synopsis with dialogue sample **Response:** 1 week query; 2 months script **Your chances:** 30/3 **Remuneration:** "Tape; if box office exceeds expenses, the playwright gets a share." **Advice:** "Literate writing."

RAFT THEATRE
432 W. 42nd St., New York, NY 10036
(212) 947-8389 Contact: Martin Zurla, Artistic Director **Theatre:** professional not-for-profit **Works:** full-length plays, one-acts **Specifications:** maximum cast: 7; no more than 2 sets or unit set **Stage:** 2-sided L **Audience:** middle class; professionals **Policy:** inquire **Best time:** spring **Response:** 4 months **Your chances:** 500/4 **Remuneration:** option **Advice:** Request statement of artistic purposes; theatre is dedicated to new plays by American playwrights; do not type scripts in European format.

RAINBOW COMPANY CHILDREN'S THEATRE
821 Las Vegas Blvd., Las Vegas, NV 89101
(702) 386-6553 Contact: Brian Strom, Acting Director **Theatre:** community/non-professional **Works:** full-length

plays, one-acts, adaptations, children's plays **2nd productions**: yes **Stages**: proscenium; thrust; arena; black box **Audience**: families **Policy**: query/synopsis **Best time**: Feb.-Jun. **Response**: 1 year **Your chances**: 25/1-2 **Remuneration**: royalty

RAIN COUNTRY PLAYERS
c/o Ralph Eaton, Treasurer, 17319 32nd Ave. W., Lynwood, WA 98037   (206) 743-4240
Theatre: community/non-professional **Works**: full-length plays **Special interest**: "Family-oriented plays." **Specifications**: cast of 2-10, various ages; single set **Stage**: proscenium, 92 seats **Audience**: "Approximately 40% over 60, 50% adult, 10% children 12 and under." **Policy**: unsolicited script **Best time**: fall-spring **Response**: 6 months **Remuneration**: "Reasonable royalty." **Comment**: Theatre has not produced new plays for several years but is willing to do so.

R.A.P.P. RESIDENT THEATRE COMPANY
220 E. 4th St., New York, NY 10009
(212) 529-5921   Contact: R. Jeffry Cohen, Artistic Director **Theatre**: professional not-for-profit **Works**: full-length plays, one-acts, translations **2nd productions**: "Occasionally." **Special interests**: "Classical themes, experimental directors, large casts." **Maximum cast**: 20 **Stages**: proscenium/flexible, 299 seats; flexible, 85-99 seats; flexible, 50 seats **Policies**: unsolicited script; query/synopsis **Best time**: Jan.-Mar. **Response**: 2-4 months **Your chances**: 100-200/2-5 **Remuneration**: "For production." **Programs**: workshop productions, internships **Advice**: "We are looking for new voices on relevant, universal issues." **Comment**: See Anderson, Wayne. "Artist's Oasis: The R.A.P.P. Arts Center" (*Theater Week*, Mar. 7-13, 1988), 12-15.

RED BARN THEATRE
Box 707, Key West, FL 33040   (305) 296-9911
Contact: Richard A. Magesis, Artistic Director **Theatre**: professional not-for-profit **Works**: full-length plays, one-acts, translations, adaptations, musicals, children's plays, cabaret/revues **Maximum cast**: 8 for mainstage, 6 for cabaret **Tours**: 1 children's play each season **Stages**:

proscenium, 94 seats; proscenium, 94 seats   **Policy:**
query/synopsis with dialogue sample and resume **Best time:**
Aug.–Oct. **Response:** 1 month

REFLECTIONS THEATRE ENSEMBLE
Chicago, IL   Our 1989 questionnaire was returned as
"undeliverable," and this theatre's phone has been disconnected.

REMAINS THEATRE
1300 W. Belmont, Chicago, IL 60657
(312) 549-7725 Contact: Amy Morton, Artistic Director
Theatre: professional not-for-profit **Works:** full-length
plays, adaptations **Special interests:** political works; local
issues; adaptations **Specifications:**   maximum cast: 15;
large stage area   **Stage:**   flexible, 235 seats **Policy:**
query/synopsis **Response:** 3 weeks query; 3 months script

RENDEZVOUS PRODUCTIONS
317 Tenth Ave. #4, New York, NY 10001
(212) 695-2484 Contact: Zu Stears, Literary Manager
Theatre: off off Broadway **Works:**   full-length plays,
one-acts, translations, adaptations **2nd productions:** yes
Special interest: "American Realism." **Specifications:**
maximum cast: 10; single set   **Stage:**   thrust, 75 seats
Audience: "Mixed." **Policy:** query/synopsis with resume
Best time: Dec.–Mar. **Response:** 6-8 weeks **Your
chances:** 20/3-8 including one-acts **Comment:**   Theatre
has in-house playwrights.

REPERTORIO ESPAÑOL
138 E. 27th St., New York, NY 10016
(212) 889-2850 Contact: Rene Buch, Artistic Director
Theatre: professional not-for-profit **Works:** full-length
plays, adaptations, children's plays, operas **Exclusive
interests:** Hispanic themes only; plays in Spanish or plays in
English suitable for translation into Spanish **Specifications:**
maximum cast: 10; single set **Stage:** proscenium, 140 seats
Audience: "Predominantly Hispanic audience; some English-
speaking audience for musical and dance events." **Policy:**
unsolicited script **Best time:** May **Response:** 2 months

THE REPERTORY THEATRE OF ST. LOUIS
130 Edgar Rd., St. Louis, MO 63119
(314) 968-7340   Contact: Steven Woolf, Artistic Director **Theatre:** professional not-for-profit **Works:** full-length plays, translations, adaptations, musicals, children's plays **2nd productions:** yes **Special interest:** "Social/political themes." **Specifications:** maximum cast: 14; single set **Stages:** thrust, 735 seats; flexible, 125 seats; storefront, 40 seats **Audience:** "30 and up, literate, cultured, middle and upper class, educated, professionals, conservative." **Policies:** query/synopsis; professional recommendation; agent submission **Best time:** spring-summer **Response:** 1 month query; 4 months script **Your chances:** 100+/"number depends upon need and quality of work" **Program:** workshop productions **Advice:** "Single set, fewer than 8 characters, good story, strong emotions. Send query and manuscripts to Susan Gregg, Associate Artistic Director."

RICHMOND SHEPARD THEATRES
6476 Santa Monica Blvd., Hollywood, CA 90038
(213) 462-9399   Contact: Richmond Shepard, Artistic Director **Theatre:** Equity-waiver **Works:** full-length plays **2nd productions:** yes **Specifications:** maximum cast: 10, fewer preferred; no large spectacles **Stage:** proscenium **Audience:** varied **Policy:** unsolicited script **Response:** 2-7 weeks **Your chances:** 200/2 **Remuneration:** "In initial production, royalty after recoupment of investment; subsequently, straight royalty." **Advice:** "Write a hit: great story, brilliant dialogue, depth, pith."

RITES & REASON
Box 1148, Brown University, Providence, RI 02912
(401) 863-3558   Contact: Karen Baxter, Managing Director; George Houston Bass, Artistic Director **Theatre:** professional not-for-profit, university/college **Works:** full-length plays, one-acts **2nd productions:** yes **Special interest:** plays by or about Afro-Americans **Stage:** black box, 150 seats **Policy:** query/synopsis with resume and references **Response:** 1 month query; 3 months script **Remuneration:** "Varies." **Programs:** readings, staged readings, workshop productions, development **Advice:** "Rites & Reason is interested in developing new plays and ideas by and

about Afro-Americans using our research to performance method." **Comment:** Theatre produces 2-4 new plays each season.

RIVER ARTS REPERTORY
Box 1166, Woodstock, NY 12498 (914) 679-2100
Contact: Literary Manager **Theatre:** off off Broadway **Works:** full-length plays, translations **2nd productions:** yes **Stage:** flexible **Audience:** "Broad spectrum." **Policy:** professional recommendation **Best time:** fall **Response:** several months **Your chances:** "infinite number"/3 plus 4 staged readings **Remuneration:** "Generally a fee against percentage." **Programs:** staged readings, development

RIVERWEST THEATER
155 Bank St., New York, NY 10014
(212) 243-0259 Contact: Nat Habib, Artistic Director **Theatre:** off off Broadway **Works:** full-length plays, musicals **2nd productions:** "Only occasionally." **Stage:** proscenium, 28'x18' **Audience:** "Eclectic. People who go to the theatre once a month and find nothing pleasing on Broadway." **Policies:** unsolicited script; professional recommendation; commission **Best time:** fall **Response:** "Depends upon the play and our interest in it—the number of people who want to read it." **Your chances:** 250/5-6 (4 plays, 2 musicals or 5 plays, 1 musical) **Remuneration:** negoitable royalty **Advice:** "The play should be ready for an audience to see it."

THE ROAD COMPANY
Box 5278-EKS, Johnson City, TN 37603
(615) 926-7726 Contact: Christine Murdock **Theatre:** professional not-for-profit, community-based **Works:** full-length plays **2nd productions:** no **Special interest:** "Social value. We do plays that can teach us something and make us think." **Maximum cast:** 8 **Stage:** proscenium, 150 seats **Audience:** "Young to middle age, liberal, college educated, rural." **Policies:** query/synopsis; professional recommendation **Response:** 3 months query; 1 year script **Your chances:** 20/1-2 **Remuneration:** negotiable royalty **Advice:** "Non-traditional form, social significance, small cast, Southern or rural in location."

ROADSIDE THEATER
Box 743, Whitesburg, KY 41858 (606) 633-0108
Contact: Dudley Cocke, Director **Theatre:** professional not-for-profit **Works:** full-length plays **2nd productions:** no **Exclusive interest:** Appalachian subject matter **Specifications:** maximum cast: small cast; simple sets suitable for touring **Stage:** thrust, 150 seats **Audience:** "All ages, educated and uneducated, largely 'working class.'" **Policies:** unsolicited script; query/synopsis with dialogue sample **Response:** 2 weeks query; 1 month script **Programs:** readings, workshop productions, residencies

ROCHESTER CIVIC THEATRE
Mayo Park, Rochester, MN 55901 (507) 282-7633
Contact: Craig Peterson, General Manager **Theatre:** community/non-professional **Works:** full-length plays, one-acts, musicals, children's plays **Stage:** proscenium, 299 seats **Audience:** "Bi-polar: half are highly educated professionals." **Policy:** request all submission guidelines

THE ROOFTOP REPERTORY COMPANY, INC.
425 W. 57th St. Apt. 2J, New York, NY 10019
(212) 265-6284 Contact: Norman Biem, Artistic Director
This theatre is inactive in 1989.

ROUNDABOUT THEATRE COMPANY
100 E. 17th St., New York, NY 10003
(212) 420-1360 Contact: Mark Michaels, Literary Manager **Theatre:** professional not-for-profit **Works:** full-length plays, translations, adaptations **2nd productions:** yes **Stages:** proscenium; thrust **Audience:** "Diverse, sophisticated New York audience." **Policies:** query/synopsis; professional recommendation; agent submission **Response:** 2 months query; 1 year script **Your chances:** 200/"0-1 plus 1-3 readings on mainstage" **Programs:** readings, classes, Roundabout Theatre's Creative Connection (see Special Programs)

ROUND HOUSE THEATRE
12210 Bushey Dr., Silver Spring, MD 20902
(301) 468-4233 Contact: Jerry Widdon, Artistic Director **Theatre:** professional not-for-profit **Works:** full-length plays, translations, adaptations, children's plays

Special interests: contemporary social/political issues; experimental pieces; new translations of lesser-known classics Specifications: maximum cast: 7-8; single set preferred Stage: modified thrust, 216 seats Policy: professional recommendation Response: 1 year or more

ROYAL COURT REPERTORY
300 W. 55th St., New York, NY 10019
(212) 956-3500 Contact: Phyllis Craig, Artistic Director Theatre: professional Works: full-length plays, musicals Special interests: murder mysteries, musicals Policy: unsolicited script Response: 2 weeks Advice: "We are particularly interested in promoting musicals."

THE RYAN REPERTORY COMPANY, INC.
2442 Bath Ave., Brooklyn, NY 11214
(718) 373-5208 Contact: Script Review Committee Theatre: non-Equity not-for-profit Works: full-length plays, one-acts, musicals 2nd productions: no Specifications: cast of 1-7 preferred; minimal set; "no nudity" Policy: unsolicited script

SACRAMENTO THEATRE COMPANY
1419 H. St., Sacramento, CA 95814
(916) 446-7501 Contact: Mark Cuddy, Producing Director Theatre: professional not-for-profit Works: full-length plays, one-acts, translations, adaptations, cabaret/revues Maximum cast: 7 for black box Stages: proscenium, 297 seats; black box, 80 seats Policy: solicited script Best time: Nov.-Jan. Response: 8-12 months

ST. BART'S PLAYHOUSE
109 E. 50th St., New York, NY 10022
(212) 751-1616 Contact: Christopher Catt, Artistic Director Theatre: professional not-for-profit Works: full-length plays, musicals Special interest: American musicals Policy: query/synopsis Response: 2 weeks

THE SALT LAKE ACTING COMPANY
168 W. 500 N, Salt Lake City, UT 84103
(801) 363-0526 Contact: Shaun Elam, Literary Manager Theatre: professional not-for-profit Works: full-length plays, one-acts, translations, musicals Special interests:

contemporary western social issues; experimental, non-traditional works **Stage:** proscenium-thrust, 140-200 seats **Policy:** query/synopsis with sas postcard **Response:** 2-3 weeks postcard; 6 months script **Program:** readings

SANDCASTLE PLAYERS, INC.
Box 1596 Cathedral Station, New York, NY 10025 **(212) 932-1508 Contact:** Amy Phillips, Chairwoman of the Board **Theatre:** professional not-for-profit **Works:** full-length plays, one-acts **2nd productions:** "Yes, if not previously produced in New York." **Special interest:** "Contemporary plays of social significance." **Specifications:** simple sets **Policy:** unsolicited script **Remuneration:** negotiable **Comment:** Theatre produces 4 new plays each year.

SAN DIEGO REPERTORY THEATRE
79 Horton Plaza, San Diego, CA 92101 **(619) 231-3586 Contact:** Walter Schoen, Associate Producer **Theatre:** professional not-for-profit **Works:** full-length plays, translations, adaptations, musicals, literary cabaret **Special interests:** U.S. and West Coast premieres; innovations in form and perspective; works by and about women and minorities; multi-media works **Specifications:** no fly space **Stages:** proscenium, 212 seats; modified thrust, 535 seats; flexible, 225 seats **Audience:** "Middle to upper middle class, white, 35-50." **Policy:** unsolicited script **Response:** 4-6 months **Remuneration:** negotiable **Programs:** readings, workshop productions, residencies **Comment:** Theatre receives 500 new scripts each year.

SAN FRANCISCO REPERTORY
San Francisco, CA Our 1989 questionnaire was returned as "undeliverable," and this theatre's phone has been disconnected.

SAN JOSE REPERTORY COMPANY
Box 2399, San Jose, CA 95109 (408) 294-7595 This theatre is not presently interested in new scripts and has requested that we discontinue its listing.

SEASIDE MUSIC THEATRE
Daytona Beach, FL This theatre has requested that we discontinue its listing.

SEATTLE CHILDREN'S THEATRE
Seattle Center, 305 Harrison, Seattle, WA 98109
(206) 443-0807 Contact: Linda Hartzell, Artistic Director **Theatre:** professional not-for-profit **Works:** children's plays, adaptations and musicals **Special interest:** contemporary issues for young audiences **Stage:** proscenium, 280 seats **Policy:** professional recommendation **Best time:** Feb.–Dec. **Response:** 6 months

THE SEATTLE GROUP THEATRE
3940 Brooklyn Ave. NE, Seattle, WA 98105
(206) 545-4969 Contact: Tim Bond, Literary Manager **Theatre:** professional not-for-profit **Works:** full-length plays, one-acts, translations, adaptations, musicals **2nd productions:** yes **Special interests:** "Plays suitable for multi-ethnic casting; serious plays on social/cultural issues; satires or comedies with bite." **Specifications:** maximum cast: 10; unit or simple set preferred **Tours:** yes **Stage:** modified thrust, 200 seats **Audience:** "Median age 35, liberal, socially conscious; college graduates; variety of occupations; various ethnic backgrounds; middle income." **Policy:** query/synopsis with dialogue sample and resume **Best times:** spring, fall **Response:** 6 weeks query; 9–12 months script **Your chances:** 400/"6–8 as part of Playwrights' Festival; regular season varies" **Remuneration:** "Royalty, fee negotiable." **Programs:** readings, staged readings, workshop productions, development, Multicultural Playwrights' Festival (see Contests) **Comment:** Formerly The Group Theatre Company.

SEATTLE REPERTORY THEATRE
155 Mercer St., Seattle, WA 98109
(206) 443-2210 Contact: Shelley Starr Mason, Literary Manager/Dramaturg **Theatre:** professional not-for-profit **Works:** full-length plays, translations, adaptations **Tours:** "Each season at least 1 play tours throughout the states of WA, CA and HI." **Stages:** proscenium, 862 seats; arena, 160 seats **Policies:** unsolicited script; no synopsis or dialogue sample; commission **Response:** 2–3 months **Your chances:** "up to 1000/at least 2 on mainstage and Second Stage combined plus at least 4 in workshop" **Remuneration:** travel, per diem for workshop production **Programs:** workshop productions, internships, residencies **Advice:** "The Seattle Repertory

Theatre is not interested in conventional domestic melodramas or 'sit-com'-like material. Rather, it seeks playwrights with unique voices to whom language and authentic theatricality are most important."

THE SECOND STAGE
Box 1807 Ansonia Station, New York, NY 10023
(212) 787-8302 Contact: Anne Cattaneo, Dramaturg **Theatre:** professional not-for-profit **Works:** full-length plays, adaptations, musicals **2nd productions:** exclusively **Special interests:** social/political issues; "heightened realism" **Stage:** endstage, 110 seats **Policy:** unsolicited script with production history **Response:** 2-3 months **Program:** Theatre produces readings of 6-8 new and previously produced plays each year.

SENIOR ACTING PROGRAM OF THE BARN PLAYERS
Box 713, Shawnee Mission, KS 66201
(913) 341-8834 Contact: Winnie Laas, Chairman, Steering Committee **Theatre:** community service touring theatre **Works:** one-acts **2nd productions:** no **Exclusive interest:** "Works suitable for performers over 55 years of age." **Specifications:** no scenery for touring; minimum props; works must be no more than 30 minutes in length **Stages:** "Various spaces—from platforms to living rooms." **Audience:** retired persons; elementary, high school and college students **Policy:** unsolicited script **Your chances:** 125/6 **Remuneration:** $10 per performance **Comment:** See The Barn Players listing in this section.

SEVEN STAGES
c/o George Wren, Director, 956 Seville Dr.,
Clarkston, GA 30021 (404) 523-7647
Theatre: professional not-for-profit **Works:** full-length plays, translations, adaptations **2nd productions:** yes **Special interests:** socio/political works; non-traditional, experimental works on contemporary issues **Specifications:** maximum cast: 10, fewer preferred; small space **Stages:** flexible modified thrust, 250 seats; L-shape, 100 seats **Audience:** "Racially and culturally mixed; inner-city, professional and working class." **Policy:** unsolicited or solicited script **Best time:** summer-fall **Response:** 3-8 months **Your chances:** 150/3 **Remuneration:** commission;

royalty; per diem; residency **Programs:** readings, staged readings, workshop productions, development, internships **Advice:** "No domestic melodramas. Avoid realism. Be a poet--include music."

SEVENTH SIGN THEATRE COMPANY
Box 1698 Murray Hill Station, New York, NY 10156 Contact: Anthony Osnato, Artistic Director **Theatre:** off off Broadway **Works:** full-length plays, one-acts, translations, adaptations, children's plays **2nd productions:** "We might consider them." **Specifications:** moderate cast size; simple sets **Stage:** open arena, 60-80 seats **Audience:** "Varying, with quite a number of senior citizens." **Policies:** unsolicited script with resume; professional recommendation; agent submission; in-house commission **Response:** 1 month **Remuneration:** no **Program:** Writer's Roundtable: monthly readings (request application)

SHAKESPEARE & COMPANY
The Mount, Lenox, MA 01240 (413) 637-1197 Contact: Tina Packer, Artistic Director **Theatre:** professional not-for-profit **Works:** two-act plays, one-acts, adaptations, children's plays (1 hour in length) **2nd productions:** yes **Special interests:** adaptations of works by Henry James, Edith Wharton and their contemporaries; works dealing with social change, c. 1900-1910 **Maximum cast:** small cast; single set **Stages:** outside ampitheatre, 500 seats; outside ampitheatre, 150 seats; flexible, 100 seats **Audience:** "Mixed: city, rural, area people and people from across U.S.A." **Policy:** query/synopsis **Best time:** Feb. **Response:** 4 weeks **Programs:** staged readings, workshop productions **Comment:** Theatre receives approximately 100 new scripts each year. The Mount, Edith Wharton's former home, may be used as a set. **Advice:** "Irish plays; Protestant/Catholic problem; Irish playwrights."

THE SHAKESPEARE THEATRE AT THE FOLGER
301 E. Capitol St. SE, Washington, DC 20003 (202) 547-3230 Contact: Michael Kahn, Artistic Director **Theatre:** professional not-for-profit **Works:** translations, adaptations **2nd productions:** yes **Exclusive interest:** translations and adaptations of classics **Stage:**

thrust, 254 seats **Audience:** "White, professional, college educated, over 40." **Policy:** professional recommendation **Best time:** summer **Response:** 2 months

THE SHAZZAM PRODUCTION COMPANY
418 Pier Ave. Suite 104, Santa Monica, CA 90405
(213) 396-0984 Contact: Edward Blackoff, Producer **Theatre:** off off Broadway **Works:** full-length plays **2nd productions:** no **Specifications:** maximum cast: 15; 1 or 2 sets **Stages:** proscenium; thrust; arena **Policies:** unsolicited script; query/synopsis; professional recommendation; agent submission **Response:** 6 weeks **Your chances:** 100/2 **Remuneration:** $15 per performance

SHEBOYGAN COMMUNITY PLAYERS
607 S. Water St., Sheboygan, WI 53081
(414) 459-3779 Contact: Ralph Maffongelli, Director of Theatre **Theatre:** community/non-professional **Works:** full-length plays, children's plays **2nd productions:** "We would consider it." **Specifications:** maximum cast: 6-8; simple sets **Stage:** thrust **Audience:** "Conservative!" **Policy:** query/synopsis **Response:** 2 weeks query; 2 months script **Your chances:** 3-4/"1 every few years" **Remuneration:** "Small stipend." **Program:** readings **Advice:** "We do new shows for our Readers' Theatre program, a series of staged readings; shows must be appropriate for such. We will consider new plays for mainstage, but must be very careful as our box office must support a substantial part of our budget."

SIDEWALKS THEATER
40 W. 27th St., New York, NY 10001
(212) 481-3077 Contact: Gary Beck, Artistic Director **Theatre:** off off Broadway, professional not-for-profit **Works:** full-length plays, one-acts, translations, adaptations **2nd productions:** "Possibly." **Special interests:** "We want serious playwrights, not amateurs with first plays. Serious, meaningful, sophisticated plays." **Specifications:** maximum cast: 12; single set; "nothing set in bars or cafes" **Stage:** black box, 74 seats **Audience:** "Depends on play; New York." **Policy:** query/synopsis with resume **Response:** 6-12 months **Remuneration:** negotiable **Programs:** readings, staged readings, workshop

productions, internships, residencies **Advice:** "Work through our workshop development procedure. All plays are done in this manner: reading, workshop, production." **Comment:** Theatre produces 1-2 new plays each year.

SIERRA REPERTORY THEATRE
Box 3030, Sonora, CA 95370 (209) 532-3120
See Marvin Taylor Playwriting Award listing in Contests.

SMITH COLLEGE THEATRE
Northampton, MA   This theatre has requested that we discontinue its listing.

THE SNOWMASS REPERTORY THEATRE
Box 6275, Snowmass Village, CO 81615
(303) 923-3773   Contact: Susan Short, Managing Director **Theatre:** professional not-for-profit **Works:** full-length plays, translations, adaptations, musicals **2nd productions:** yes **Specifications:** maximum cast: 10; single set preferred **Tours:** yes **Stage:** thrust **Audience:** "Tourists interested in healthy fun." **Policy:** unsolicited script **Best time:** Oct.-Nov. **Response:** 2 weeks query; 6 months script **Your chances:** 300/2 **Remuneration:** percentage **Program:** workshop productions

SOCIETY HILL PLAYHOUSE
507 S. 8th St., Philadelphia, PA 19147
(215) 923-0210   Contact: Walter Vail, Director, Development **Theatre:** professional not-for-profit **Works:** full-length plays, one-acts, translations, adaptations, musicals, children's plays **Stages:** proscenium, 223 seats; flexible, 50 seats **Audience:** "General theatre-goers from the Delaware Valley." **Policies:** query/synopsis preferred; unsolicited script; professional recommendation; agent submission **Response:** 1 month query; 6 months script **Your chances:** 300+/2-6 **Remuneration:** negotiable **Programs:** staged readings, workshop productions

SOHO REPERTORY THEATRE
80 Varick St., New York, NY 10013
(212) 925-2588   Contact: Jerry Engelback, Artistic Director **Theatre:** off off Broadway **Works:** full-length plays, one-acts, translations, adaptations, musicals **2nd**

productions: "Yes, but not off off Broadway shows."
Special interests: "Plays that are intellectually stimulating, use 3-dimentional space imaginatively, have plenty of action and are unlikely to be done by other theatres; high-quality mixed-media and experimental works; offbeat new musicals and operas with superb music." **Specifications:** high ceilings **Stage:** proscenium, 100 seats **Audience:** "Educated, sophisticated, median age about 50." **Policy:** query (no synopsis) describing ways the play "will be perceived by an audience and as a physically theatrical event," with resume **Response:** 1 week query; 90 days script **Your chances:** 100/1-2 **Remuneration:** "About $400 for 30 performances." **Programs:** First Look staged readings; One Night Stand Series "non-play works such as performance pieces and music" (inquire) **Advice:** "Request guidelines; if you have a director interested in staging your play, his/her input might be useful."

SOURCE THEATRE COMPANY
1809 14th St. NW, Washington, DC 20009
(202) 462-1073 Contact: Pat Murphy Sheehy, Artistic Director **Theatre:** professional not-for-profit **Works:** full-length plays, one-acts, translations, adaptations, musicals **2nd productions:** yes **Specifications:** small stage; suggestive settings **Policy:** query/synopsis with resume **Best time:** Sept. 15-Mar. 15 **Response:** June 1 **Programs:** readings, SourceWorks and The Washington Theatre Festival productions (see Special Programs), Source Theatre National Playwriting Competition (see Contests)

SOUTH COAST REPERTORY
Box 2197, Costa Mesa, CA 92628 (714) 957-2602
Contact: Jerry Patch, Dramaturg; John Glore, Literary Manager **Theatre:** professional not-for-profit **Works:** full-length plays **2nd productions:** yes **Tours:** yes **Stages:** proscenium, 507 seats; thrust, 161 seats **Audience:** "Cosmopolitan." **Policies:** query/synopsis; professional recommendation; agent submission **Response:** 2 weeks query; 4 months script **Your chances:** 600-700/5-6 **Remuneration:** "Negotiable percentage, usually about 5%." **Programs:** readings, staged readings, workshop productions, development, Hispanic Playwrights Project (see Contests)

SOUTHERN APPALACHIAN REPERTORY THEATRE
SART, Box 53, Mars Hill, NC 28754
(704) 689-1384, -1203 Contact: James W. Thomas, Managing Director **Theatre:** professional not-for-profit **Works:** full-length plays, musicals **2nd productions:** "Sometimes." **Special interest:** "Southern Appalachian themes, but not exclusively." **Stage:** proscenium, 152 seats **Audience:** "Well educated; upper-middle income; generally about 45-50 years of age; many retired and summer residents." **Policies:** unsolicited script with resume; query/synopsis with resume; professional recommendation **Best time:** fall **Response:** 1 month query; 6 months script **Your chances:** 30-40/1-2 or more **Remuneration:** "$500 plus expenses while attending rehearsals and/or performances." **Programs:** readings, staged readings, development, Southern Appalachian Playwrights Conference held each Jan. (inquire) **Advice:** "Submit finished draft in proper form."

SOUTH JERSEY REGIONAL THEATRE
Bay Ave, Somers Point, NJ 08244 (609) 653-0554
Contact: Joanna Papada, Producing Director **Theatre:** professional not-for-profit **Works:** adaptations, musicals, cabaret/revues **Specifications:** maximum cast: 6; minimal or unit set; no fly space **Stage:** proscenium, 299 seats **Policy:** query/synopsis **Response:** 3 weeks query; 3-6 months script

SPECTRUM THEATRE
151 First Ave. Suite 199, New York, NY 10003
(212) 475-5529 Contact: Beno Haehnel, Producing Artistic Director **Theatre:** professional not-for-profit **Works:** full-length plays, one-acts, translations, adaptations, children's plays, cabaret/revues **2nd productions:** yes **Special interest:** "Plays that deal with social issues that are important in the last years of the 20th century." **Maximum cast:** 6 **Stage:** proscenium **Policies:** unsolicited script; query/synopsis, professional recommendation; agent submission **Response:** 1 month query; 3-4 months script **Your chances:** 500/3-4 **Remuneration:** "Varies." **Programs:** readings, staged readings, workshop productions, development, classes

SPOKANE INTERPLAYERS ENSEMBLE
Box 1961, Spokane, WA 99210 (509) 455-7529
Contact: Robert A. Welch, Managing Director **Theatre:** professional not-for-profit **Works:** full-length plays, translations, adaptations, cabaret/revues **Specifications:** maximum cast: 8 preferred; single set **Stage:** thrust, 253 seats **Policy:** unsolicited script **Best time:** Jun.-Aug. **Response:** 6-12 months

SPRINGBOARD THEATRE
15 Cheever Pl., Brooklyn, NY 11231
(718) 875-2405 Contact: Sasha Nanus, Artistic Director **Theatre:** off off Broadway **Works:** full-length plays, one-acts **2nd productions:** yes **Specifications:** some limitations on sets **Stages:** proscenium; thrust; flexible **Audience:** "Educated New York audience." **Policies:** unsolicited script; query/synopsis; agent submission **Response:** 1 week query; 1 month script **Your chances:** 75-100/5-10 **Remuneration:** "Depends upon each individual project." **Programs:** readings, staged readings, workshop productions **Advice:** "Contemporary, realistic works; age range 20-40; more female roles."

STAGE #1
Dallas, TX This theatre did not respond to our 1989 questionnaire, and its phone has been disconnected.

STAGE ONE: LOUISVILLE CHILDREN'S THEATRE
425 W. Market St., Louisville, KY 40202
(502) 589-5946 Contact: Moses Goldberg, Producing Director **Theatre:** professional not-for-profit **Works:** children's full-length plays, one-acts, translations, adaptations and musicals **2nd productions:** yes **Special interests:** "Stageworthy and respectful dramatizations of the classic tales of childhood, both ancient and modern; plays relevant to the lives of young people and their families; plays directly related to school curriculum." **Maximum cast:** 12 **Tours:** yes **Stages:** thrust, 626 seats; arena, 350 seats **Audience:** "Young people ages 5-18, or some portion of that span. Some plays are done for 'Family Audiences,' which may include all ages." **Policies:** unsolicited script; professional recommendation; agent submission **Best time:** Nov. **Response:** 4 months **Your chances:** 100-200/1-2

Remuneration: varies **Program:** readings **Advice:** "Please do not send plot summaries or reviews. Include author's resume, if desired."

STAGES
118 E. 4th St. #14, New York, NY 10003
Contact: Joe Miloscia, Artistic Director **Theatre:** off off Broadway **Works:** musicals **2nd productions:** "Yes, if it has not had a full-scale production." **Stages:** rented spaces **Audience:** general **Policy:** unsolicites script with tape of score **Best time:** spring-summer **Response:** 2-3 **Your chances:** 100/20 **Remuneration:** no **Programs:** workshop productions, development **Advice:** "We want works of imagination by people who collaborate well."

STAGES REPERTORY THEATRE
3201 Allen Pkwy. Suite 101, Houston, TX 77019
(713) 527-0220 Contact: Brenda Dubay, Producing Director **Theatre:** professional not-for-profit **Works:** full-length plays, one-acts, children's plays, cabaret/revues **Special interest:** new plays by Texas authors **Specifications:** small cast, simple set preferred **Tours:** children's plays **Stages:** thrust, 195 seats; arena, 248 seats **Policy:** unsolicited script with synopsis **Programs:** Women Playwrights Repertory; Texas Playwrights Festival (contact Carla Webbles)

STAGE WEST
One Columbus Center, Springfield, MA 01103
(413) 781-4470 Contact: Gregory Boyd, Artistic Director **Theatre:** professional not-for-profit **Works:** full-length plays, translations **Special interests:** adaptations of material from non-dramatic genres; new translations and adaptations of neglected classic and 20th-century European plays **Stages:** thrust, 480 seats; flexible, 99 seats **Policy:** query/synopsis **Response:** 3 months **Program:** staged readings

STAGE WEST
Box 2587, Ft. Worth, TX 76113 (817) 332-6265
Contact: Jerry Russell, Artistic Director **Theatre:** professional not-for-profit **Works:** full-length plays,

translations, adaptations, musicals, cabaret/revues **2nd productions:** yes **Special interest:** contemporary problems **Maximum cast:** 9 preferred **Stage:** flexible, 175 seats **Policy:** query/synopsis **Best time:** Jan.-Mar. **Response:** 1 month **Remuneration:** varies

STAGEWRIGHTS, INC.
165 W. 47th St., New York, NY 10036
(718) 946-5891 Contact: John Albanese, Literary Manager **Theatre:** off off Broadway **Works:** full-length plays, one-acts **2nd productions:** yes **Special interest:** "Works emphasizing present action." **Policy:** query/synopsis with 1st scene **Response:** 3 months **Program:** Manhattan Monday Night Playwrights Workshop (inquire)

STAMFORD THEATRE WORKS
95 Atlantic St., Stamford, CT 06901
(203) 359-4414 Contact: Steve Karp, Artistic Director **Theatre:** professional not-for-profit resident company **Works:** full-length plays **2nd productions:** yes **Special interest:** "Quality work on any subject matter that speaks to our audience." **Stage:** pit stage with raked audience, 150 seats **Audience:** "Stamford area, affluent and sophisticated." **Policy:** unsolicited script **Response:** 3-6 months **Remuneration:** royalty **Programs:** "We anticipate greater work with playwrights in the future."

STANLEY HOTEL THEATRE
333 Wonderview Rd., Estes Park, CO 80517
(303) 586-3371 (hotel) **Contact:** Melody Page, Producer **Theatre:** non-Equity **Works:** full-length plays, musicals **Special interests:** mysteries, melodramas, dramas, comedies, farces, musicals **Specifications:** maximum cast: 10; simple, moveable sets; no sit-coms **Policy:** query/synopsis

STEPPENWOLF THEATRE COMPANY
2851 N. Halsted St., Chicago, IL 60657
(312) 472-4515 Contact: Randall Arney, Jeff Perry, Artistic Directors **Theatre:** professional not-for-profit **Works:** full-length plays, adaptations **Stage:** modified thrust, 211 seats **Policy:** query/synopsis **Best time:** Oct.-Dec. **Response:** 1 month query; 6 months script

STONEWALL REPERTORY THEATER
Box 94 Old Chelsea Station, New York, NY 10011
(212) 677-2392 **Contact:** Jacqueline Allen, William Cunningham, Artistic Directors **Theatre:** off off Broadway **Works:** full-length plays, one-acts, translations, adaptations, musicals **2nd productions:** yes **Exclusive interest:** "Gay characters and themes." **Specifications:** simple sets **Stage:** black box **Audience:** "Gay and straight; men and women." **Policies:** unsolicited script; query/synopsis **Response:** 3 months **Your chances:** 100/4 **Remuneration:** percentage **Programs:** readings, development

STOP-GAP COMPANY
523 N. Grand Ave., Santa Ana, CA 92701
(714) 648-0135 **Contact:** Don Laffoon, Executive Director **Theatre:** professional not-for-profit **Works:** full-length plays, one-acts **2nd productions:** no **Special interest:** "Social issues and disabilities: alcoholism, death, drug abuse, seniors, etc." **Specifications:** maximum cast: 6; some limitations on sets **Stage:** proscenium, 200 seats **Audience:** "General audience and those interested in specific social themes presented." **Policies:** unsolicited script; query/synopsis **Your chances:** 20/2 **Remuneration:** no

STOREFRONT THEATRE
615 NW Couch, Portland, OR 97209
(503) 224-9598 **Contact:** Gary O'Brien, Producing Director **Theatre:** professional not-for-profit **Works:** full-length plays, adaptations, small musicals **2nd productions:** yes **Stages:** flexible (usually proscenium), 300 seats; proscenium, 150 seats **Policies:** query/synopsis with dialogue sample; professional recommendation **Response:** 1 month query; 6 months script **Your chances:** 50-100/1-2 **Remuneration:** standard royalty **Advice:** "We are Portland's 'alternative' theatre--not interested in mainstream, Broadway-type material."

STRAND STREET THEATRE
2317 Mechanic St., Galveston, TX 77550
(409) 763-4591 **Contact:** Susan Permenter, Managing Director **Theatre:** professional not-for-profit **Works:** full-length plays, one-acts, adaptations **Specifications:**

small cast; single-story set, unit preferred **Policy:** inquire **Programs:** readings, workshop productions

THE STREET THEATER
228 Fisher Ave. Room 226, White Plains, NY 10606 (914) 761-3307   Contact: Gray Smith, Executive Director **Theatre:** professional not-for-profit **Works:** one-acts, plays for young audiences **Special interests:** ensemble pieces; plays for young audiences (not children's plays) **Specifications:** minimal production requirements **Tours:** yes **Stages:** summer: outdoor mobile stages; winter: school stages **Policies:** query/synopsis; commission **Best time:** Nov.-Feb. **Response:** 2-4 weeks **Comment:** Playwrights interested in commissions to write for or collaborate with the company should write for information.

STUDIO ARENA THEATRE
710 Main St., Buffalo, NY 14202 (716) 856-8025 Contact: Ross Wasserman, Associate Director/Dramaturg **Theatre:** professional not-for-profit **Works:** full-length plays, translations, adaptations, children's plays **2nd productions:** yes **Special interests:** "We are seeking plays which deal with issues of power in America and plays which explore in original ways the roles of women and minorities in our society. We also are looking for work that celebrates theatricality and the act of performance itself." **Specifications:** maximum cast: 12; limited wing space; no fly system **Stage:** thrust, 637 seats **Audience:** "Broad spectrum." **Policies:** query/synopsis with dialogue sample; agent submission   **Response:** 2 weeks query; 3 months script **Your chances:** 300/1-2 **Remuneration:** "Fee." **Program:** staged reading with 1-week residency

THE STUDIO THEATRE
1333 P St. NW, Washington, DC 20005 (202) 232-7267   Contact: Maynard Marshall, Literary Manager **Theatre:** professional not-for-profit **Works:** full-length plays, translations, adaptations, musicals **Special interests:** American "lyric realism"; translations of new Asian and European plays **Stage:** thrust, 110 seats **Policy:** professional recommendation **Best times:** Aug.-Sept., Dec.-Jan. **Response:** 2 months

STUDIO X
The Ashland Performing Arts Center, 208 Oak St., Ashland, OR 97520 (503) 488-2011
Contact: Scott Avery, Artistic Director **Theatre:** professional not-for-profit **Works:** full-length plays, one-acts **2nd productions:** yes **Maximum cast:** 8 **Stage:** flexible **Audience:** "All types." **Policy:** unsolicited script **Best time:** Mar. **Your chances:** 150/13 **Remuneration:** "Varies." **Programs:** staged readings, classes

SUNSET PLAYHOUSE, INC.
800 Elm Grove Rd., Elm Grove, WI 53122
(414) 782-4430 Contact: Alan Furlan, Managing Director **Theatre:** community not-for-profit **Works:** full-length plays **Special interest:** comedies with appeal to an older audience **Stage:** proscenium **Audience:** "Mature--30-70." **Policy:** unsolicited script **Your chances:** 50/"0 perhaps" **Remuneration:** royalty **Comment:** "Season normally consists of Broadway plays--as soon as they become available."

SYNTHAXIS THEATRE COMPANY
Box 15036, North Hollywood, CA 91606
(213) 877-4726 Contact: Estelle Busch, Executive Director **Works:** full-length plays, one-acts **2nd productions:** no **Special interests:** plays for women, children, the elderly **Specifications:** maximum cast: 6-7; single set **Policy:** inquire

SYRACUSE STAGE
820 E. Genessee St., Syracuse, NY 13210
(315) 443-4008 Contact: Howard A. Kerner, Literary Manager **Theatre:** professional not-for-profit **Works:** full-length plays, one-acts, translations **2nd productions:** yes **Maximum cast:** 12 preferred **Stages:** proscenium, 199 seats; flexible, 499 seats **Audience:** "Cultural cross-section; high school to senior citizen." **Policies:** unsolicited script; query/synopsis with dialogue sample; professional recommendation; agent submission **Best time:** May-Jun. only for unsolicited script; Apr.-Oct. preferred for query/synopsis **Response:** 1 month if interested in query; 3-6 months script **Your chances:** 150/1-2 **Remuneration:** "Standard royalty." **Program:** staged readings

TACOMA ACTORS GUILD
1323 S. Yakima Ave., Tacoma, WA 98405
(206) 272-3107 Contact: William Becvar, Artistic Director **Theatre:** professional not-for-profit **Works:** full-length plays, translations, adaptations, musicals **2nd productions:** no **Specifications:** maximum cast: 14; unit set preferred **Stage:** modified thrust, 298 seats **Audience:** "Older, middle-of-the-road, not adventurous." **Policy:** query/synopsis **Best time:** spring-summer **Response:** 1-2 months query; 6-12 months script **Remuneration:** "Negotiable." **Your chances:** 30/0 **Program:** staged readings **Advice:** "No overabundance of strong language or provocative situations involving nudity."

TALE SPINNERS THEATER
Bldg. C Room 200, Ft. Mason Center,
San Francisco, CA 94123 (415) 776-8470
Contact: Kate Mendeloff, Artistic Director **Theatre:** professional not-for-profit **Works:** full-length plays **2nd productions:** yes **Exclusive interest:** "The development of new plays from Bay Area oral history." **Tours:** yes **Stages:** proscenium, usually 99 seats; thrust, usually 99 seats **Audience:** "Varied." **Policy:** inquire **Remuneration:** "Royalty for mainstage productions." **Programs:** readings, staged readings, workshop productions, development

THE TALKING BAND
New York, NY This theatre is developing its own material and has requested that we discontinue its listing.

THE TAMPA PLAYERS
601 S. Florida Ave., Tampa, FL 33602
(813) 254-0444 Contact: Bill Lelbach, Artistic/Managing Director **Theatre:** professional not-for-profit **Works:** full-length plays, musicals **2nd productions:** yes **Stage:** flexible, 250 seats **Policy:** professional recommendation **Response:** "No response guaranteed." **Programs:** staged readings, development

TENNESSEE REPERTORY THEATRE
427 Chestnut St., Nashville, TN 37203
(615) 244-4878 Contact: Jennifer Orth, Production Manager **Theatre:** professional not-for-profit **Works:**

full-length plays, one-acts,   adaptations, musicals **Special interest**: new American musicals **Stages**: proscenium, 1050 seats; 2nd stage workshop setting, 90 seats **Policy**: query/synopsis with dialogue sample **Best time**: Dec.-Jan. **Response**: 6 months **Your chances:** 6-12/0 to date **Advice:** "Tennessee Repertory Theatre has a playreading committee of actors, designers and directors who evaluate submitted scripts. Because of limited resources and a very conservative audience base, the number of new works actually produced is extremely small. No new works on mainstage; we might consider them for 2nd stage only."

TEXAS A & I UNIVERSITY THEATRE
Box 178, Texas A & I University,
Kingsville, TX 78363 (512) 595-2614
Contact: Randall J. Buchanan, Director of Theatre **Theatre:** university/college **Works:** full-length plays, one-acts, translations, children's plays **2nd productions:** yes **Specifications:** single set or space **Tours:** yes **Stages:** proscenium, 1000 seats; proscenium, 240 seats; flexible, 100 seats **Audience:** "Fairly conservative; mixture of university and community; Hispanic and Anglo; small Black population." **Best time**: spring **Response:** 1 month query; 3-4 months script **Your chances:** 3-4/0-1 **Remuneration:** standard royalty **Advice:** "Cast of 8-10 with at least as many female as male roles."

THALIA SPANISH THEATRE
Box 4368, Sunnyside, NY 11104 (718) 729-3880
Contact: Silvia Brito, Artistic/Executive Director **Theatre:** professional not-for-profit **Works:** full-length plays, translations, adaptations **Exclusive interest:** plays in Spanish **Specifications:** maximum cast: 6; single set **Stage:** proscenium, 74 seats **Policy:** unsolicited script **Best time**: Dec.-Jan. **Response:** 3 months

THEATER ARTISTS OF MARIN
Box 473, San Raphael, CA 94915 (415) 454-2380
Contact: Charles Brousse, Artistic Director **Theatre:** professional not-for-profit **Works:** full-length plays, one-acts, musicals **2nd productions:** yes **Special interest:** "Plays which illuminate contemporary American life in a broader sense, not merely personal relationships."

Audience: "Varied in age, well educated, affluent, liberal." **Policies:** unsolicited script; query/synopsis **Response:** 2 months query; 6 months script **Your chances:** 80-100/1 plus 3 staged readings **Remuneration:** "$400 for full production." **Programs:** staged readings, workshop productions, development

THE THEATER AT MONMOUTH

Box 385, Monmouth, ME 04259 (207) 933-4371 **Contact:** Margaret M. Sterling, Business Manager **Works:** full-length plays, children's plays **Special interest:** traditional plays for young audiences **Specifications:** simple set **Stage:** thrust, 275 seats **Policy:** query/synopsis **Best time:** Nov. **Response:** 4-6 weeks query; 4-6 months script

THEATER FOR THE NEW CITY

155 First Ave., New York, NY 10003 **(212) 254-1109 Contact:** Crystal Field, George Bartenieff, Artistic Directors **Theatre:** off off Broadway, professional not-for-profit **Works:** full-length plays, one-acts, musicals, operas, cabaret/revues, dance, performance art **2nd productions:** no **Special interests:** social issues; experimental American works; plays integrating music, dance and poetry **Tours:** "Annual Street Theatre production tours throughout New York City." **Stages:** proscenium, 140 seats; arena, 80-90 seats; black box, 45 seats; cabaret, 45 seats **Policies:** unsolicited script; professional recommendation; commission **Best time:** spring **Response:** 9-18 months **Your chances:** 780/40 **Remuneration:** "For a play that we commission and when the playwright attends every performance." **Programs:** readings, staged readings, classes, internships **Comment:** TNC is committed to "the creation and performance of new American theatre and to new artists, lesser known writers and young performers."

THEATER LUDICRUM, INC.

64 Charlesgate E. #83, Boston, MA 02215 **(617) 424-6831 Contact:** George Bistransin, President **Theatre:** professional not-for-profit **Works:** full-length plays, one-acts **2nd productions:** yes **Special interest:** "Works which rely upon the written word and acting."

Specifications: "We are unable to present works that require expensive or difficult sets and effects." **Stages:** various spaces **Policy:** unsolicited script **Response:** 1 month **Your chances:** 50/1 **Remuneration:** $15-$30 per performance **Programs:** readings, staged readings

THE THEATER STUDIO
750 Eighth Ave., New York, NY 10019
(212) 581-9425 Contact: Lawrence Anziviao, Managing Director **Theatre:** professional not-for-profit **Works:** full-length plays, one-acts, translations, adaptations, musicals **2nd productions:** yes **Special interest:** "Family plays." **Stage:** flexible open space **Specifications:** maximum cast: 6-20; limited space; limited production requirements **Audience:** "New Yorkers and some tourists." **Policies:** unsolicited script; query/synopsis with resume and sample dialogue **Response:** 9 months **Your chances:** 24/1-2 **Remuneration:** no **Programs:** staged readings, workshop productions **Comments:** "We go to schools and work with children and youth. We emphasize workshop productions."

THEATRE AMERICANA
Box 245, Altadena, Ca 91001-1235
(818) 791-4497 Contact: Leone Jones, Chairman, Playreading Committee **Theatre:** community/non-professional **Works:** full-length plays **Specifications:** cast of 4-10 preferred; simple sets; minimum set changes; no elaborate, expensive costumes; no musicals **Stage:** "Simple raised stage with curtains, 100-150 seats." **Audience:** "Mostly conservative; middle-aged and senior citizens." **Policy:** unsolicited script **Response:** 2-3 months query; several months script **Your chances:** 200-250/4 **Remuneration:** "No; however, there is an annual $500 award to the best of the 4 plays produced each year." **Program:** David James Ellis Memorial Award (see Contests)

THEATRE ARTS GROUP
1612 Metropolitan, Las Vegas, NV 89102
(702) 877-6463 Contact: Lori Noble, Trustee **Theatre:** community not-for-profit **Works:** full-length plays **Specifications:** maximum cast: 20; small stage **Stage:** proscenium, 90 seats **Audience:** "Mainly middle class white."

Policy: unsolicited script **Response:** 6 weeks **Your chances:** 1/1 in 2 and a half years **Remuneration:** "Would depend." **Programs:** workshop productions, classes **Advice:** "Appeal to a general audience."

THEATRE DE LA JEUNE LUNE
Box 25170, Minneapolis, MN 55458-6170
(612) 332-3968 Contact: Emily Stevens, Business Director **Theatre:** professional not-for-profit **Works:** full-length plays, translations, adaptations, musicals **2nd productions:** yes **Tours:** yes **Stages:** prosenium, 200 seats; thrust, 325 seats **Audience:** "Age 25-65, college educated." **Policies:** unsolicited script; query/synopsis with resume; professional recommendation **Response:** 2 months **Your chances:** 10/0 **Remuneration:** "Negotiated fee."

THEATRE EXCHANGE
11855 Hart St., North Hollywood, CA 91605
(818) 765-9005 Contact: Rob Zapple, Managing Director **Theatre:** off off Broadway **Works:** full-length plays, translations, adaptations, children's plays **2nd productions:** yes **Special interests:** "Modern political works; good, fast-paced comedy." **Specifications:** maximum cast: 35; abstract sets if more than 2 **Tours:** yes **Stage:** 3/4 thrust, 50 seats **Audience:** "Mostly upscale professionals and people from the arts." **Policies:** unsolicited script; query/synopsis; professional recommendation **Response:** 1 year **Your chances:** 75/4-5 **Remuneration:** standard royalty **Programs:** readings, staged readings, workshop productions **Advice:** "Simple settings; clear, concise ideas in writing."

THEATREFEST
c/o Phillip Oesterman, Producer-Artistic Director, 529 W. 42nd St #9T, New York, NY 10036
Theatre: professional try-out center; university/college **Works:** full-length plays, musicals **2nd productions:** if not previously produced in New York **Stages:** mainstage, 1009 seats; studio, 199 seats **Policies:** unsolicited script with synopsis; query/synopsis **Best time:** no submissions before fall 1989 **Program:** developmental workshops **Comment:** Theatre is located at Montclair State College, Montclair, NJ.

THEATRE IV

114 W. Broad St., Richmond, VA 23220
(804) 783-1688 Contact: Russell Wilson, Production Associate **Theatre:** professional not-for-profit **Works:** full-length plays, translations, adaptations, musicals, children's plays **2nd productions:** yes **Special interest:** children's plays **Specifications:** moderate production budget **Stages:** proscenium, 650 seats; flexiable 100 seats **Audience:** "Broad base." **Policies:** query/synopsis with resume; professional recommendation; commission **Response:** 2 months **Your chances:** 50/3-7 **Remuneration:** "Negotiated royalty." **Programs:** readings, staged readings **Comment:** The theatre rarely produces new plays other than new children's plays.

THEATRE IN THE PARK

Box 12151, Raleigh, NC 27605 (919) 755-6936
Contact: Ira D. Wood, Executive Director **Theatre:** professional not-for-profit, community/non-professional **Works:** full-length plays, one-acts, translations, adaptations, musicals, children's plays **2nd productions:** yes **Maximum cast:** 60 **Tours:** yes **Stage:** flexible **Audience:** college community; young professionals **Policy:** unsolicited script **Your chances:** 50/1 **Remuneration:** "Negotiated royalty." **Programs:** staged readings, workshop productions, classes

THEATRE-IN-THE-WORKS

Box 532016, Orlando, FL 32853 (305) 857-6364
Contact: Literary Manager **Theatre:** professional not-for-profit **Works:** full-length plays, one-acts, translations, adaptations, musicals, children's plays, operas **2nd productions:** "Only after a workshop with our theatre." **Exclusive interest:** Florida playwrights **Stage:** flexible **Audience:** "Varies from show to show." **Policy:** inquire **Best time:** fall **Response:** 1 year **Your chances:** 40/2 **Remuneration:** "At least $100 plus travel/accommodations." **Programs:** staged readings, workshop productions, development

THEATRE KENT & PORTHOUSE THEATRE FESTIVAL
B141 M and Sp. Bldg., Kent State University, Kent, OH 44242 (216) 672-2082
Contact: Michael Nash, Artistic Director **Theatre:** professional not-for-profit, university/college **Works:** full-length plays, one-acts, translations, musicals **2nd productions:** yes **Specifications:** "Balance of male/female roles; no fly system." **Tours:** "Rarely." **Stage:** thrust, 500 seats **Policies:** unsolicited script; query/synopsis; professional recommendation; agent submission **Response:** 3 weeks-1 month **Remuneration:** "We would try!" **Comment:** "We produce 1 new play every 2 years or so. Unsolicited submission is _very_ difficult, given the lack of any literary staff."

THEATRE NOUVEAU
539 Tremont St., Boston, MA 02116
(617) 451-6360 Contact: Barry Finch, Company Manager **Theatre:** professional not-for-profit **Works:** full-length plays, one-acts, translations **2nd productions:** "We want new or relatively new plays." **Specifications:** maximum cast: 6; minimal and simple sets **Stage:** black box, 60-70 seats **Audience:** "Educated, sophisticated people interested in new theatre." **Policy:** query/synopsis with resume and 1-page dialogue sample **Best time:** late spring-early summer **Response:** 2-3 weeks **Your chances:** 150/25-30 **Remuneration:** "No royalty, with some exceptions." **Programs:** staged readings, development: "We are a development program and are interested in helping the playwright; we want the playwright to attend rehearsals and be involved." **Advice:** "Write for educated people. Comedies with value."

THEATRE OFF PARK
224 Waverly Pl., New York, NY 10014
(212) 627-2556 Contact: Albert Harris, Artistic Director **Theatre:** professional not-for-profit **Works:** full-length plays, one-acts, musicals **2nd productions:** "Occasionally." **Special interest:** small-cast contemporary plays **Specifications:** maximum cast: 8; single set **Stage:** 99 seats **Policy:** agent submission **Best time:** summer **Response:** 2-3 months **Remuneration:** yes **Programs:** readings, staged readings, internships, classes

THEATRE OF YOUTH COMPANY
681 Main St., Buffalo, NY 14205 (716) 856-4410
Contact: Meg Pantera, Artistic Director **Theatre:** professional not-for-profit **Works:** full-length plays, translations, adaptations, children's plays **2nd productions:** yes **Special interest:** contemporary issues for young audiences **Specifications:** maximum cast: 6; small sets for touring shows **Stages:** proscenium; thrust; arena; school auditoriums **Audience:** "Children pre-K and grades K-12, adults." **Policies:** unsolicited script; query/synopsis with dialogue sample; commission **Response:** Sept. **Your chances:** 5/3 **Remuneration:** fee plus royalty **Programs:** development, internships

THEATRE ON THE SQUARE
450 Post St., San Francisco, CA 94102
(415) 433-6461 Contact: Jonathan Reinis, Owner **Theatre:** off off Broadway **Works:** full-length plays, musicals **2nd productions:** yes **Special interests:** musicals, comedies **Specifications:** maximum cast: 5; no more than 6 sets **Tours:** yes **Stages:** proscenium, 700 seats; thrust **Policies:** professional recommendation; agent submission **Best time:** spring **Response:** immediate query; 3 months script **Your chances:** 40-50/1-2 **Remuneration:** percentage

THEATRE PROJECT COMPANY
4219 Laclede, St. Louis, MO 63108
(314) 531-1301 Contact: Fontaine Syer, Artistic Director **Theatre:** professional not-for-profit **Works:** full-length plays, translations, children's plays **Maximum cast:** 15; no more than 2 sets **Stage:** thrust, 200 seats **Policy:** query/synopsis **Best time:** Apr.-Jun. **Response:** 2 weeks query; 2 months script

THEATRE RAPPORT
8128 Gould Ave., Hollywood, CA 90046
(213) 464-2662 Contact: Crane Jackson, Artistic Director **Theatre:** professional not-for-profit **Works:** full-length plays **2nd productions:** "Yes, if West Coast premieres." **Special interests:** "Unique, issue-oriented dramas; fast-moving farce-comedies; contemporary work." **Specifications:** maximum cast: 8; single set **Stage:**

proscenium **Audience:** "Aware, sophisticated." **Policy:** inquire **Your chances:** 50/4 **Remuneration:** 20% of box office **Programs:** staged readings, workshop productions, internships

THEATRE RHINOCEROS
2926 16th St., San Francisco, CA 94103
(415) 522-4100 Contact: Kenneth R. Dixon, Artistic Director **Theatre:** community/non-professional **Works:** full length plays, one-acts, musicals **2nd productions:** yes **Special interest:** "Gay/lesbian issues." **Specificiations:** "Small casts, easy sets." **Tours:** yes **Stages:** 2 flexible spaces **Audience:** "60% male, 40% female, 15% people of color." **Policies:** unsolicited script; query/synopsis; professional recommendation **Response:** 1 month query; 6 months script **Your chances:** 200/6-10 **Remuneration:** royalty **Programs:** readings, staged readings, workshop productions, development **Advice:** "Contemporary subject matter with lesbian/gay characters, people of color, other minorities functioning together."

THEATRE SOUTHWEST
3767 Harper St., Houston, TX 77005
(713) 661-9505 Contact: Anita Sampson, President
This theatre is not accepting submissions in 1989.

THEATRE THREE
Dallas, TX This theatre has requested that we discontinue its listing.

THEATRE THREE PRODUCTIONS
Box 512, Pt. Jefferson, NY 11777 (516) 928-9202
Contact: Jerry Friedman, Associate Artistic Director **Theatre:** professional not-for-profit **Works:** full-length plays, children's plays, cabaret/revues **Specifications:** single set or suggested settings **Stages:** thrust, 475 seats; 3/4 thrust, 75 seats **Policy:** unsolicited script **Response:** 6 months **Program:** staged readings

THEATREVIRGINIA
2800 Grove Ave., Richmond, VA 23221-2466
(804) 367-0840 Contact: Bo Wilson, Literary Manager **Theatre:** professional not-for-profit **Works:** full-length

plays, adaptations, musicals **2nd productions:** yes **Tours:** "Possibly." **Stage:** proscenium, 500 seats **Policy:** query/synopsis with dialogue sample **Best time:** late spring **Response:** 2-3 weeks query; 2 months script **Remuneration:** negotiable

THEATRE WEST
3333 Cahuenga Blvd. W, Los Angeles, CA 90068 (213) 851-4839 Contact: Jan Harris, Writer's Workshop Moderator **Theatre:** professional not-for-profit membership workshop **Works:** full-length plays, one-acts, translations, adaptations, musicals, children's plays **2nd productions:** yes **Specifications:** very limited wing and fly space **Tours:** occasionally **Stage:** proscenium, 200 seats **Audience:** "Fairly sophisticated theatrically; wide financial spectrum; considerable entertainment-industry audience." **Policies:** sponsorship by 1 or more of approximately 200 members; unsolicited script from playwright desiring membership **Response:** 2 months **Your chances:** 30-40/1-3 **Remuneration:** negotiable **Program:** Theatre West Writer's Unit: a membership workshop offering developmental programs and full productions; $66 initiation fee, $34 monthly dues **Advice:** "L.A. area writers can increase their chances for production greatly by applying to join our Writer's Unit. Theatre West does not accept unsolicited scripts for production."

THEATRE WEST VIRGINIA
Box 1205, Beckley, WV 25802 (304) 253-8317 Contact: Charles Kennedy, Artistic Director **Theatre:** professional not-for-profit touring company **Works:** full-length plays, one-acts, translations, adaptations, musicals, children's plays **Special interests:** adaptations of well-known works; historical subjects **Specifications:** maximum cast: 5; single set suitable for touring **Audience:** family-oriented **Policy:** unsolicited script **Best time:** Sept. **Response:** 2 months

THEATREWORKS
1305 Middlefield Rd., Palo Alto, CA 94301 (415) 328-0600 Contact: Robert Kelley, Artistic Director **Theatre:** professional not-for-profit **Works:** full-length plays, translations, adaptations, musicals **2nd**

productions: yes   **Special interest:** new musicals **Stages:** proscenium, 425 seats; proscenium, 275 seats; flexible outdoor, 300 seats; flexible, 70 seats **Audience:** "Wealthy and educated; heavily subscribed, very active." **Policies:** unsolicited script; professional recommendation, agent submission **Best time:** Oct.-Dec. **Response:** 6 months **Your chances:** 100/0-1 **Remuneration:** royalty **Advice:** "Extremely well-written work; interesting subject matter."

THEATREWORKS/USA
131 W. 86th St., New York, NY 10024
(212) 628-5785 Contact: Barbara Pasternack, Artistic Associate   **Theatre:** professional not-for-profit touring **Works:** children's musicals **2nd productions:** yes **Special interests:** "Historical plays, fairy tales, issues, classics and contemporary literature." **Specifications:** maximum cast: 5-6; single, touring set   **Stages:** proscenium; flexible **Audience:** "6-14 year olds."   **Policies:** query/synopsis preferred; unsolicited script **Best time:** summer **Response:** 3 months query; 6 months-1 year script **Your chances:** 100/3 **Remuneration:** "$1500 available for commission (advance against royalty); 6% total divided among collaborators." **Programs:** readings, workshop productions, Theatreworks/USA Commissioning Program (see Contests)

THEATRE X
Box 92206, Milwaukee, WI 53202 (414) 278-0555
Contact: John Schneider, Associate Artistic Director **Theatre:** professional not-for-profit **Works:** full-length plays **2nd productions:** yes **Special interests:** plays written with or for the company; performance art; avant garde works **Specifications:** small cast **Stage:** flexible, 99 seats **Audience:** "Mixed, educated." **Policy:** professional recommendation   **Response:** 6 months   **Your chances:** 20/0-1   **Remuneration:** standard royalty   **Program:** readings **Advice:** "Get to know us and our work; get us to see your work somewhere."

THEATRICAL OUTFIT
Atlanta, GA   This theatre is undergoing reorganization and has requested that we discontinue its listing in 1989.

THIRD STEP THEATRE COMPANY
1179 Broadway, New York, NY 10001
(212) 545-1372 Contact: Margit Ahlin, Literary Manager **Theatre:** off off Broadway, professional not-for-profit **Works:** full-length plays, one-acts, adaptations, children's plays **2nd productions:** no **Stage:** rented space, 99 seats **Audience:** "General New York audience." **Policy:** query/synopsis with character analysis and 15-page dialogue sample **Best time:** Sept. 1-Jan. 15 only **Response:** 3 months **Your chances:** 70/10 in staged reading festival, 3 possible productions **Remuneration:** cash award for winners of festival **Comment:** Other plays may be produced by other theatres.

THE THIRTEENTH STREET
CHILDREN'S THEATRE ENSEMBLE
The Thirteenth Street Repertory Theatre,
50 W. 13th St., New York, NY 10011
(212) 675-6677 Contact: Tom Oliver, Director **Theatre:** off off Broadway, professional not-for-profit **Works:** children's musicals, adaptations of classic fairy tales, original non-musicals for children **2nd productions:** yes **Specifications:** works must be 45-60 minutes in length and suitable for adult ensemble company; small cast; sets suitable for small spaces **Tours:** all shows **Stage:** proscenium, 70 seats **Audience:** "Parents and children ages 3-8." **Policy:** unsolicited script with resume **Response:** 2 weeks **Your chances:** 10-15/5 **Remuneration:** no **Advice:** "Send cassette tape of songs, sample lead sheets and/or piano arrangements."

THE THIRTEENTH STREET REPERTORY COMPANY
50 W. 13th St., New York, NY 10011
(212) 675-6677 Contact: Gordon Farrell, Literary Manager **Theatre:** off off Broadway **Works:** short full-length plays, one-acts, musicals, children's plays **2nd productions:** New York premieres **Specifications:** maximum cast: 10; uncomplicated sets--"simple and fun!" **Tours:** "Not yet--may." **Audience:** "City dwellers from New York, Brooklyn, New Jersey--mixed." **Policy:** unsolicited script **Best time:** summer **Response:** 6 months **Your chances:** 200/10 **Remuneration:** no **Programs:** readings, development **Advice:** "Come to our

theatre; see our productions." **Comment:** Theatre is interested in working with playwrights to develop new plays.

THREE BROTHERS THEATRE
216 Falmouth Rd., Scarsdale, NY 10583
(914) 723-8169 Contact: Wendell Batts, Artistic Director **Theatre:** professional not-for-profit **Works:** full-length plays, one-acts, translations, adaptations, musicals, children's plays **2nd productions:** yes **Special interest:** "The contemporary Black male experience, particularly from 1964 to present—post Civil Rights." **Specifications:** simple **Tours:** yes **Stage:** proscenium, 388 seats **Audience:** "Black and white, middle class." **Policy:** query/synopsis with resume **Best time:** Sept.-Mar. **Response:** 3 months **Your chances:** 30-35/1 **Remuneration:** no **Programs:** readings, staged readings, workshop productions **Advice:** "Emphasis on the Black experience; good writing."

THREE RIVERS SHAKESPEARE FESTIVAL
B-39 CL, University of Pittsburgh,
Pittsburgh, PA 15260 (412) 624-6805 Contact: Attilio Favorini, Producing Director **Theatre:** professional not-for-profit, university/college **Works:** full-length plays, translations, adaptations **Special interest:** new translations and adaptations of classics **Stage:** modified thrust, 600 seats **Policy:** query/synopsis with resume **Best time:** fall **Response:** 3 months

THE THUNDERBIRD THEATER COMPANY
Box 468, Venice, CA 90204-0468 (213) 306-5176
Contact: Samuel Miller, Literary Manager **Theatre:** professional not-for-profit **Works:** full-length plays, one-acts **2nd productions:** yes **Special interests:** "Mature writing concerned with or featuring characters under the age of 30." **Stages:** rented spaces **Policies:** unsolicited script; query/synopsis; professional recommendation; agent submission **Response:** 1 week query; 2 months script **Your chances:** 200/2-3 **Remuneration:** "Varies: as much as possible, sometimes very little." **Advice:** "Please send us strong and serious work. TTC yearns for comedic scripts but only those packing a punch. Please do not submit scripts that resemble sitcoms, as it is never our intention to serve as a

Hollywood showcase. Please write with a big heart and a sharp mind, and please create plays that are emotionally vital, intellectually rigorous and structurally flawless."

TOLEDO REPERTORY THEATRE
16 Tenth St., Toledo, OH 43624 (419) 243-9277
Contact: Paul Causman, Resident Director **Theatre:** community/non-professional **Works:** full-length plays, one-acts, children's plays **Tours:** yes **Stage:** proscenium **Policies:** unsolicited script; query/synopsis with dialogue sample **Remuneration:** yes

TOUCHSTONE THEATRE
908 E. 5th St., Bethlehem, PA 18105
(215) 867-1689 Contact: Bill George, Producing Director **Theatre:** professional not-for-profit **Works:** ensemble pieces **Specifications:** maximum cast: 4; small performance space **Stage:** black box, 74 seats **Policy:** query with proposal for project to be created in collaboration with ensemble

THE TOWER PLAYERS OF HILLSDALE COLLEGE
Hillsdale, MI 49242 (517) 437-7341
Contact: R. J. Pentzell, Professor of Theatre Arts **Theatre:** university/college **Works:** full-length plays, one-acts, translations, adaptations **2nd productions:** yes **Specifications:** maximum cast: 20 (cast of 8-16 preferred); single set, "including multi-scene 'space staging' shows" **Stage:** thrust, 180 seats **Audience:** "Students and townspeople; tendency toward intelligent political and religious conservatism." **Policies:** unsolicited script; professional recommendation **Best time:** Sept.-Jan. **Response:** 2 weeks script; 1 month or more script **Your chances:** 5-10/0-1 **Remuneration:** "Standard royalty and possible residency during dress rehearsals and performance." **Program:** workshop productions **Advice:** "We always have more female than male performers available for casting. Our directors, overall, prefer 'theatricalist' or 'Brechtian' styles. We react negatively to run-of-the-mill Leftist cliches and the use of standard, too-easy targets of satire."

TRIANGLE THEATRE COMPANY
316 E. 88th St., New York, NY 10128
(212) 860-7245 Contact: Molly O'Neil, Associate Executive Director **Theatre:** off off Broadway **Works:** full-length plays, musicals **2nd productions:** no **Special interests:** "Small chamber productions. Primarily interested in non-naturalistic, theatrical plays and musicals." **Specificiations:** maximum cast: 8; simple unit set or skeleton; "we are not interested in '60's avant garde, experimental" **Stages:** proscenium; arena; 3/4 flexible **Audience:** "Yorkville area of Upper East Side New York. Many young professionals." **Policies:** unsolicited script with resume; professional recommendation; agent submission **Best time:** Jun.-Jul. **Response:** 1 month **Your chances:** 200-300/4 **Remuneration:** "Depends--$500-$1000." **Programs:** readings, staged readings

TRINITY REPERTORY COMPANY
201 Washington St., Providence, RI 02903
(401) 521-1100 Contact: Richard Cumming, Literary Manager **Theatre:** professional not-for-profit **Works:** full-length plays, translations, adaptations, musicals **Stages:** thrust, 500 seats; thrust, 297 seats **Policy:** query/synopsis **Best time:** Aug.-Oct. **Response:** 1 month query; 12 months script

TRINITY SQUARE ENSEMBLE
Box 1798, Evanston, IL 60204 (312) 328-0330
Contact: Karen L. Erickson, Artistic Director **Theatre:** professional not-for-profit **Works:** full-length plays, translations, adaptations, children's plays **2nd productions:** yes **Stages:** "Variety of spaces, 70-190 seats." **Audience:** "Upper middle class, white and some minorities; college educated, white-collar workers and professionals, 30-60 years of age." **Policies:** query/synopsis; professional recommendation **Response:** 2-8 months **Your chances:** 10/1 **Remuneration:** "Sometimes. Varies." **Program:** staged readings **Advice:** "Get to know our ensemble and what our seasonal theme is--in advance!"

T.W.E.E.D. (THEATRE WORKS: EMERGING AND EXPERIMENTAL DIRECTIONS)

496 Hudson St. #6-36, New York, NY 10014
(212) 741-1812 Contact: Kevin Maloney, Artistic Director **Theatre:** professional not-for-profit **Works:** one-acts, adaptations, musicals **2nd productions:** no **Special interests:** "Experimental, performance art, mixed-media." **Stages:** rented spaces **Audience:** "Young, downtown New York crowd. Offbeat." **Policy:** query/synopsis with resume **Best times:** late fall, late spring **Response:** 1 month **Your chances:** 50-100/14; "estimates include short works as part of an Annual Festival" **Remuneration:** "Stipend; often $200-$500." **Program:** workshop productions **Advice:** "We are not interested in the well-made play or in discovering the great new playwright. We seek work that we feel deserves a platform because it is indicative of new theatrical forms."

UBU REPERTORY THEATER

149 Mercer St., New York, NY 10012
(212) 925-0999 Contact: Catherine Temerson, Literary Manager **Theatre:** professional not-for-profit theatre center **Works:** translations **2nd productions:** no **Exclusive interest:** English translations of contemporary full-length plays and one-acts originally written in French **Tours:** "Perhaps in the future." **Stage:** flexible **Audience:** "New York off Broadway." **Policies:** unsolicited script; query/synopsis; professional recommendation; agent submission; commission **Best time:** summer **Response:** 3 months **Your chances:** 100/2 plus readings **Remuneration:** royalty **Programs:** readings, staged readings, workshop productions, script evaluations, translation referrals, international theatre panels and workshops, reference library, publications (inquire) **Comment:** "Most of our submissions come from France or other French-speaking countries."

UKIAH PLAYERS THEATRE

Box 705, Ukiah, CA 95482 (707) 462-1210
Contact: Lesley Schisgall **Theatre:** community not-for-profit **Works:** full-length plays, children's plays **Tours:** yes **Stage:** proscenium, 133 seats **Programs:** staged readings, workshop productions, New American Comedy Festival (see Contests)

UNDERGROUND RAILWAY THEATER
21 Notre Dame Ave., Cambridge, MA 02140
(617) 497-6136 Contact: Wes Sanders, Artistic Director
Theatre: professional not-for-profit **Works:** full-length plays, one-acts, translations, adaptations, musicals, children's plays **2nd productions:** "We could." **Special interests:** "Social/political themes; possibility of combining actors, puppets and music; collaboration." **Maximum cast:** 6 **Tours:** preferred **Stages:** proscenium; thrust; arena; flexible **Audience:** "Diverse." **Policies:** professional recommendation preferred; unsolicited script with resume; query/synopsis with resume **Response:** 4 weeks **Your chances:** 5/"none so far" **Remuneration:** "We raise grants to pay collaborating artists." **Programs:** staged readings, workshop productions **Comment:** "So far we have worked with playwrights we know, but we are always open."

UNICORN THEATRE
3820 Main St., Kansas City, MO 64111
(816) 531-7529 Contact: Cynthia Levin, Artistic Director
Theatre: professional not-for-profit **Works:** full-length plays **Special interest:** social issues **Specifications:** maximum cast: 10; contemporary settings and themes **Stage:** thrust, 150 seats **Policy:** query/synopsis **Best time:** Mar.-May **Response:** 1 month query; 6 months script **Program:** Unicorn Theatre National Playwright Competition (see Contests)

UNIVERSITY OF ARIZONA DEPARTMENT OF DRAMA
Tucson, AZ 85721 (602) 621-7008
Contact: Patricia Van Metre, Acting Dept. Head **Theatre:** university/college **Works:** full-length plays, one-acts, adaptations, musicals **2nd productions:** yes **Special interest:** "Hispanic or Native American themes." **Specifications:** unit set preferred **Tours:** yes **Stages:** proscenium, 330 seats; proscenium, 120 seats; flexible, 100 seats **Audience:** "Varies; majority are university-affiliated." **Policies:** unsolicited script with resume; professional recommendation; university's playwriting program **Best time:** fall **Response:** 2-6 weeks **Your chances:** 75/3-4 **Remuneration:** "Non-student playwright receives royalty." **Programs:** readings, staged readings, workshop productions, development, classes

THE UNIVERSITY OF WEST FLORIDA
Pensacola, FL   This theatre is not seeking scripts in 1989 and has requested that we discontinue its listing.

UPSTAIRS DINNER THEATRE
221 S. 19th St., Omaha, NE   68102
(402) 344-3858 Contact: Deborah Denenberg, Producer
Theatre: non-Equity dinner **Works:** full-length plays, musicals **Exclusive interests:** comedies and musicals **Maximum cast:** 14 **Policy:** unsolicited script

VERMONT THEATRE COMPANY
31 Green St., Brattleboro, VT 05301
(802) 257-0607 Contact: Ray Jenness, Artistic Director
Theatre: community/non-professional **Works:** full-length plays, one-acts, children's plays **2nd productions:** no
Special interest: "Vermont and other New England writers."
Tours: yes **Stage:** flexible **Audience:** "Cross section."
Policies: unsolicited script; query/synopsis with resume; agent submission **Response:** 2 weeks query; 6 months script
Remuneration: "$500-$1000." **Programs:** readings, staged readings, workshop productions, development, contest (inquire)

VETCO
c/o HBO, 1100 6th Ave. 13th Floor,
New York, NY 10019 (212) 512-1960
Contact: Thomas Bird, Artistic Director **Theatre:** professional not-for-profit **Works:** full-length plays **Special interest:** "Political statements." **Specifications:** maximum cast: 8; single, flexible set **Tours:** yes **Stages:** rented spaces **Audience:** general **Policies:** unsolicited script; query/synopsis; professional recommendation **Best time:** summer **Response:** 6 weeks **Your chances:** 200/3
Remuneration: "Option; royalty; 6%-7% of box office."
Programs: staged readings, development **Advice:** "Present plays in a professionally typed format with a synopsis. A polite follow-up will indicate the author's seriousness."
Comment: Formerly Vietnam Veterans Ensemble Theatre Company.

VICTORIAN THEATRE
4201 Hooker St., Denver, CO 80211
(303) 433-5050 Contact: S. Jenkins, Artistic Director **Theatre:** community/non-professional **Works:** full-length plays, one-acts **2nd productions:** yes **Specifications:** maximum cast: 8; single set; no fly space; small wings; modest light and sound facilities **Tours:** "Possibly, not normally." **Stage:** proscenium, 90 seats **Audience:** "Mixed urban and suburban, wide age range." **Policies:** unsolicited script; query/synopsis; professional recommendation **Best time:** fall **Response:** 4 months **Your chances:** 20/0-1 **Remuneration:** standard royalty

VICTORY GARDENS THEATER
2271 N. Lincoln Ave., Chicago, IL 60614
(314) 549-5778 Contact: Charles Smith, Literary Associate **Theatre:** professional not-for-profit **Works:** full-length plays, one-acts, musicals **2nd productions:** yes **Special interests:** "Plays which address contemporary social issues; plays by Chicago and Midwest playwrights; plays by or about minorities." **Specifications:** maximum cast: 8; small stage; no wing space **Tours:** yes **Stages:** thrust, 200 seats; thrust, 60 seats **Policies:** unsolicited script; query/synopsis; professional recommendation; agent submission **Response:** 1 month query; 6 months script **Your chances:** 800/3-4+ **Remuneration:** standard royalty **Programs:** readings, staged readings, workshop productions, development, internships, classes, contests (inquire)

VICTORY THEATRE
3326 W. Victory Blvd., Burbank, CA 91505
(818) 843-9253 Contact: Tom Ormeny, Maria Gobette, Artistic Directors **Theatre:** professional not-for-profit **Works:** full-length plays, one-acts, musicals **2nd productions:** yes **Special interest:** "Relationships." **Specifications:** maximum cast: 12; low ceiling; musicals must be small-scale **Policy:** unsolicited script **Response:** 6 months

VIETNAM VETERANS ENSEMBLE THEATRE COMPANY
New York, NY See VetCo.

VINEYARD THEATRE
309 E. 26th St., New York, NY 10010
(212) 683-0696 Contact: Douglas Aibel, Artistic Director **Theatre:** professional not-for-profit **Works:** full-length plays, one-acts, musicals **2nd productions:** musicals in need of revision **Special interests:** works with strong poetic quality, unique incorporation of music; musicals with strong narrative **Stages:** thrust, 70 seats; black box, 175 seats **Policy:** unsolicted script **Response:** 4-6 months **Programs:** readings, developmental program for musicals

VIRGINIA STAGE COMPANY
Box 3770, Norfork, VA 23514 (804) 627-6988
Contact: Christopher Hanna, Associate Artistic Director **Theatre:** professional not-for-profit **Works:** full-length plays, adaptations, musicals **2nd productions:** yes **Special interests:** "Talented writers who understand the stage's unique requirements for theatricality, vital language and metaphor, as distinct from television and movie media; developing writers who are giving voice to the current American experience." **Tours:** "Perhaps in the future." **Stages:** proscenium, thrust, arena, flexible--125-600 seats **Audience:** "All ages from students to senior citizens; ethnically diverse; the majority of adults are college educated." **Policy:** professional recommendation **Best time:** May-Aug. **Response:** 12 months **Your chances:** 100/1 **Remuneration:** negotiable **Programs:** readings, staged readings, workshop productions

WALDEN THEATRE COMPANY
New York, NY This theatre is permanently closed.

WALNUT STREET THEATRE
9th and Walnut Sts., Philadelphia, PA 19107
(215) 574-3550 Contact: Charlie Hensley, Associate Director **Theatre:** professional not-for-profit **Works:** full-length plays, one-acts, translations, adaptations, musicals **2nd productions:** yes **Special interests:** "Historical plays; plays with bite." **Specifications:** maximum cast: 10, 6 or fewer preferred; simple technical requirements **Stages:** proscenium, 1050 seats; proscenium, 100 seats; flexible, 80 seats **Audience:** "Conservative; prefer modern plays. We are open, however, to 'wild' material that is well

written." **Policies:** query/synopsis with dialogue sample and resume; agent submission **Best time:** Jun.-Aug. **Response:** 1 month query; 4 months script **Your chances:** 450/3-4 **Remuneration:** negotiable royalty; possible residency **Program:** classes

WASHINGTON UNIVERSITY PERFORMING ARTS DEPARTMENT
Campus Box 1108, St. Louis, MO 63130
(314) 889-5877   Contact: Henry Schvey, Chair **Theatre:** university/college **Works:** full-length plays, one-acts, translations, adaptations, children's plays **Tours:** yes **Stages:** proscenium; arena **Policies:** unsolicited script; agent submission **Response:** 1 week query; 4 weeks script **Your chances:** 50/1 **Remuneration:** "Sometimes; $500 or transportation and lodging." **Programs:** staged readings, development, classes **Comment:** Theatre also receives submissions from the St. Louis Playwrights Festival (inquire).

WATERLOO COMMUNITY PLAYHOUSE/ BLACK HAWK CHILDREN'S THEATRE
Box 433, Waterloo, IA 50704 (319) 235-0367
Contact: Charles Stilwill, Managing Director **Works:** full-length plays, one-acts, adaptations, musicals, children's plays **2nd productions:** yes **Specifications:** no fly space **Tours:** elementary schools **Stage:** proscenium **Audience:** "All ages, 3% black." **Policies:** unsolicited script; query/ synopsis with dialogue sample; agent submission **Best time:** winter-spring **Response:** 3 months query; 3 years script **Your chances:** 400/1 or more **Remuneration:** "Royalty plus travel if money is available."

THE WAYSIDE THEATRE
Box 260, Middletown, VA 22645 (703) 869-1782
Contact: Christopher Owens, Producing Director **Theatre:** professional not-for-profit **Works:** contemporary full-length plays **Specifications:** maximum cast: 10-12; no more than 2 sets **Tours:** "Small-cast plays for young audiences; simple 1-set mainstage shows." **Stage:** proscenium, 195 seats **Policy:** unsolicited script **Best time:** winter **Response:** 2 months **Your chances:** 20/1 **Advice:** "Send synopsis; if we are interested we will request full script." **Comment:** Theatre season (8 mainstage shows) is May-Dec.

WESTBETH THEATRE CENTER
151 Bank St., New York, NY 10014
(212) 691-2272 Contact: Arnold Engelman, Producing Director **Theatre:** off off Broadway, professional not-for-profit **Works:** full-length plays **2nd productions:** "In special circumstances." **Specifications:** maximum cast: 10; no more than 1-2 sets **Stage:** proscenium, 60-99 seats **Audience:** "Downtown New York City, industry and Greenwich Village." **Policies:** professional recommendation; agent submission **Best time:** summer **Response:** 2 months **Your chances:** 150/5 **Programs:** readings, development, American Playwright Program (see Special Programs)

WEST COAST ENSEMBLE
Box 38728, Los Angeles, CA 90038
(213) 871-8673 Contact: Les Hanson, Artistic Director **Theatre:** professional not-for-profit **Works:** full-length plays, one-acts, translations, adaptations, musicals **2nd productions:** "If not previously produced in Southern California." **Specifications:** maximum cast: 15, 5-12 preferred; simple sets preferred **Stages:** flexible, 70 seats; flexible, 99 seats **Audience:** "A broad spectrum from throughout Southern California." **Policies:** unsolicited script; professional recommendation; agent submission **Best times:** Jan.-Jun. for full-length plays, Sept.-Dec. for one-acts **Response:** 2-6 months **Your chances:** 700/12 one-acts, 200/1-2 full-length plays **Remuneration:** negotiated **Programs:** readings, staged readings, workshop productions, development, classes, Celebration of One-Acts (see Contests), West Coast Ensemble Full-Length Play Competition (inquire)

WEST END DINNER THEATRE
4615 Duke St., Alexandria, VA 22304
(703) 823-9061 Contact: James J. Matthews, Producer **Works:** full-length plays, musicals **Special interests:** family-oriented comedies, farces and musicals **Specifications:** maximum cast: 20-25; no fly space **Policy:** unsolicited script

THE WESTERN STAGE OF HARTNELL COLLEGE
156 Homestead Ave., Salinas, CA 93901
(408) 755-6987 Contact: Joyce Lower, Dramaturg **Theatre:** university/college **Works:** full-length plays,

one-acts, translations, adaptations, musicals, children's plays **2nd productions:** yes **Specifications:** maximum cast: 20; some limitations on sets; limited fly space **Tours:** "Possible." **Stages:** proscenium, 540 seats; modified thrust, 200 seats; 3/4 stage, 120 seats; "environmental staging on our large stage" **Policies:** unsolicited script with resume; professional recommendation; agent submission **Response:** 2 weeks **Your chances:** 500/readings (6 in 1988) **Remuneration:** "$25-$50 for a reading." **Programs:** readings, staged readings, workshop productions, development, contests (inquire)

THE WHOLE THEATER
544 Bloomfield Ave., Montclair, NJ 07042
(201) 744-2996 **Contact:** Daniel De Raey, Associate Artistic Director **Theatre:** professional not-for-profit **Works:** full-length plays **Specifications:** small cast; single or unit set **Stage:** endstage, 200 seats **Policy:** query/ synopsis **Best time:** Oct.-Apr. **Response:** 3 weeks query; 8 weeks script **Programs:** readings, staged readings, workshop productions, The Gathering (see Special Programs) **Comment:** See Ledford, Larry S. with Bonnie Kramen. "On Becoming The Whole Theater" (*Theater Week*, Feb. 8-14, 1988), 28-29.

THE WILL GEER THEATRICUM BOTANICUM
Box 1222, Topanga, CA 90290 (213) 455-2322
Contact: Ellen Geer, Artistic Director **Theatre:** professional not-for-profit **Works:** full-length plays, one-acts, translations, adaptations, musicals, cabaret/revues **2nd productions:** yes **Special interests:** social issues; new translations of classics **Specifications:** maximum cast: 5-10; works must be suitable for large outdoor stage **Stage:** outdoor arena, 350 seats **Policies:** query/synopsis with dialogue sample preferred; unsolicited script **Best time:** Sept. **Response:** 3-4 weeks query; 4-5 months script **Your chances:** 100-150/1 **Remuneration:** negotiable royalty **Programs:** Sunday workshops; series of one-acts (inquire)

WILLIAMSTOWN THEATRE FESTIVAL
Box 517, Williamstown, MA 01267
(413) 597-3377 **Contact:** Bonnie J. Monte, Associate Artistic Director **Theatre:** professional not-for-profit **Works:** full-length plays, translations, adaptations **2nd**

productions: no **Specifications:** maximum cast: 10; simple set **Stages:** proscenium, 500 seats; flexible, 96 seats; outdoor theatre, several hundred seats **Audience:** "Wide range." **Policies:** query/synopsis with dialogue sample; professional recommendation; agent submission **Best time:** Oct.-Mar. **Response:** 1 month query; 3 months script **Your chances:** 300-400/4-7 **Remuneration:** "A modest fee." **Program:** staged readings **Advice:** "Small cast, simple production values, important subject matter."

THE WILMA THEATRE
2030 Sansom St., Philadelphia, PA 19103
(215) 963-0249 Contact: Jiri Zizka, Artistic Director **Theatre:** professional not-for-profit **Works:** full-length plays, translations, adaptations, musicals **2nd productions:** yes **Specifications:** maximum cast: 12; "simple but inventive sets" **Tours:** yes **Stages:** proscenium; flexible **Policies:** query/synopsis with dialogue sample; professional recommendation; agent submission **Response:** 8 months **Remuneration:** fee and royalty **Comment:** Theatre produces 1-2 new plays each season.

WINGS THEATRE COMPANY
112 Charlton St., New York, NY 10014
(212) 645-9630 Contact: Jeffery Corrick, Artistic Director **Theatre:** off off Broadway **Works:** full-length plays, musicals, children's plays **2nd productions:** seldom **Special interest:** "Strong themes." **Specifications:** maximum cast: 12; small stage **Stage:** flexible, 60 seats **Audience:** "Very mixed, New York City." **Policies:** unsolicited script; professional recommendation; agent submission **Best time:** Sept.-Dec. **Response:** 9 months **Your chances:** 500/8-10 **Remuneration:** "$100 advance against 3% of box office gross." **Programs:** readings, staged readings, workshop productions, internships, Wings Theatre Company 1989 New Plays Contest (see Contests)

WISDOM BRIDGE THEATRE
1559 W. Howard St., Chicago, IL 60626
(312) 743-0486 Contact: Richard E. T. White, Artistic Director **Theatre:** professional not-for-profit **Works:** full-length plays, translations, adaptations, musicals **2nd productions:** yes **Special interests:** "New plays that deal

with contemporary social/political issues; plays by women and minority writers; adventurous treatments of classic texts." **Audience:** "Ethnically diverse; Chicago dwellers as well as people from the suburbs; largely in the 30-40 age range." **Policies:** query/synopsis; professional recommendation; agent submission **Best time:** summer **Response:** 4 months query; 6 months script **Your chances:** 800/4 **Remuneration:** "Negotiable, based on a guarantee against a percentage." **Program:** in-house readings

WOMEN IN THEATRE NETWORK
Box 1147 FDR Station, New York, NY 10150
(718) 797-1852 Contact: Susan Gitenstein, Executive Director **Theatre:** off off Broadway, professional not-for-profit **Works:** full-length plays, one-acts, translations, adaptations, children's plays **Special interests:** "Translations. We would love a good play on the Middle East crisis. International relations, cross-cultural themes, women in a contemporary light." **Specifications:** maximum cast: 15; single set **Stage:** flexible **Policies:** unsolicited script; query/synopsis **Best time:** late spring-Jun. **Response:** 3 months query; 6 months script **Remuneration:** negotiable **Programs:** staged readings, workshop productions, Fall Festival (inquire)

WOMEN'S INTERART CENTER
549 W. 52nd St., New York, NY 10019
(212) 246-1050 Contact: Jean Rowan, Literary Coordinator **Theatre:** off off Broadway **Works:** full-length plays **2nd productions:** "Yes, co-producing." **Special interest:** "Women's plays and themes." **Specifications:** small cast; simple set **Stage:** flexible **Policy:** query/synopsis with dialogue sample **Response:** "We do our best but are very backlogged and have a very small staff." **Program:** staged readings **Advice:** "Invite us to your workshop production, if possible."

THE WOMEN'S THEATRE PROJECT
St. Paul, MN This theatre is not accepting submissions and has requested that we discontinue its listing.

WOODSTOCK PLAYHOUSE ASSOCIATION
Box 396, Woodstock, NY 12498 (914) 679-6000
Contact: Harris A. Gordon, Executive Director **Theatre:** professional not-for-profit **Works:** full-length plays, translations, adaptations, children's plays, operas **Special interest:** social issues **Specifications:** maximum cast: 15; single set preferred **Stage:** proscenium, 560 seats **Policies:** professional recommendation; agent submission **Best time:** Sept.-Jan. **Response:** 3 weeks query; 8 months script

WOOLLY MAMMOTH THEATRE COMPANY
Box 32229, Washington, DC 20007 (202) 393-3939
Contact: Neil Steyskal, Literary Manager **Theatre:** professional not-for-profit **Works:** full-length plays, translations, adaptations **2nd productions:** yes **Exclusive interest:** "Plays that are highly unusual, either in form or content." **Maximum cast:** 12 **Stage:** flexible, 130 seats **Audience:** "Yuppies and older." **Policy:** query/synopsis **Response:** 3 weeks query; 6 months script **Your chances:** 120/1-2

WORCESTER FOOTHILLS THEATRE COMPANY
Box 236, Worcester, MA 01602 (508) 754-3314
Contact: Greg DeJarnett, Literary Manager **Theatre:** professional not-for-profit **Works:** full-length plays, translations, adaptations, musicals **2nd productions:** yes **Special interest:** plays of interest to a multi-generational audience **Specifications:** maximum cast: 10; single or simple set; small scale musicals only; "no strong language or gratuitous violence" **Stage:** proscenium, 349 seats **Policy:** query/synopsis **Response:** 3-4 weeks query; 1-4 months script

WORKS BY WOMEN
11 Fifth Ave. #14P, New York, NY 10003
(212) 674-7381 Contact: Laura Padula, Script Consultant **Theatre:** off off Broadway, professional not-for-profit **Works:** full-length plays, one-acts, translations **2nd productions:** "If not previously produced in New York City, or if it is a completely new draft." **Specifications:** some limitations on sets; minimal lighting **Stage:** flexible, 150 seats **Audience:** "Sophisticated New Yorkers, professional-habitual theatre-goers." **Policies:** unsolicited script;

professional recommendation; agent submission **Response:** 3 weeks query; 3-5 months script **Your chances:** varying number/8-10 **Remuneration:** "Small honorarium for staged reading."**Advice:** "We do not consider works-in-progress."

WORKS IN DEVELOPMENT
New York, NY Our 1989 questionnaire was returned as "undeliverable," and no phone number is listed for this theatre.

WPA THEATRE
519 W. 23rd St., New York, NY 10011
(212) 691-2274 Contact: Patricia Hoag, Literary Advisor **Theatre:** professional not-for-profit **Works:** full-length plays, musicals **2nd productions:** no **Special interest:** "Contemporary American realism dealing with important social issues." **Specifications:** maximum cast: 10; single set preferred **Tours:** "No, but several have had commercial transfers." **Stage:** proscenium, 124 seats **Policies:** query/ synopsis with dialogue sample; agent submission **Best time:** summer **Response:** 3 weeks query; 6 months script **Your chances:** 250/1 **Remuneration:** $1500 **Programs:** readings, staged readings

THE WRITERS THEATRE
145 W . 46th St., New York, NY 10036
(212) 869-9770 Contact: Byam Stevens, Literary Manager **Theatre:** professional not-for-profit **Works:** full-length plays, one-acts, adaptations **2nd productions:** "Only if the playwright wants to do substantial rewriting." **Exclusive interest:** "Scripts for development." **Specifications:** "No finished works." **Stage:** flexible, 74 seats **Policies:** unsolicited script; professional recommendation; agent submission **Response:** 6 months **Your chances:** 350/2-3 **Remuneration:** "Favored nations on Actors Equity Association Tier Code basis." **Programs:** readings, staged readings, workshops productions, development **Advice:** "The Writers Theatre is primarily a developmental theatre. If the playwright feels that a work is finished and is looking for immediate production, he or she would be better served submitting to another company."

YALE REPERTORY THEATRE
222 York St., New Haven, CT 06520
(203) 436-8492 Contact: Literary Manager **Theatre:** professional not-for-profit, university/college **Works:** full-length plays, translations, adaptations, musicals **Special interests:** new plays; new translations of classics and contemporary foreign plays **Stage:** modified thrust, 487 seats **Policy:** query/synopsis **Response:** 6 weeks query; 3 months script **Remuneration:** yes **Comment:** Theatre produces 3-4 new plays each winter.

YORK COMMUNITY SCHOOL
355 W. Charles Rd., Elmhurst, IL 60126
(312) 617-PLAY, 279-PLAY Contact: Les Zunkel, Director of Drama and Speech **Theatre:** high school **Works:** musicals, children's plays, reader's theatre **Stages:** thrust; arena; flexible **Audience:** community and school **Policies:** query/synopsis; commission **Best time:** spring **Response:** 4 months **Remuneration:** stipend based upon work

THE YORK THEATRE COMPANY
2 E. 90th St., New York, NY 10128
(212) 534-5366 Contact: R. David Westfall, Literary Manager **Theatre:** off off Broadway **Works:** full-length plays, musicals **2nd productions:** no **Specifications:** maximum cast: 10; some limitations on sets; "theatre is located in Episcopal Church and thereby somewhat limited in plays (language, violence, sex, etc.)" **Stage:** flexible **Audience:** "Adults with New York demands for good theatre." **Policies:** unsolicited script; professional recommendation **Response:** 6 months **Your chances:** 80-90/1 **Remuneration:** no **Programs:** readings, staged readings

YOUNG PEOPLE'S THEATRE COMPANY OF DELAWARE VALLEY
121 South Dr., Newtown, PA 18940
(215) 860-6888 Contact: Karin Kasdin, Executive Director **Theatre:** professional not-for-profit **Works:** full-length plays, adaptations, musicals, children's plays **2nd productions:** yes **Exclusive interests:** "Family-oriented theatre—dramatic, comic or musical; subjects relevant to the lives of young people in the 80's; historical subjects; nothing

for children under 8 years old." **Specifications:** maximum cast: 35, always including adults, teens and children; simple unit set **Audience:** "Affluent, well-educated suburban families." **Policies:** unsolicited script; query/synopsis with dialogue sample; professional recommendation; agent submission **Best time:** Jun.-Aug. **Response:** 8-12 weeks **Your chances:** 200/2 **Remuneration:** negotiable

YOUNG PERFORMERS THEATRE
Ft. Mason Center Bldg. C Room 300,
San Francisco, CA 94123 (415) 346-5550
Contact: Matilda Kunin, Executive Director **Theatre:** professional not-for-profit **Works:** children's plays **2nd productions:** yes **Special interest:** "Family entertainment." **Specifications:** maximum cast: 12; no more than 3 set changes; limited lighting **Tours:** yes **Stages:** thrust; flexible **Audience:** "Urban, 3-12 years of age, ethnic mixture, poor to wealthy." **Policies:** unsolicited script with resume; professional recommendation **Response:** 2-6 weeks **Your chances:** 15-20/1 **Remuneration:** negotiable **Programs:** readings, staged readings **Advice:** "Dont' write 'down' to children; don't try to write 'hip' scripts; have a mixed cast of adults and children. Keep show to 60-70 minutes. Make submitted material neat and easy to read."

YOUNG PERFORMERS THEATRE ADULT WING
Ft. Mason Center Bldg. C Room 300,
San Francisco, CA 94123 (415) 346-5550
Contact: Matilda Kunin, Executive Director **Theatre:** professional not-for-profit **Works:** full-length plays, one-acts, translations, adaptations, musicals **2nd productions:** yes **Special interests:** "Thought-provoking plays; politics, religion." **Maximum cast:** 12-16 **Stage:** flexible **Policies:** unsolicited script with resume; professional recommendation **Response:** 2-6 weeks **Your chances:** 150/2 **Remuneration:** "7% of gate." **Advice:** "A good, solid play with a story line."

ZACHARY SCOTT THEATER CENTER
Box 244, Austin, TX 78744 (512) 476-0597
Contact: Candace Thompson, Office Manager **Theatre:** professional performing arts school, community/non-professional **Works:** full-length plays, children's plays **2nd**

productions: no **Specifications**: maximum cast: 8; unit set **Tours**:   "INTER ACT--professional children's theatre." **Stages**: thrust, 200 seats;   arena **Audience**: university students, professionals, retirees **Policies**: unsolicited script; professional recommendation **Best time**: summer-early fall **Response**: 6 months   **Your chances**: 100-300/1 **Remuneration**: travel; 2-week residency **Advice**: "Take a course in playwriting. Learn your craft. Only 1 out of every 100 scripts we read has possibilities."

ZEPHYR THEATRE
25 Van Ness Ave. Suite 50,
San Francisco, CA 94102 (415) 861-6655
Contact: Michael Lojkovic, Operations Manager **Theatre**: 3 not-for-profit theatres **Works**: full-length plays, translations, adaptations, musicals **2nd productions**: "Yes, but not a priority." **Special interests**:   musicals, political works **Maximum cast**: 22 **Tours**: yes **Stages**: proscenium, 50 seats; thrust, 99 seats; flexible, 140 seats **Audience**: "All ethnic groups, highly educated, ages 25-60." **Policies**: query/synopsis with dialogue sample; agent submission **Response**: 1 month query; 6 months script **Your chances**: 120/2 **Remuneration**: 4%-6% of box office gross **Programs**: staged readings, workshop productions, development

ZOILUS II PRODUCTIONS
281 Ninth Ave., New York, NY 10011
(212) 255-2334 Contact: Leslie Hoban Blake, Co-Artistic Director **Theatre**: off off Broadway, professional not-for-profit **Works**: translations, adaptations **2nd productions**: "Possibly." **Special interests**: "Broad interests, including TV scripts." **Stages**: proscenium; thrust; arena **Audience**: "Sharp and knowledgeable, New York off off Broadway." **Policies**: unsolicited script; query/synopsis with dialogue sample and resume; professional recommendation **Best time**: Sept.-Jun. **Response**: 2 months **Your chances**: 75-100/ 2-3 plus 25-30 readings **Remuneration**: Dramatists Guild contracts **Programs**: staged readings, development **Advice**: "Be willing to start with a reading and to work on development." **Comment**: "We are attached to, but separate from, the New Theatre."

Since June 1988, the following theatres have issued calls for new scripts. As we have been unable to reach these theatres, playwrights are advised to write for information before submitting materials.

The American Line, 810 W. 183rd St. #5C, New York, NY 10033 (212) 740-9277 Contact: Richard Hoehler

Bingham/Nagy Productions, 300 Mercer St. #8G, New York, NY 10003 (212) 740-3534

The Byrdcliffe Festival, 34 Tinker St., Woodstock, NY 12498 (914) 679-2100, 657-2988 Contact: Erika Block

Centenary Stage Company, Centenary College, Hackettstown, NJ 07840 Contact: M. E. Schmidt, Women Playwrights Project

Coyote Radio, c/o David Maltby, 1026 E. Main, Ashland, OR 97520

The Cutting Edge Theatre Company, c/o M. Stone, C.N.S., 210 W. 80th St., New York, NY 10024

The Formative Stage of The Theatre of Newburyport, 24 Center St., Newburyport, MA 01950 (508) 462-3332

Fountainhead Theatre Company, Box 4515, New York, NY 10185-0038 (212) 777-6512

Heartland Productions, Inc., McLean County Arts Center, 601 N. East St., Bloomington, IL 61701 (309) 829-0011 Contact: Carol Reitan

The Laughing Horse Summer Theatre, Box 1412, Ellensburg, WA 98926 Contact: Sydney Moe, Chairman of the Board

Mark Keyloun Productions, c/o McMinn Management, 8721 Sunset Blvd. #104, Los Angeles, CA 90069

The New Place Theatre, c/o Phyllis Murphy, 204 Lincoln Blvd. #6, Venice, CA 90291 (213) 396-2653

No Empty Space Theatre, Box 010422, Staten Island, NY 10301-0001 Contact: Program Director

Polaris Repertory Company, c/o Michael Irwin, 400 W. 43rd St. #9-0, New York, NY 10036

The Story People, 2170 Broadway Suite 2161, New York, NY 10024

Zimmer-Bees Productions, 186 Claremont Ave. #25, New York, NY 10027 (212) 541 7600 Contact: Kathy Zimmer, (212) 840-1234 Contact: Jackie Bees

Zone Productions, c/o Richard Weiss, 533 W. 49th St., New York, NY 10019

Announcements

Feedback Services and Feedback Theatrebooks are pleased to announce the results of the Little Nashville Playwriting Award Competition 1987:

Winner: **David Muschell** for BIRDS IN THE WEATHER

Finalists and Semifinalists: **Lary Campbell** for ROBBY; **Robert J. Canning** for IN CAHOOTS; **John Crews** for EASTER'S CHILDREN; **Thomas L. Durkin** for THE GOLDEN APPLES; **Vincent Eaton** for STAY, RANDOM VIOLENCE, NEGATIVE SPACE and NUTS; **Josepha Gutelius** for VERONICA CORY; **George Hammer** for CAPTAIN BRAVEHEART FLIES; **Manuel Martin, Jr.** for THE LEGEND OF THE GOLDEN COFFEE BEAN; **Michael Morse** for UNDER SIEGE, OVERWROUGHT; **Mary S. Ryzuk** for THE FAMILY DELI; **Janet Schecter** for THE THIRD PARTY; **Alan Stolzer** for MOST PRIZED POSSESSION; **Dorothy Velasco** for OPEN HOUSE; **Judith Zivanovic** for CARRIE, HARRY AND THE RELUCTANT STORY WIZARD

We received many well-written and interesting entries and take this opportunity to thank every playwright who participated in the competition.

Because *The Playwright's Companion 1989* had earlier deadlines this year, the results of the FS Drama Award 1988 will be announced in our 1990 edition.

Contests

Suggestions for entering plays in the competitions listed in *The Playwright's Companion 1989* :

Read each entry carefully and observe all regulations.

Request guidelines for all competitions; space does not allow us to provide full details of every contest, and any contest may change its regulations and/or deadline during the year.

Always enclose a stamped, self-addressed business envelope when requesting application forms, guidelines or other information.

Submit well in advance of deadlines.

Include all appropriate materials with each submission (see The Playwright's Checklist and individual contest guidelines). After a script has been submitted, do not send revisions or other materials unless the competition sponsor requests that you do so.

Do not expect a competition to return any material not accompanied by a stamped, self-addressed mailer.

ACTORS ALLEY REPERTORY THEATRE'S
ANNUAL NEW PLAY COMPETITION (AART) 1989
4334 Van Nuys Blvd., Sherman Oaks, CA 91403
(818) 986-AART Contact: Alvin Ross, Literary Manager
Award: $350, possible production **Works:** full-length plays
Regulations: entries must be unpublished and unproduced
Procedure: request guidelines **Deadline:** Sept. 30, 1989 postmark

ACTORS REPERTORY THEATRE
PLAYWRIGHTS CONTEST
303 E. 44th St., New York, NY 10017
(212) 687-6430 This contest is inactive in 1989.

AGGIE PLAYERS PLAYWRITING COMPETITION
Texas A & M University, College Station, TX 77843
(409) 854-2526 Contact: Roger Shultz, Director of Theatre **Frequency:** annual **Award:** $1000, production, entry in American College Theatre Festival 1989, $1000

expenses to attend rehearsals **Works:** full-length plays **Regulations**: authors must be American playwrights; entries must be unpublished, unproduced and must deal with "the American experience"; winning author must be in residence in fall 1989 **Specifications**: cast size: 5-12; works must be suitable for cross-cultural casting **Procedure:** send script with 1-page synopsis **Deadline**: Feb. 1, 1989 **Notification**: Apr. 1989

ALLEN CLARK MEMORIAL AWARD
La Pensee Dicovery! Theatre New Plays Discovery Festival, 511 N. 179th Pl., Seattle, WA 98133 (206) 542-8648 Contact: Willy Clark, Artistic Director **Frequency:** annual **Awards:** $300, production; staged reading of several entries **Works:** full-length plays, single and related one-acts, fully scored musicals, children's plays **Regulations:** authors must be residents of AK, ID, OR, WA or British Columbia; entries must be unproduced except in readings or workshop productions; no more than 1 entry per author; no collaborations; previous winners ineligible; winning playwright must be in residence during rehearsal and production period and must participate in script development **Specifications:** maximum cast: 10; sets must be suitable for an intimate stage **Stage:** flexible, 50-75 seats **Procedure:** request guidelines **Deadline:** Jan. 15, 1990 postmark **Notification:** May 15, 1990 **Comment:** All entries will be considered for the Fletcher Cross Award (see listing in this section).

AMERICAN COLLEGE THEATRE FESTIVAL AWARDS
ASCAP FOUNDATION
COLLEGE MUSICAL THEATRE AWARD
Michael Kanin Playwriting Awards Program, John F. Kennedy Center, Washington, DC 20566 (202) 254-3437 Contact: David Young, Producing Director **Frequency:** annual **Awards:** $1000 each for lyrics, music and book **Regulations:** authors must be full-time students in accredited institutions of higher learning; entries must be original, copyrighted works produced by ACTF participating schools **Procedure:** request guidelines; application form to be completed by producing school; fee upon entry **Deadline:** Dec. 1, 1989 postmark **Notification:** spring 1990

COLUMBIA PICTURES
TELEVISION PLAYWRITING AWARD
Michael Kanin Playwriting Awards Program,
John F. Kennedy Center, Washington, DC 20566
(202) 254-3437 **Contact**: David Young, Producing Director **Frequency**: annual **Award**: assignment to write a completed teleplay for one of Columbia Pictures Television's series, expenses for story conference in Los Angeles, Writers Guild Scale for completed teleplay, fellowship to Shenandoah Valley Playwrights Retreat (see Special Programs) **Works**: full-length comedies **Regulations**: authors must be full-time students in accredited institutions of higher learning; entries must be original, copyrighted works produced by ACTF participating schools **Procedure**: request guidelines; application form to be completed by producing school; fee upon entry **Deadline**: Dec. 1, 1989 **Advice**: "Scripts should be sent as soon as possible after the last performance on campus."

DAVID LIBRARY AWARD ON AMERICAN FREEDOM
Box 748, Washington Crossing, PA 18977
(215) 493-6776 **Contact**: Ezra Stone, National Chairman **Frequency**: annual **Awards**: 1st prize $2000, fellowship to Shenandoah Valley Playwrights Retreat (see Special Programs); 2nd prize $1000 **Works**: full-length plays **Regulations**: authors must be full-time students in accredited institutions of higher learning; entries must be produced by ACTF participating schools and must "examine or reflect some aspect of Americana and reveal, either in primary statement or underlying theme, the nature of freedom in its broadest sense" **Procedure**: request guidelines; application form to be completed by producing school; fee upon entry **Deadline**: Oct. 15, 1989, or 12 weeks prior to 1st performance, whichever is earlier **Notification**: spring 1990

LORRAINE HANSBERRY PLAYWRITING AWARD
National Program for Cultural Diversity,
John F. Kennedy Center, Washington, DC 20566
(202) 254-3437 **Contact**: David Young, Producing Director **Frequency**: annual **Awards**: 1st prize $2500, fellowship to Shenandoah Valley Playwrights Retreat (see Special Programs); 2nd prize $1000; grants ($750 and

$500) to schools producing   1st and 2nd place winners **Works**: full-length plays   **Regulations**: authors must be full-or part-time students in   accredited institutions of higher learning; entries must be   produced by ACTF participating schools and must deal with the   black experience **Procedure**: request guidelines; application form to be completed by producing school; fee upon entry **Deadline**: Dec. 1, 1989 **Advice**: Playwrights may submit scripts to ACTF regional playwriting chairs for assistance in securing productions.

NATIONAL STUDENT PLAYWRITING AWARD
Michael Kanin Playwriting Awards Program,
John F. Kennedy Center, Washington, DC 20566
(202) 254-3437   Contact: David Young, Producing Director **Frequency**: annual **Awards**: $2500, production at Kennedy   Center, offer of contract with William Morris Agency (see   Agents), active membership in The Dramatists Guild (see Special   Programs), publication by Samuel French (see Publishers), cash   award to producing school **Works**: full-length plays, musicals **Regulations**: authors must be full-time students in accredited   institutions of higher learning; entries must be produced by ACTF   participating schools **Procedure**: request guidelines; application   form to be completed by producing school; fee upon entry **Deadline**: Dec. 1, 1989   **Comment**:   The producing department   of each regional winner is eligible for The Angels New Play   Production Award of $500 to be used for production costs of the   next production entered in the Michael Kanin Playwriting Awards Program within 3 years; a request for the award should accompany the entry form for the second original play.

THE SHORT PLAY AWARDS PROGRAM
Michael Kanin Playwriting Awards Program,
John F. Kennedy Center, Washington, DC 20566
(202) 254-3437   Contact: David Young, Producing Director **Frequency**: annual **Awards**: $1000, publication by Samuel   French (see Publishers), membership in The Dramatists Guild (see   Special Programs), offer of contract with William Morris Agency   (see Agents), possible production at Kennedy Center; awards to   each of 2-3 winners **Regulations**: authors must be full-time students

in accredited institutions of higher learning; entries must be produced by ACTF participating schools and must be 20-40 minutes in length; entries are not eligible for other ACTF playwriting awards, but performers are eligible for ACTF's Irene Ryan Acting Scholarship **Procedure:** request guidelines; application form to be completed by producing school; fee upon entry **Deadline:** Dec. 1, 1989 **Comment:** See American College Theatre Festival New Play Preview Program listing in Special Programs.

AMERICAN MUSICAL THEATER FESTIVAL
Frohman Foundation, Box I, Carmel, CA 93921
(408) 625-9900 Contact: Moss Hall, Dramaturg
Frequency: annual **Award:** $2000, possible production and/or staged reading **Works:** full-length musicals **Regulations:** entries must be unpublished and unproduced **Stage:** flexible, 160 seats **Audience:** general **Procedure:** request guidelines and application form; $15 fee upon entry **Deadline:** late fall (inquire)

AMERICAN STAGE DIRECTIONS
PLAYWRITING CONTEST
San Francisco, CA This contest has been discontinued.

ANNA ZORNIO MEMORIAL CHILDREN'S THEATRE
PLAYWRITING AWARD
Theater Dept., Paul Arts Center M211,
University of New Hampshire, Durham, NH 03824
(603) 862-2291 Contact: Carol Lucha-Burns, Director of Youth Drama **Frequency:** annual **Award:** $250, production, publication by Action Press (see Publishers) with negotiable royalty **Works:** children's plays **Regulations:** authors must be U.S. or Canadian residents; entries must be unpublished, unproduced and no more than 1 hour in length; no more than 3 submissions per author **Procedure:** request guidelines **Deadline:** Oct. 1, 1989

ANNUAL AT THE UPRISING PLAYWRIGHT'S AWARD
Uprising Productions, 3125 E. 7th St.,
Long Beach, CA 90804 (213) 438-8922
Contact: Ken Rugg, Dramaturg **Awards:** full-length category 1st prize $300, 2nd prize $150, possible production; short category 1st prize $150, 2nd prize $75, possible

production **Works:** full-length plays (80 minutes or longer), single one-acts (up to 60 minutes)   **Regulations:** entries must not be published, professionally produced or committed **Specifications:** maximum cast: 8; 1-2 interiors or simultaneous settings **Stage:** flexible, 32 seats **Procedure:** request guidelines **Deadline:** Sept. 30, 1989 postmark **Notification:** Nov. 1, 1989 **Your chances:** 30/3/3 or more **Advice:** "Submit plays for a theatre that is very small." **Comment:** The judges reserve the right to withhold the award if, in their opinion, no entry merits it.

THE ANN WHITE THEATRE
6TH ANNUAL NEW PLAYWRIGHTS CONTEST
5266 Gate Lake Rd. Ft. Lauderdale, FL 33319
(305) 722-4371 Contact: Ann White, Founder/Director **Award:** $500, production for full-length play; possible staged reading for one-act **Works:** full-length plays, one-acts **Regulations:** entries must be unpublished, unproduced and free of royalty and copyright restrictions **Specifications:** small cast, simple set preferred **Procedure:** send script **Deadline:** Nov. 15, 1989; no submissions before Aug. 1 **Notification:** Mar. 1990 **Your chances:**   400/6/8 **Comment:**   The screening committee reserves the right to select no winner or more than one winner.

ARNOLD AND DOROTHY BURGER
PLAYWRITING COMPETITION
Euclid Recreation Dept.,
23131 Lake Shore Blvd., Euclid, OH 44123
(216) 449-8624 Contact: Mary Thompson, President **Frequency:** annual **Award:** "Up to $1000—varies depending upon funding." **Works:** full-length plays, related one-acts, adaptations, musicals, children's plays **Regulations:** authors must be residents of OH; entries must be unpublished and unproduced except in a staged reading **Stage:** proscenium, 200 seats **Audience:** "Mixed." **Procedure:** send script **Deadline:** Aug. 1, 1989 postmark **Notification:** Oct. 15, 1989 **Your chances:** 45/5/1 or more

ARNOLD WEISSBERGER AWARD
**New Dramatists, 424 W. 44th St.,
New York, NY 10036 (212) 757-6960**
Contact: Kirk Aanes, Director of Artist Services
Frequency: annual **Award:** $5000 **Works:** full-length
plays **Regulations:** entries must not be published or
professionally produced; no more than 1 entry per author
Procedure: request guidelines **Deadline:** Feb. 1, 1989
Notification: Sept. 1989 **Your chances:** 700/3 final
round judges/1in 1st round, 2 in 2nd round, 3 in 3rd round

A.R.T. RADIO SCRIPT WRITING COMPETITION
**1616 W. Victory Blvd. Suite 104,
Glendale, CA 91201 (213) 460-2464** This contest is
inactive in 1989.

ASF TRANSLATION PRIZE
**The American-Scandinavian Foundation,
127 E. 73rd St., New York, NY 10021**
(212) 879-9779 Contact: Publishing Office **Frequency:**
annual **Works:** translations from a Scandinavian language into
English **Award:** $1000, publication of excerpt in *Scandinavian
Review* **Regulations:** entries must be unpublished; minimum
length: 75 pages prose, 35 pages poetry; original work must be
written by a Scandinavian born after 1880 **Procedure:** send
4 copies of script, 1 copy of original work and letter of
permission from copyright holder **Deadline:** Jun. 1, 1989
Notification: Nov. 1, 1989

ATA AWARD FOR LITERARY TRANSLATION FROM GERMAN
**American Translators Association,
109 Croton Ave., Ossining, NY 10562**
(216) 234-6345 Contact: Betty Becker-Theye, Chair,
Honors and Awards Committee **Frequency:** biennial odd years
Award: $1000, certificate **Regulations:** entries must have
been published in U.S. after Jan. 1, 1987, and must conform to
P.E.N. guidelines **Procedure:** any party directly associated
with publication of the book may request application form and
guidelines; ATA members may nominate books **Deadline:** Mar.
1989 (inquire)

ATLANTIC COMMUNITY COLLEGE PLAYWRIGHTS' WEEKEND

Humanities Division, Atlantic Community College, Mays Landing, NJ 08330 (609) 343-5040
Contact: John Pekich, Producer, Playwrights' Weekend **Frequency:** annual **Award:** reading, possible production **Works:** one-acts **Regulations:** entries must be unpublished and not under consideration or option elsewhere; no more than 1 entry per author **Specifications:** minimum cast: 4-6; limited sets; limited scene changes; no musicals, adaptations, film or TV scripts **Procedure:** send script **Deadline:** Jan. 31, 1989 **Notification:** Feb. 20, 1989 **Comment:** "The reviewers reserve the right to accept or reject any and all manuscripts."

BARN PLAYERS PLAYWRIGHTING CONTEST

Box 713, Shawnee Mission, KS 66201
(913) 381-4004 Contact: Don Ramsey, President, Board of Directors **Frequency:** annual **Award:** $500, production, possible playwriting seminar with stipend **Works:** full-length plays, related one-acts, musicals **Regulations:** entries must be unpublished, unproduced and approximately 2 hours in length; related one-acts must constitute a full evening's entertainment; piano scores must accompany musical entries; no more than 1 submission per author **Specifications:** simple production requirements **Procedure:** request guidelines **Deadline:** inquire (Sept. 15 in 1988) **Comment:** "Tapes of music are appreciated but not necessary."

BEVERLY HILLS THEATRE GUILD– JULIE HARRIS PLAYWRIGHT AWARD COMPETITION

2815 N. Beachwood Dr., Los Angeles, CA 90068
(213) 465-2703 Contact: Marcella Meharg, Competition Coordinator **Frequency:** annual **Awards:** 1st prize $5000 plus $2000 to a theatre company to help finance a showcase production in the Los Angeles area within 1 year after receipt of award; 2nd prize $1000; 3rd prize $500 **Works:** full-length plays **Regulations:** entries must be unpublished, unproduced and unoptioned; authors must be U.S. citizens; no more than 1 entry per author; previous entries and plays that have won other contests are ineligible **Procedure:** request guidelines and application form **Deadline:** Nov. 1, 1989

postmark; no submissions before Aug. 1 **Notification:** Jun. 1990 **Your chances:** 500+/5/2+ **Advice:** "Don't send 1st draft--competition is tough; play should be as well-developed as possible without a production."

BIENNIAL PROMISING PLAYWRIGHT AWARD
Colonial Players, Inc., c/o Doris Cummins, 104 Stewart Dr., Edgewater, MD 21307 (301) 956-3397
Frequency: biennial, even years **Award:** $750, possible production **Works:** full-length plays, adaptations **Regulations:** authors must reside in U.S. or U.S. possession; entries may not have been formally produced and must be free of restrictions; no more than 2 entires per author; adaptations must be accompanied by permission in writing from copyright holders **Specifications:** maximum cast: 20, 12 or fewer preferred; works must be suitable for arena staging **Procedure:** request guidelines; $5 fee upon entry **Deadline:** inquire (Dec. 31 in 1988) **Comment:** The judges reserve the right to withhold the award if no play is deemed suitable for production in Colonial Players' theatre.

BLOOMINGTON PLAYWRIGHTS PROJECT CONTEST
409 S. Walnut St., Bloomington, IN 47401 (812) 332-0822 Contact: Rita Kniess, Literary Manager **Frequency:** annual **Award:** $250, production, staged reading **Works:** full-length plays **Regulations:** entries must be unpublished and unproduced **Specifications:** simple set **Stage:** flexible, 50 seats **Audience:** young adults, college students **Procedure:** send script and cover letter **Deadline:** Oct. 15, 1989 **Notification:** 6 weeks **Your chances:** 15/3/3 or more **Advice:** "We consider the playwright's ability to take part in the rehearsal process."

BMI UNIVERSITY MUSICAL SHOW COMPETITION
320 W. 57th St., New York, NY 10019 (212) 586-2000 ext. 258 Contact: Jean Banks, Director, Musical Theater Dept. **Frequency:** periodic **Awards:** $2500 to each composer of best music, writer of best lyrics, organization or class sponsoring winning show; $1000 to librettist **Regulations:** authors must be students in accredited institutions of higher learning and must be under 26 years of age as of Dec. 31, 1988; entries must be

certified by a dean of students and must be sponsored during the 1987-88 academic year as a recognized student activity; no more than 1 entry per author **Procedure:** request guidelines **Deadline:** Jun. 1989 (inquire) **Comment:** "If, in the opinion of the judges, the quality of the entries does not warrant the awarding of any prizes, the amount not awarded shall be added to the awards for the following year's competition."

BOB CLARK NEW PLAYWRIGHT CONTEST
University of Miami, Dept. of Theatre Arts,
Box 248273, Coral Gables, FL 33124
(305) 284-6439 Contact: Robert Ankrom, Chairman **Frequency:** annual **Award:** $1500, production, student showcase in New York **Works:** full-length plays, musicals **Specifications:** works must be suitable for college students **Procedure:** send script **Deadline:** Mar. 31, 1989 **Notification:** Aug. 1989

BREAKTHROUGH SERIES
University of Missouri Press, 200 Lewis Hall,
Columbia, MO 65211 (314) 882-7641
Contact: Janice Smiley, Administrative Assistant "The contest is in the formative stages of being updated in the very near future." Interested playwrights should inquire for details.

CAC NEW PLAY COMPETITION
Contemporary Arts Center, 900 Camp St.,
New Orleans, LA 70130 (504) 523-1216
Contact: Linda Gregoric, Performing Arts Education Coordinator **Frequency:** annual **Awards:** 1st prize $300; 3 plays receive staged readings **Works:** full-length plays, musicals **Regulations:** authors must reside in AL, GA, LA or MS; entries must be unpublished and unproduced; no more than 2 entries per author; previous entries ineligible **Procedure:** request guidelines **Deadline:** Oct. 15, 1989 **Notification:** Feb. 1990

CALIFORNIA YOUNG PLAYWRIGHTS PROJECT
The Gaslamp Quarter Theatre Company,
547 4th Ave., San Diego, CA 92101-6904
(619) 232-9608 Contact: Deborah Salzer, Director **Frequency:** annual **Award:** variable cash award, production,

script development, variable travel **Works:** full-length plays, single and related one-acts, musicals, children's plays **Regulations:** authors must be residents of CA under 19 years of age at date of submission; entries must not be published or professionally produced **Stage:** 3/4 round, 95 seats **Audience:** "Many young people (over 12 years usually), families and theatre patrons. We don't cater to any element in the audience." **Procedure:** send script with cover letter giving date of birth and biographical information **Deadline:** May 1, 1989 postmark **Notification:** late fall 1989 **Your chances:** 170/6 or more/2 or more **Advice:** "We consider the quality of script as follows: sense of truth, imagination, skillful use of language, grasp of dramatic format. Writers are encouraged to write about ideas of importance to them, using whatever subject matter, form or language they choose." **Comment:** Scripts are not returned.

CAROL BURNETT YOUNG PLAYWRIGHTS' COMPETITION

A Director's Theatre, 6404 Hollywood Blvd. Suite 329, Hollywood, CA 90028 (213) 465-8431
Contact: Dorothy Lyman, Artistic Director **Frequency:** annual **Awards:** $1000 savings bond, production with expenses, for each of 3 winners; $500 savings bond to teachers of winning playwrights **Works:** one-acts **Exclusive interest:** humorous works **Regulations:** authors must be under 19 years of age and enrolled in public or private schools; entries must be unproduced and 30-40 minutes in length **Procedure:** request guidelines; 3 copies of script required for entry **Deadline:** spring 1989 (inquire)

CELEBRATION OF ONE-ACTS

West Coast Ensemble, Box 38728,
Los Angeles, CA 90038 (213) 871-8673
Contact: Les Hanson, Artistic Director **Frequency:** annual **Award:** production **Guidelines:** no more than 3 entries per author; previous entries ineligible **Specifications:** limits on cast size, sets and technical requirements **Stages:** flexible, 70 seats; flexible, 99 seats **Procedure:** send script **Deadline:** Dec. 1, 1989 postmark **Your chances:** 700/15/5

CHARLOTTE FESTIVAL/NEW PLAYS IN AMERICA
Charlotte Repertory Theatre, Spirit Square,
110 E. 7th St., Charlotte, NC 28202
(704) 375-4796 Contact: Claudia C. Covington, Literary Manager **Frequency**: annual **Awards**: production with royalty for 6 winners **Works**: full-length plays **Regulations**: entries must not be professionally produced; playwrights must participate in Festival process **Procedure**: send script with resume **Deadline**: ongoing program **Notification**: 3-4 months **Your chances**: 600/3 judges **Advice**: "Just your best work."

CHARLOTTE REPERTORY THEATRE
NEW SCRIPT COMPETITION
Charlotte, NC This contest has been discontinued.

CHARLOTTE REPERTORY THEATRE
PLAY COMMISSION
Charlotte Repertory Theatre, Spirit Square,
110 E. 7th St., Charlotte, NC 28202
(704) 375-4796 Contact: Claudia C. Covington, Literary Manager **Award:** $6000 commission **Works:** full-length plays **Exclusive interest:** animal rights, "particularly (but not exclusively) the abuse of those rights in science (including education, product testing and research)" **Regulations:** theatre may produce play within 18 months **Specifications:** maximum cast: 9; no animals on stage; no musicals **Procedure:** request guidelines **Deadline:** Apr. 1, 1989 **Advice:** "We're more interested in focusing on the fact that people (characters) change or don't change in the face of new information or discoveries." **Comment:** For research needs contact Tom Eagan, 3509 Eden Croft Dr., Raleigh, NC 27612 (919) 782-3739.

CHICANO LITERARY CONTEST
Dept. of Spanish and Portuguese, University of California at Irvine, Irvine, CA 92717
(714) 856-5702   Contact: Julie Foraker, Coordinator **Frequency:** annual **Awards:** 1st prize $400, 2nd prize $250, 3rd prize $150 **Works:** full-length plays, one-acts, children's plays **Special interest:** one-acts **Regulations:** authors must be U.S. residents, either Chicano playwrights or playwrights with strong identification with Chicano community;

entries must be unpublished and may be written in Spanish, English or both **Procedure:** "Manuscripts must be typed, double-spaced and submitted in triplicate. The Title page must bear the title 'Fifteenth Annual Chicano Literary Contest' and the author's full name, address, telephone number and social security number and should be signed by the author. The author's name should not appear anywhere else on the script." **Deadline:** Jan. 6, 1989 **Notification:** May 1, 1989

CHRISTINA CRAWFORD AWARDS
ATHE Playwrights' Theater Workshop, Dept. of Speech, Box 2201, South Dakota State University, Brookings, SD 57007 (605) 688-6131
Contact: Judith Zivanovic, Vice-President for Workshop **Frequency:** annual **Awards:** 1st prize $1000, 2nd prize $500, 2 Honorable Mention Awards: of $150 each; staged readings at annual conference in Aug. **Works:** full-length plays, one-acts **Regulations:** for 1st and 2nd prizes, authors must have been enrolled in college on or since Jun. 1, 1988; no more than 1 entry per author; winners must attend conference **Procedure:** request guidelines **Deadline:** Feb. 1, 1989 postmark **Advice:** "Short plays have an advantage because of convention session length."

CLAUDER COMPETITION FOR EXCELLENCE
New Voices, 511 Tremont St., Boston, MA 02108
(617) 357-5667 Contact: Stanley Richardson, Artistic Director **Frequency:** biennial even years **Awards:** $3000, production; runners-up may receive $500 and staged reading **Works:** full-length plays **Regulations:** authors must be residents of New England states; entries must not be published or professionally produced **Specifications:** maximum cast: 8; no more than 1 unit set **Procedure:** request guidelines **Deadline:** inquire **Your chances:** 200/6/2 or more **Advice:** "Focus on ideas, language. Forget psychological motivation. Care."

COLUMBIA THEATRE PLAYERS' ANNUAL NEW PLAY CONTEST
603 E. Robert, Hammond, LA 70401
(504) 345-2098 Contact: Larry Gray, Vice President **Award:** $300, staged reading, possible production **Works:** full-length plays **Regulations:** entries must be unpublished

Stage: black box, 100 seats **Audience:** "Community theatre; cross section, all kinds." **Procedure:** send script **Deadline:** Feb. 1, 1989 **Notification:** Mar. 1, 1989 **Your chances:** 50-100/"usually 3/1 1st reading, usually 3 for finalists" **Advice:** "Use standard script form. Binding makes our life easier and makes your script look better." **Comment:** "We want the best quality. We promise a staged reading. A full production is possible if we think we can do it justice. The award will be given to the best play, regardless."

CORNERSTONE: PENUMBRA THEATRE COMPANY NATIONAL PLAYWRIGHT COMPETITION
270 N. Kent St., St. Paul, MN 55102
(612) 224-4601 Contact: Lou Bellamy, Artistic Director **Frequency:** annual **Award:** $1000, production with royalty, travel **Works:** full-length plays **Regulations:** works must not be professionally produced and must deal with the Afro-American experience **Stage:** thrust/proscenium, 150 seats **Procedure:** send script and resume **Deadline:** Mar. 15, 1989 **Notification:** Sept. 1, 1989 **Your chances:** 60/4/3

THE COUNCIL OF JEWISH THEATRE PLAY COMMISSIONS
New York, NY This contest has been discontinued.

DALTON LITTLE THEATRE/ WORLD CARPET INC. NEW PLAY PROJECT
Box 841, Dalton, GA 30722-0841 (404) 226-6618
Contact: Jimmy E. Nations, President, Dalton Little Theatre **Frequency:** annual **Award:** $400, production **Works:** full-length plays, musicals **Regulations:** entries must be unproduced; no more than 2 submissions per author **Specifications:** small playing area **Procedure:** request guidelines **Deadline:** inquire (Nov. 30 in 1988) **Notification:** Mar. 1989 **Your chances:** 200/6/6

THE DAVID B. MARSHALL AWARD IN MUSICAL THEATRE
Musical Theatre Program, University of Michigan, 911 N. University, Ann Arbor, MI 48109
(313) 763-5213 This contest is inactive in 1989.

DAVID JAMES ELLIS MEMORIAL AWARD
**Theatre Americana, Box 245,
Altadena, CA 91001-1235 (818) 791-4497
Contact:** Mrs. Leone Jones, Chairman, Playreading Committee
Frequency: annual **Award:** $500, production **Works:**
full-length plays **Regulations:** entries must be unpublished
and 90 minutes-2 hours in length and must deal with "the
American scene" **Specifications:** maximum cast: 20, 4-10
preferred; simple sets; minimal set changes; no elaborate,
expensive costumes **Procedure:** send script **Deadline:** Apr.
1, 1989 postmark **Notification:** time varies **Your
chances:** 200-250/3/2-7 **Advice:** "No pornography!
Originality is important. Oscenity for shock value is
unacceptable. Preference is given to American authors. No
musicals, TV or movie scripts." **Comment:** Season runs from
Jul. 1-Jun. 30 with 1 award each season for the best of 4 plays
produced.

DAYTON PLAYHOUSE PLAYWRITING COMPETITION
**1301 E. Siebenthaler Ave., Dayton, OH 45414
(513) 222-7000 Contact:** Jim Payne, Managing Director
Frequency: annual **Award:** $1000, possible production
Works: full-length plays, translations, adaptations **Special
interests:** "Plays for and about, but not limited to, women
and minorities." **Regulations:** entries must be unpublished
and unproduced except in staged readings and/or workshops
Stage: flexible, 180 seats **Audience:** "Open." **Procedure:**
request guidelines **Deadline:** Nov. 30, 1989 postmark; no
submissions before Sept. 1 **Notification:** May 30, 1990
Your chances: 150/5-8/at least 3 **Comment:** The judges
reserve the right to withhold the award if, in their opinion, no
entry merits it.

THE DOGWOOD NATIONAL ONE-ACT PLAY COMPETITION
**2040 Old Salem Rd., Watkinsville, GA 30677
(404) 769-6576 Contact:** David Muschell, Contest
Coordinator **Frequency:** annual **Award:** $100, staged
reading **Regulations:** entries must be unpublished **Stages:**
300 seats; 150 seats **Procedure:** send script with $5 fee
Deadline: Jul. 15, 1989 **Notification:** Sept. 15, 1989
Your chances: 50+/7/2+

DRAMA LEAGUE OF NEW YORK
PLAYS-IN-PROGRESS COMPETITION
165 W. 46th St. Suite 601, New York, NY 10036
(212) 302-2100 **Contact:** Carolyn French, Chair, Playwrights Awards Committee **Frequency:** annual **Award:** $1000, reading, script development **Works:** full-length plays **Special interests:** "We like to see human beings represented at their best; we prefer plays that resonate to the community rather than plays about narrow psychological perceptions; we invariably choose plays of literary as well as theatrical merit." **Regulations:** authors must be U.S. citizens; entries must be unpublished and unproduced **Procedure:** request guidelines and application form **Deadline:** Oct. 1, 1989 postmark **Notification:** Mar. 1, 1990 **Your chances:** 300/15/2-15

DRAMARAMA89
Playwright's Center of San Francisco, 3225 Laguna #3, San Francisco, CA 94123 (415) 931-2392
Contact: Bill Lees, Producer **Frequency:** annual **Awards:** concert readings of 6 plays; 3 $100 post-performance awards **Works:** full-length plays **Regulations:** entries must not have been produced in Bay Area; no more than 1 entry per author **Specifications:** small stage; no children's plays, musicals, pageants, TV scripts or pornographic works **Stage:** 50 seats **Audience:** general **Procedure:** send script **Deadline:** Dec.. 1, 1989 postmark **Notification:** Apr. 1990 **Your chances:** 140/9/3 **Advice:** "Send the best script you have available for a small stage; script-in-hand staged reading."

DRURY COLLEGE 1-ACT PLAYWRITING CONTEST
900 N. Benton Ave., Springfield, MO 65802
(417) 865-8731 **Contact:** Sandy Asher, Writer-in-Residence **Frequency:** biennial even years **Awards:** 1 prize of $300, 2 prizes of $150 each; possible production **Regulations:** works must not be committed, published or professionally produced; no more than 1 entry per author **Specifications:** "Some preference is given to small cast, one-set plays running between 20 and 45 minutes." **Stage:** proscenium, 200 seats **Audience:** "College students, faculty, staff, general public." **Procedure:** request guidelines **Deadline:** Dec. 1, 1990 postmark **Notification:** Mar. 1, 1991 **Your chances:** 200/14/1-3

DUBUQUE FINE ARTS PLAYERS
12TH ANNUAL ONE-ACT PLAYWRITING CONTEST
569 S. Grandview, Dubuque, IA 52001
(319) 582-5558 Contact: Sally T. Ryan, Contest Director **Awards:** 1st prize $200, 2nd prize $150, 3rd prize $100; production **Regulations:** entries must be unpublished, unproduced and no more than 45 minutes in length **Maximum cast:** 6-8 **Procedure:** request guidelines and application form; $5 fee upon entry **Deadline:** Jan. 31, 1989 postmark; no submission before Nov. 1 **Notification:** May 1989 **Your chances:** 180/2/2-5 **Advice:** "Small cast, minimum scene changes, minimal costume requirements."

EMERGING PLAYWRIGHT AWARD
Playwrights Preview Productions, 1160 Fifth Ave. #304, New York, NY 10029 (212) 289-2168
Contact: Thais Fitzsimmons, Literary Manager **Frequency:** annual **Award:** $500, staged reading, expenses to attend rehearsals **Works:** full-length plays, one-acts **Special interests:** "Minority playwrights, among all other writers"; full-length plays and related one-acts preferred **Guidelines:** entries must not have been produced in New York **Maximum cast:** 8 **Procedure:** request guidelines **Deadline:** ongoing program **Notification:** spring 1990 **Comment:** The judges reserve the right to withhold the award if no play of merit is found.

FEAT PLAYWRITING FESTIVAL
Phoenix Theatre, 37 E. 9th, Indianapolis, IN 46204
(317) 635-2381 Contact: Brian Fonseca, Artistic Director **Frequency:** annual **Awards:** $500 for full-length play, $250 for one-act; production, housing **Works:** full-length plays, single and related one-acts, translations, adaptations, children's plays **Regulations:** entries must not be published or professionally produced; no more than 2 entries per author **Specifications:** maximum cast: 6-8 preferred; single set **Stage:** proscenium, 93 seats **Audience:** "University educated, liberal, interested in social issues." **Procedure:** send script, biography "of self and play," $5 entry fee **Deadline:** Apr. 30, 1989 **Notification:** Jun. 1989 **Your chances:** 300/14-15/1-3 **Comment:** "Children's plays are less likely to be chosen."

FERNDALE REPERTORY NEW WORKS COMPETITION
Box 892, Ferndale, CA 95536 (707) 725-2378
Contact: Peter Buckley, Artistic Director **Frequency:** annual **Award:** production with royalty **Works:** full-length plays **Regulations:** entries must be unproduced **Stage:** small thrust **Procedure:** request guidelines **Deadline:** Oct. 1, 1989 **Notification:** Dec. 1, 1989

FESTIVAL OF FIRSTS PLAYWRITING COMPETITION
Sunset Center, Box 5066, Carmel, CA 93921
(408) 624-3996 **Contact:** Richard Tyler, Director **Frequency:** annual **Award:** $1000, possible production **Works:** full-length plays, related one-acts, adaptations **Regulations:** entries must be unpublished and unproduced; related one-acts must constitute a full evening's entertainment **Stage:** 28' x 35', 700 seats **Audience:** "Local patrons who see a great many productions in this area." **Procedure:** request guidelines and application form; $5 fee upon entry **Deadline:** inquire (Nov. 11 in 1988) **Your chances:** 200/3/1-3

FESTIVAL OF SOUTHERN THEATRE
Dept. of Theatre, University of Mississippi, University, MS 38677 (601) 232-5816
Contact: Scott McCoy, Producing Director **Frequency:** annual **Awards:** 3 awards of $1000, expenses to attend productions **Works:** full-length plays **Regulations:** entries must not be published or professionally produced; authors must be Southerners, or plays must have "markedly Southern" themes; winning writers must be in residence in mid-July, 1990 **Stage:** proscenium **Audience:** "General; we must avoid extreme and unwarranted vulgarity." **Procedure:** request guidelines **Deadline:** Dec. 15, 1989 **Notification:** Mar. 1990 **Advice:** "Theatricality and resolution—we're tired of dialogue pieces." **Comments:** Competition normally receives approximately 150 entries. "National critics are on hand for critique of winners; there are usually printed reviews."

FESTIVAL THEATRE OF BIOGRAPHY AND HISTORY COMMISSIONS

Division of the Wooden O, Inc., 600 W. 58th St. Suite 9194, New York, NY 10019 (212) 874-6147
Contact: Gayther Myers, Artistic Director   **Frequency**: ongoing program   **Award**: $500 commission, possible production   **Works**: full-length plays, one-acts **Exclusive interest**: historical and biographical topics **Regulations**: plays must be written in consultation with the theatre and based on topics proposed by the theatre **Procedure**: send 2 full-length scripts as work samples

FIU PLAYWRIGHTS' FESTIVAL

Dept. of Theatre, Florida International University, Miami, FL 33199   (305) 554-2895
Contact: Therald Todd, Chairperson   **Frequency**: annual **Awards**: awards to be announced, production   **Works**: full-length plays, one-acts   **Regulations**: entries must be unproduced works by FL playwrights; winning author must be available for production meetings and rehearsals **Stage**: flexible, 140 seats   **Audience**: "Mixed--community and university."   **Procedure**: request guidelines   **Deadline**: inquire **Your chances**: 80+/6/at least 2

FLETCHER CROSS AWARD

La Pensee Discovery! Theatre New Plays Discovery Festival, 511 N. 179th Pl., Seattle, WA 98133 (206) 542-8648   Contact: Willy Clark, Artistic Director **Frequency**: annual   **Awards**: $300, production; staged reading of several entries **Works**: full-length plays, single and related one-acts, fully-scored musicals, children's plays **Regulations**: authors must be U.S. residents; entries must be unproduced except in readings or workshop productions; no more than 1 entry per author with exception of thematically related one-acts; collaborations and previous winners ineligible; winning author must be in residence and must participate in script development **Specifications**: maximum cast: 8-10; sets must be suitable for intimate stage **Stage**: flexible, 50-75 seats   **Procedure**: request guidelines **Deadline**: Jan. 15, 1990 **Notification**: May 1990 **Your chances**: 200-300/3-5/3-5 **Comment**: Entries in Allen Clark Memorial Award competition (see listing in this section) will automatically be considered for this award.

FMCT MIDWEST PLAYWRIGHT COMPETITION
Fargo-Moorhead Community College, Box 644, Fargo, ND 58107 This contest is inactive in 1989.

FOREST A. ROBERTS/
SHIRAS INSTITUTE PLAYWRITING AWARD
Forest A. Roberts Theatre, Northern Michigan University, Marquette, MI 49855-5364 (906) 227-2553 Contact: James A. Panowski, Director of Theatre **Frequency**: annual **Award**: $1000, production, housing **Works**: full-length plays **Regulations**: entries must be unpublished and unproduced **Stages**: proscenium; flexible **Audience**: "University theatre, wide age range." **Procedure**: request guidelines and application form **Deadline**: Nov. 18, 1989 **Notification**: Mar. 1990 **Your chances**: 400-500/3/2 or more **Advice**: "Read the directions!"

FRANK McCLURE ONE-ACT PLAY AWARD
Amelia **Magazine, 329 E St., Bakersfield, CA 93304 (805) 323-4064 Contact**: Frederick A. Raborg, Jr., Editor **Frequency**: annual **Award**: $150, publication, free copy **Works**: one-act plays, translations, adaptations and children's plays **Regulations**: entries must be unpublished and no more than 45 minutes in length; adaptors must provide permission from copyright holder if original is under copyright protection **Audience**: "International, catholic readership that is predominantly well-educated but representative of all walks of life." **Procedure**: send script, resume and $10 entry fee; "list acknowledgements" **Deadline**: May 15, 1989 **Notification**: approximately 3 months **Your chances**: 90-100/3/3-4 **Advice**: "Be professional. All previous winners, we have noted, were members of The Dramatists Guild. Have something important to say. We look for social or humane insights, strong plotting and conflict, intensity, fully developed characters and situations, daring and inventiveness. In short, does it play?"

FS DRAMA AWARD
305 Madison Ave. Suite 411, New York, NY 10165 This contest is inactive in 1989.

GALLERY PLAYERS OF THE LEO YASSENOFF JEWISH CENTER PLAYWRITING CONTEST

1125 College Ave., Columbus, OH 43209
(614) 231-2731 Contact: Teri Devlin, Drama Director
Frequency: biennial odd years **Award**: $1000, production
Works: full-length plays, children's plays **Procedure**: send
script **Deadline**: Jan. 1, 1989 **Notification**: Feb. 1, 1989

GEORGE R. KERNODLE PLAYWRITING COMPETITION

Dept. of Drama, University of Arkansas, Kimpel Hall
406, Fayetteville, AR 72701 (501) 575-2953
Contact: Thomas R. Jones **Frequency**: annual **Awards**: 1st
prize $300, 2nd prize $200; production **Works**: one-acts
Regulations: authors must be citizens or residents of U.S. or
Canada; entries must be unpublished, unproduced except in
workshops and no more than 1 hour in length; no more than 2
entries per author **Maximum cast**: 6-8 **Procedure**:
request guidelines; fee upon entry **Deadline**: Apr. 1, 1989
Notification: Aug. 1, 1989

GERALDINE R. DODGE FOUNDATION NEW AMERICAN PLAY AWARD

Playwrights Theatre of New Jersey, 33 Green
Village Rd., Madison, NJ 07940 (201) 514-1194
Contact: Buzz McLaughlin, Project Coordinator
Frequency: biennial odd years **Awards**: $10,000,
developmental residency with professional company at
conference at Princeton University (Aug. 6-12, 1989) staged
reading, expenses, for each of 2 winners **Works**: full-length
plays, related one-acts **Regulations**: authors must be U.S.
citizens or permanent residents; entries must not have
received professional productions or extensive professional
workshops; no more than 1 entry per author **Procedure**: send
script with separate 1-page biography including author's
name, address, phone number and title of entry and "a history
of developmental work on the submitted play, if any; other
plays written, along with their production history; and how you
heard about the award; title page of script must include name,
address and phone number of author or person submitting the
play" **Deadline**: Jan. 15, 1989 postmark; no submission
before Sept. 1 **Notification**: Apr. 3, 1989

GOLDEN GATE ACTORS ENSEMBLE PLAYWRIGHTS COMPETITION
580 Constanzo St., Stanford, CA 94305
(415) 326-0336 Contact: Contest Administrator **Frequency**: annual **Award**: $1000, staged reading, possible production; all entries receive a written critique **Works**: full-length plays, related one-acts **Regulations**: authors must be U.S. residents; entries must be unproduced and at least 60 minutes in length **Procedure**: request guidelines and application form; $20 fee upon entry **Deadline**: Mar. 1, 1989 **Notification**: Nov. 1, 1989

THE GREAT ALASKAN PLAYRUSH
Perseverance Theatre, 914 3rd St.,
Douglas, AK 99824 This contest is inactive in 1989.

HAROLD MORTON LANDON TRANSLATION AWARD
The Academy of American Poets, 177 E. 87th St.,
New York, NY 10128 (212) 427-5665
Contact: Nancy Schoenberger, Executive Director **Frequency**: annual **Award**: $1000 **Exclusive interest**: verse drama translated from any language into English verse **Regulations**: authors must be U.S. citizens; entries must have been published after Dec. 31, 1988; anthologies and collaborations ineligible **Procedure**: request guidelines **Deadline**: Dec. 31, 1989

HELEN EISNER AWARD FOR YOUNG PLAYWRIGHTS
Streisand Center at UCLA Hillel, 900 Hilgard Ave.,
Los Angeles, CA 90024 (213) 208-3081
Contact: Avi Davis, Program Coordinator **Frequency**: annual **Award**: $1000, possible production **Works**: full-length plays, one-acts, translations, adaptations, musicals, children's plays **Regulations**: authors must be under 30 years of age; entries must deal with "the struggle to express Jewish values in the contemporary world" **Procedure**: request guidelines and application form **Deadline**: inquire

THE HENRY FONDA YOUNG PLAYWRIGHTS PROJECT
Very Special Arts, Education Office,
John F. Kennedy Center, Washington, DC 20566
(202) 662-8899 Contact: Michael Anderson, Administrator, Field Services **Frequency**: annual **Award**:

production or staged reading; travel, housing **Works:** full-length plays, single and related one-acts, children's plays **Regulations:** authors must be students, 12-18 years of age; entries must be unproduced and must address some aspect of disability **Stage:** flexible **Audience:** "Children and adults, many disabled individuals." **Procedure:** request guidelines and application form **Deadline:** Feb. 15, 1989 **Notification:** Apr. 1989 **Your chances:** 100+/7/2 **Comments:** Scripts are not returned. See Henry Fonda Young Playwrights Project listing in Special Programs.

HISPANIC PLAYWRIGHTS PROJECT
South Coast Repertory, Box 2197,
Costa Mesa, CA 92628 (714) 957-2602
Contact: José Cruze Gonzalez, Project Director **Frequency:** annual **Awards:** summer workshop productions of 6 plays **Works:** full-length plays, one-acts **Regulations:** authors must be Hispanic-American playwrights; entries may be written partially in Spanish **Policy:** send script **Deadline:** Apr. 15, 1989 **Notification:** 1 month **Your chances:** 100/3/2

HUMBOLDT STATE UNIVERSTY
SEASON OF NEW AMERICAN PLAYS
Theatre Arts Dept., Humboldt State University,
Arcata, CA 95521 (707) 826-3566, -4606
Contact: Louise Williams, New Play Season Coordinator **Frequency:** biennial even years **Awards:** $1000, production and residency for each of 4-5 winners **Works:** full-length plays, related one-acts; choreographic pieces; scenarios for choreographic pieces and mime works **Regulations:** authors must be professional playwrights and must be available for 2-3 week residency; entries must be unproduced except in readings or workshops; choreographic pieces must be 7-30 minutes in length; no more than 1 entry per author **Procedure:** request guidelines; 2 copies of script required **Deadline:** inquire (Oct. 1 in 1988)

ILLINOIS STATE
FINE ARTS PLAYWRITING CONTEST
Illinois State University, Normal, IL 61761
(309) 438-8783 Contact: John W. Kirk, Contest Director **Frequency:** annual **Award:** $1000, production, publication

Works: full-length plays **Regulations:** entries must be unproduced except in stage reading or productions for which no admission has been charged and must be no more than 90 minutes in length **Stages:** proscenium, 400 seats; thrust, 320 seats **Procedure:** request guidelines **Deadline:** Oct. 15, 1989 **Notification:** Feb. 1990 **Your chances:** 300-400/18/3 **Advice:** "Strong action, conflict."

INDIANA UNIVERSITY-PURDUE UNIVERSITY AT INDIANAPOLIS CHILDREN'S THEATRE PLAYWRITING COMPETITION

Dept. of Theatre, IUPUI, 525 N. Blackford St., Indianapolis, IN 46202 (317) 274-0554
Contact: Dorothy Webb, Director **Frequency:** biennial even years **Awards:** 1st prize $1500 ($750 to encourage 1st production or rehearsed reading, $750 for residency); 3 semi-finalists receive $500 each (for residency at rehearsed reading); "winning plays are showcased at the National Children's Theatre Playwriting Symposium in March"; certificates **Works:** children's plays, one-acts and adaptations **Special interest:** "Well-crafted plays with strong story lines, compelling characters and careful attention to language. May include music." **Regulations:** works must not be professionally produced and must be 45-90 minutes in length; for adaptations of works not in the public domain, authors must provide written proof of permission from copyright holder **Procedure:** request guidelines and application form; 3 copies of script required upon entry **Deadline:** inquire (Nov. 1 in 1988) **Notification:** spring 1991 **Your chances:** 125/16/2 or more **Advice:** "Follow all rules and guidelines. Quality plays—write up, not down, to children. Write to the child within yourself." **Comment:** Formerly National Children's Theatre Playwriting Competition.

THE INSIDE FROM THE OUTSIDE INTERNATIONAL PROSE/POETRY CONTEST

Box 3186, Bloomington, IN 47402 (812) 876-5093, 335-1517 Contact: NormaJean McLeod, Publisher/Editor, IFTO Newsletter **Frequency:** annual **Award:** $50, publication **Works:** short plays or parts of plays **Special interests:** "Anything that is creative, well thought out, not cliche or trite and not plagarized or libelous." **Regulations:** entries must be uncommitted, unpublished and no more than

5-10 pages in length **Procedure:** request guidelines; fee upon entry **Deadline**: Nov. 1, 1989 **Notification:** Jan. 1990 **Your chances:** 150 "including poetry, prose, fiction and non-fiction"/3/1-2

INTERNATIONAL NEW MUSIC COMPOSERS COMPETITION

7114 Southwest 114 Pl. Suite E, Miami, FL 33173 (305) 271-9138 Contact: Carrie Manfrino, Coordinator **Frequency**: annual **Awards**: $2500, concert performance at Carnegie Recital Hill; possible performance for runners-up **Works:** musicals, operas, mixed-media pieces **Regulations**: entries must have been completed within the last 5 years and must not have won major competitions **Procedure:** request guidelines; $25 fee for first entry, $20 each for additional entry **Deadline**: May 15, 1989 **Notification:** Aug. 1989

THE INTERNATIONAL SOCIETY OF DRAMATISTS AWARDS

Box 1310, Miami, FL 33153   (305) 674-0538 Contact: Andrew Delaplaine, President **Frequency**: annual **Stage:** flexible, 100 seats **Procedure:** send script with synopsis and resume; specify particular contest on all submissions and correspondence

ADRIATIC AWARD

Award: $250, staged reading **Works:** full-length plays **Regulations**: entries must not have been produced more than once **Deadline**: Nov. 1, 1989 postmark **Notification:** Feb. 1, 1990

LINCOLN MEMORIAL ONE-ACT CONTEST

Award: $50, staged reading **Regulations**: entries must not be published or professionally produced **Deadline**: Oct. 1, 1989 **Notification:** Jan. 1, 1990

PERKINS PLAYWRITING CONTEST

Award: $100, staged reading **Works:** full-length plays **Regulations**: entries must not be published or professionally produced **Deadline**: Dec. 6, 1989 **Notification:** Mar. 1, 1990

JACKSONVILLE UNIVERSITY
ANNUAL PLAYWRITING CONTEST

Dept. of Theatre Arts, College of Fine Arts, Jacksonville University, Jacksonville, FL 32211 (904) 744-3950 Contact: Davis Sikes, Director **Award**: at least $1000, premiere production **Frequency**: inquire **Works**: full-length plays, one-acts **Special interests**: "Distinctive quality and outstanding theatrical value." **Regulations**: entries must be unproduced; no more than 3 entries per author **Procedure**: request guidelines **Deadline**: inquire after Sept. 1989

JAMES D. PHELAN LITERARY AWARD

The San Francisco Foundation, 685 Market St. Suite 910, San Francisco, CA 94105 (415) 543-0223 Contact: Adrienne Krug, Assistant Coordinator **Frequency**: annual **Award**: $2000 **Works**: full-length plays, single and related one-acts **Regulations**: authors must be California natives; entries must be unpublished and no more than 100 pages in length **Procedure**: request guidelines and application form **Deadline**: Jan. 15, 1989 **Notification**: Jun. 15, 1989 **Your chances**: 200+ entries/3judges

JCC THEATRE OF CLEVELAND
PLAYWRITING COMPETITION

The Jewish Community Center, 3505 Mayfield Rd., Cleveland Heights, OH 44118 (216) 382-4000 ext. 275 Contact: Dorothy Silver, Director, Visual and Performing Arts **Frequency**: annual **Award**: $1000, staged reading, possible production **Works**: full-length plays **Exclusive interest**: "The Jewish experience." **Regulations**: entries must be unproduced **Procedure**: request guidelines **Deadline**: Dec. 15, 1989 **Notification**: Jul. 10, 1990

JOHN DREW THEATRE NEW PLAY CONTEST

158 Main St., East Hampton, NY 11937 (516) 324-4051 Contact: Laura Lyons, Business Manager This contest is inactive in 1989.

JOHN GASSNER MEMORIAL PLAYWRITING AWARD

New England Theatre Conference, 50 Exchange St., Waltham, MA 02154 (617) 893-3120
Contact: Marie L. Philips, Executive Secretary **Frequency**: annual **Awards**: 1st prize $500, 2nd prize $250; staged reading and critique-discussion at NETC convention in Nov., referral to publishers **Works:** full-length plays, one-acts, children's plays **Regulations**: authors must be residents of U.S. or Canada; no more than 2 entries per author; see "Procedure" for other regulations **Procedure:** send 3 copies of script, synopsis and statement that the play is unpublished, not professionally produced and not under option, $5 entry fee (NETC members exempt from fee) **Deadline**: Apr. 15, 1989 postmark **Notification**: Sept. 1, 1989 **Your chances:** 150-200/3-7/3 **Advice:** See "Suggestions for Playwrights" on reverse side of contest announcement, available upon request. **Comment:** The judges reserve the right to withhold the award if, in their opinion, no entry merits it.

KUMU KAHUA/UNIVERSITY OF HAWAII AT MANOA DRAMA DEPARTMENT PLAYWRITING CONTEST

1770 East-West Rd., Honolulu, HI 96822
(808) 948-7677 Contact: Dennis Carroll, Executive Director, Kumu Kahua **Frequency**: annual **Awards**: Division 1: $500 for long play (50 pages or more), $200 for short play (15-50 pages); Division II: $250, $100; possible production with royalty of $25 per performance **Works:** full-length plays, single and related one-acts **Regulations**: Division I open to all authors, plays on Hawaiian subject matter only; Division II for Hawaiian authors only, no restrictions on subject matter **Specifications**: entries must be suitable for a small theatre **Stage:** 150-200 seats **Audience:** varies **Procedure:** request guidelines **Deadline**: Jan. 1, 1989 **Notification**: Apr. 1989 **Your chances:** 30-40/3/3-12 **Advice:** "No purely commercial material of the frothy sort."

LAWRENCE S. EPSTEIN PLAYWRITING AWARD

280 Park Ave. S #22E, New York, NY 10010
(212) 979-0865 Contact: Lawrence S. Epstein, Director **Frequency**: annual **Award**: $250, plaque **Works:** full-length plays, one-acts **Special interest:** theme varies from year to year (inquire) **Procedure:** request guidelines **Deadline**: varies annually (inquire)

LEAH PRODUCTIONS PLAYWRIGHT CONTEST

205 E. 88th St. Apt. 58, New York, NY 10128
(212) 876-1283   Contact: Michael Hardstark, Artistic
Director Frequency: periodic   Award: $500, production,
expenses to attend rehearsals   Works: full-length plays
Regulations: entries must be unpublished and unproduced
Specifications: small cast, simple set Procedure: request
guidelines Deadline: inquire (Feb. 16 in 1988)

THE LEE KORF PLAYWRITING AWARDS

The Original Theatre Works, Burnight Center,
Cerritos College, 11110 E. Alondra Blvd.,
Norwalk, CA 90650 (213) 924-2100
Contact: Nancy J. Payne, Managing Director Frequency:
annual   Award: up to $500, production, reading Works:
full-length plays or "theatre pieces"   Special interest:
"Preference will be given to authors who can arrange to join us
for pre-production festivities and rehearsals."   Stages:
Burnight Center Theatre, 362 seats; Burnight Studio Theatre,
100 seats   Procedure: send 2 copies of script Deadline:
Jan. 1, 1989   Notification: May 1989   Your chances:
70+/5/3

LETRAS DE ORO (SPANISH LITERARY CONTEST)

North-South Center, University of Miami, Box
248123, Coral Gables, FL 33124 (305) 284-4303
Contact: Ambler H. Moss, Jr., Director Frequency: annual
Awards: general prize $2000, student prize $500; possible
production, publication Works: full-length plays, one-acts,
adaptations, children's plays   Regulations: authors must be
U.S. citizens; works must be unpublished and written in Spanish
and must not have won a previous award; no more than 1 entry
per author Procedure: request guidelines   Deadline: Oct.
12, 1989   Notification: Jan. 1990   Your chances:
20/25/5

LEWIS GALANTIERE LITERARY TRANSLATION PRIZE

American Translators Association,
109 Croton Ave., Ossining, NY 10562
(914) 941-1500   Contact: Betty Becker-Theye, Chair,
Honors & Awards Committee Frequency: biennial even years
Award: $500, certificate   Works: full-length and one-act

translations **Special interest**: distinguished literary translations from any language into English **Regulations**: entries must have been published by an American publisher within the past 2 years; single volumes and works in collections are eligible **Procedure**: translator or publisher may submit entry plus 10 pages of original **Deadline**: Mar. 15, 1989 **Notification**: Aug. 31, 1989

LITTLE NASHVILLE PLAYWRITING AWARD
Nashville, IN   This contest has been discontinued.

LOIS AND RICHARD ROSENTHAL NEW PLAY PRIZE
Cincinnati Playhouse in the Park, Box 6537, Cincinnati, OH 45206   (513) 421-5440
Contact: Ara Watson, Playwright-in-Residence/Literary Manager   **Frequency**: annual **Award**: production, residency with expenses   **Works**: full-length plays, related one-acts **Regulations**: works must not be produced professionally; related one-acts must constitute a full evening's entertainment **Stages**: thrust; arena **Procedure**: send script   **Deadline**: Jan. 15, 1989 **Notification**: Mar. 1989

MARGARET BARTLE ANNUAL PLAYWRITING AWARD
Community Children's Theatre of Kansas City, 8021 E. 129th Terrace, Grandview, MO 64030 (816) 761-5775   Contact: Mrs. Blanche Sellens, Chairman, Playwriting Award   **Award**: $500, possible production **Works**: children's plays, adaptations and musicals **Regulations**: entries must be unpublished, unproduced and 1 hour in length **Specifications**: maximum cast: 8; all roles must be for adult women; sets suitable for touring elementary schools; no seasonal plays; "no gratuitous violence, mature love stories, slang, cursing" **Audience**: grades K-6 **Procedure**: request guidelines   **Deadline**: Jan. 23, 1989 **Notification**: Apr. 1989   **Your chances**: 20-50/5/5 **Advice**: "Suggested topics: legends, folklore, historical incidents, biographies, adaptations of children's classics." **Comment**: The judges reserve the right to withhold the award if, in their opinion, no entry merits it.

MARGO JONES PLAYWRITING COMPETITION

Texas Woman's University, Dept. of Music and Drama, Box 23865, Denton, TX 76204
(817) 383-3586 Contact: Mary Lou Hoyle, Chairman, Selection Committee **Frequency**: annual **Award**: $1000, production **Works**: full-length plays, one-acts **Special interest**: "Plays which are about women or feature women in leading roles." **Regulations**: entries must be unpublished and unproduced **Specifications**: small cast, simple set **Audience**: "Small but enthusiastic." **Procedure**: request guidelines **Deadline**: Feb. 1, 1989 **Notification**: Apr. 1989 **Your chances**: 250/3/1

MARC A. KLEIN PLAYWRITING AWARD

Dept. of Theatre, Case Western Reserve University, 2070 Adelbert Rd., Cleveland, OH 44106
(216) 368-2858 Contact: Robert Ornstein, Acting Chair, Dept. of Theatre **Frequency**: annual **Award**: $500, production, staged reading, travel ($500); all entries considered for staged reading **Works**: full-length plays, single and related one-acts, musicals **Regulations**: authors must be enrolled in U.S. colleges or universities; entries must be unpublished, unproduced and endorsed by a teacher of drama, a member of a theatre department, a critic, a director or another playwright **Procedure**: request guidelines **Deadline**: Apr. 1, 1989 **Notification**: mid-May 1989 **Your chances**: 35/3/3

MARVIN TAYLOR PLAYWRITING AWARD

Sierra Repertory Theatre, Box 3030, Sonora, CA 95370 (209) 532-3120
Contact: Contest Director **Frequency**: annual **Award**: $400, production **Works**: full-length plays, translations, adaptations, musicals **Regulations**: entries must have had no more than 2 productions; no more than 1 entry per author **Specifications**: maximum cast: 15; no more than 2 sets **Stages**: proscenium, 99 seats; thrust, 99 seats **Audience**: "Rural, caucasian, 30's-60's, large percentage seniors." **Procedure**: send script **Deadline**: May 15, 1989 postmark **Notification**: Sept. 1, 1989 **Your chances**: 200/3/1-3

MAUDE ADAMS PLAYWRITING CONTEST

Stephens College, Columbia, MO 65215
(314) 876-7193 Contact: Addison Myers, Project Director **Frequency**: annual **Award**: $750, public reading, travel, possible production **Works**: full-length plays **Special interest**: "Plays by women, speaking to women's issues." **Regulations**: entries must not be published or professionally produced **Stages**: proscenium, 350 seats; thrust, 250 seats **Procedure**: request guidelines **Deadline**: Jan. 15, 1989 **Notification**: Feb. 15, 1989 **Your chances**: 350/3/3

MAXWELL ANDERSON
PLAYWRIGHTS SERIES PRIZE

Stamford, CT   This contest has been discontinued.

McDONALD'S LITERARY ACHIEVEMENT AWARDS

Negro Ensemble Company,
1560 Broadway Suite 409, New York, NY 10036
(212) 575-5860 Contact: Leon Denmark, Producing Director **Frequency**: annual **Award**: $2000, developmental workshop, staged reading, travel to New York City **Works**: full-length plays, one-acts **Regulations**: authors must not have had work professionally produced; entries must be at least 20 pages in length and must deal with "the Black experience in America" **Procedure**: send script with bio and list of productions **Deadline**: inquire

MERRIMACK REPERTORY THEATRE
PLAYWRITING CONTEST

Box 228, Lowell, MA 01853 (617) 454-6324
Contact: David G. Kent, Literary Manager/Dramaturg **Frequency:** annual **Awards:** 6 finalists will receive workshop productions; 1 play will be chosen for 1989-90 MRT season **Works:** full-length plays **Special interests:** social issues **Regulations:** authors must be residents of ME, NH, VT, MA, RI or CT; entries must be unproduced **Stage:** thrust, 386 seats **Audience:** "Boston area." **Procedure:** request guidelines **Deadline:** Feb. 1, 1989 **Notification:** Jun. 1, 1989 **Your chances:** 300/6/1-2 or more **Advice:** "Not avant garde." **Comment:** The judges reserve the right to withhold the award if, in their opinion, no entry merits it.

MIDSOUTH PLAYWRIGHTS CONTEST
**Playhouse on the Square, 51 S. Cooper,
Memphis, TN 38104** (901) 725-0776, 726-4498
Contact: Jackie Nichols, Executive Director **Frequency**:
annual **Award**: $500, production **Works**: full-length plays
Regulations: entries must be unproduced and uncommitted
Specifications: maximum cast: 10; single or unit set
Stage: proscenium **Audience**: "20-50, college educated."
Procedure: send script **Deadline**: Apr. 1, 1989 postmark
Notification: Jul. 1989 **Your chances**: 500/10/3

MILLER AWARD 1989
**Deep South Writers Conference, Box 44691,
University of Southwestern Louisiana,
Lafayette, LA 70504**
Contact: John Fiero, Director **Frequency**: annual **Award**:
$1500, consideration for adaptability to TV **Works**:
full-length plays **Regulations**: works must deal with some
aspect of the life of Edward de Vere, Earl of Oxford, and/or the
English Renaissance **Procedure**: request guidelines
Deadline: Jul. 15, 1989 **Notification**: Sept. 1989 **Your
chances**: 7 in 1988/2 plus tie-breaking 3rd reader if
necessary/2 **Comment**: The judges reserve the right to
withhold the award if, in their opinion, no entry merits it.

MILL MOUNTAIN THEATRE
NEW PLAY COMPETITION
**1 Market Square, Center in the Square,
Roanoke, VA 24011** (703) 342-5730
Contact: Jo Weinstein, Literary Manager **Frequency**: annual
Award: $500, staged reading, stipend, possible production
Works: full-length plays, single and related one-acts **Special
interest**: "Mixed casts, but not to the exclusion of others."
Regulations: authors must reside in U.S.; entries must be
unpublished and unproduced except in developmental workshops;
no more than 2 entries per author **Specifications**: maximum
cast: 12; unit set preferred **Stages**: proscenium, 462 seats;
flexible, 100 seats **Audience**: "A conservative and provincial
community." **Procedure**: request guidelines **Deadline**: Jan.
1, 1989 **Notification**: Jun. 1, 1989 **Your chances**:
250/5/2-3 **Advice**: "Present your own play in a neat
professional manner."

MIXED BLOOD VERSUS AMERICA

Mixed Blood Theatre Company, 1501 S. 4th St., **Minneapolis, MN 55454 (612) 338-0937 Contact**: Jack Reuler, Artistic Director **Frequency**: annual **Award**: $2000, production **Works:** full-length plays, musicals **Regulations**: authors must have had at least 1 work produced by a professional or educational theatre (workshop production qualifies); no more than 2 entries per author **Procedure:** send script with resume or other proof of previously produced work **Deadline**: Apr. 15, 1989 **Notification**: fall 1989

THE MOBIL PLAYWRITING COMPETITION

The Royal Exchange Theatre Company, St. Ann's Square, Manchester M2 7DH, England (061) 833-9333, -9938 Contact: David Fraser, Press & Publicity Director **Frequency**: periodic **Awards**: 1st prize £10,000, 2nd prize £5000, 3rd prize £3000, international prize £3000, special prizes £1000; possible production with negotiable payment, possible publication, possible 1-year residency at Royal Exchange Theatre **Works accepted**: full-length plays **Regulations**: authors may be of any nationality; entries must be written in English, unproduced and not on offer elsewhere **Procedure**: request guidelines **Deadline**: inquire (Jan. 16 in 1988)

THE MORTON R. SARETT MEMORIAL AWARD FOR THE JERRY L. CRAWFORD PLAYWRITING COMPETITION

Dept. of Theatre Arts, University of Nevada-Las Vegas, 4505 Maryland Pkwy., Las Vegas, NV 89154 (702) 739-3666 Contact: Paul Harris, Professor of Theatre **Frequency**: biennial, even years **Award**: $3000, production **Works accepted**: full-length plays **Regulations**: entries must be unproduced **Stages:** proscenium, 570 seats; black box, 180 seats **Audience:** "Students and season subscribers." **Procedure**: request guidelines and application form; 2 copies of script required **Deadline**: inquire **Your chances:** 300/25-30 judges **Comment:** "An announced winner is not mandatory for every playwriting competition."

MULTICULTURAL PLAYWRIGHTS FESTIVAL

The Group Theatre Company, 3940 Brooklyn Ave. NE, Seattle, WA 98105 (206) 545-4969
Contact: Tim Bond, Festival Director **Frequency**: annual **Award**: $1000, workshop productions, rehearsed readings, development, travel, housing **Works**: full-length plays, single one-acts, adaptations **Regulations**: "Authors must be Asian, Black, Chicano/Hispanic or Native American and must be U.S. citizens or residents of at least 3 weeks"; entries must not have been professionally produced **Specifications**: maximum cast: 10 preferred; small sets **Stage**: modified thrust, 200-213 seats **Audience**: "Middle income, ethnically diverse." **Procedure**: send script with resume **Deadline**: Oct. 15, 1989 postmark **Notification**: Feb. 1990 **Your chances**: 200/9/1-8 **Advice**: "Send us your entries by late Sept., to avoid the last minute rush."

MYSTERY PLAY COMPETITION

The Theatre Wing of the Actors Center of Los Angeles, 11969 Ventura Blvd., Dept. 828, Studio City, CA 91604 (818) 508-3721
Contact: Pamela Printy, Contest Coordinator **Award**: $300, possible production **Works**: full-length plays **Exclusive interest**: comedies and dramas in the mystery/thriller/courtroom/international intrigue genre **Regulations**: entries must be at least 90 minutes in length, unpublished, unoptioned and unproduced (except by schools or without payment to author or actors and without an admission charge); no more than 1 entry per author **Procedure**: request guidelines and application form **Deadline**: Mar. 31, 1989 **Notification**: fall 1989 **Comment**: The judges reserve the right to select no winner.

NATIONAL ARCHIVES PLAYWRITING COMPETITION

National Archives and Records Administration, Educational Branch, NEE-E, National Archives, Washington, DC 20408 Contact: Cynthia Hightower, Public Affairs Specialist **Frequency**: annual **Awards**: 1st prize $450, 2nd prize $250; possible production **Works**: one-act plays and musicals **Exclusive interest**: "Scripts must be based on any event(s) within the past 200 years which deal with the issues raised by the Bill of Rights or issues raised by the 14th and 15th Amendments." **Regulations**: entries must be unpublished and unproduced and "must be based on records held by National Archives, and/or its field branches, and/or any of the presidential libraries" **Specifications:** maximum cast: 6-8; few scenes, minimal set and lighting requirements; no fly space; no front curtain; one wing 3'x6'; playing time: 45-90 minutes **Stage:** 26' wide by 12'6" deep **Audience:** "Interested in historic plays; general public, educators." **Procedure:** request guidelines **Deadline:** Jan. 15, 1990 **Notification:** Apr. 1990 **Your chances:** "Unknown number, as this is the first year of the contest/10/4."

NATIONAL CHILDREN'S THEATRE PLAYWRITING COMPETITION
Indianapolis, IN   See Indiana University-Purdue University at Indianapolis Children's Theatre Playwriting Competition.

NATIONAL CONTEST FOR LATINO PLAYS/CONCURSO NACIONAL PARA OBRAS DE THEATRO LATINO
New York Shakespeare Festival, 425 Lafayette St., New York, NY 10003   This contest is inactive in 1989.

NATIONAL ONE-ACT PLAY CONTEST
Actors Theatre of Louisville,   316 W. Main St., Louisville, KY 40202 (502) 584-1265
Contact: Michael Bigelow Dixon, Literary Manager **Frequency:** annual **Award:** $1000, possible production with royalty, travel, housing **Works:** single and related one-acts **Regulations:** authors must be citizens or residents or U.S.; entries must not be published or professionally produced **Stages:** thrust, 650 seats; thrust, 150 seats **Audience:** "A cross-section of the Louisville community." **Procedure:** request guidelines **Deadline:** Apr. 15, 1989 postmark **Notification:** winter 1989-90 **Your chances:** 160/ATL staff/2 **Advice:** "See contest rules in brochure."

NATIONAL ONE-ACT PLAYWRITING COMPETITION
Little Theatre of Alexandria,   600 Wolfe St., Alexandria, VA 22314 (703) 683-5778
Contact: Chairman **Frequency:** annual **Awards:** 1st prize $350, 2nd prize $250, 3rd prize $150; possible production **Works:** single one-acts **Exclusive interest:** "Stage plays only!"   **Regulations:** entries must be unpublished and

unproduced; no more than 1 entry per author **Specifications:** single set preferred; few scene changes **Stage:** proscenium, 210 seats **Audience:** "Sophisticated theatre audience; conservative." **Procedure:** send script **Deadline**: Mar. 31, 1989 postmark **Notification:** Dec. 1989 **Your chances:** 100/6-8/4-6 **Advice:** Criteria for judging are concept, dramatic action, characterization, dialogue, stageability and technical requirements; "judges are favorably inclined toward scripts which have a running time of 20-60 minutes; in which a precis of the play precedes abstract works; and in which a description of each character appears, either at the beginning or as each character first appears on stage." **Comment:** Theatre reserves the right to withhold any or all awards.

NATIONAL PLAY AWARD
National Repertory Theatre Foundation, Box 71011, Los Angeles, CA 90071 (213) 629-3762
Contact: David Parrish, Assistant Literary Manager **Frequency**: biennial even years **Awards**: $7500 to playwright; $5000 to qualified professional theatre to aid production **Works:** full-length plays, single and related one-acts **Exclusive interest**: "Original plays conceived for production on the living stage." **Regulations**: entries must not be published or professionally produced and may not have won a major award; previous entries ineligible **Procedure**: request guidelines **Deadline**: inquire **Your chances:** 1500-2000/15/2

NATIONAL PLAYWRIGHTS CONFERENCE/ NEW DRAMA FOR TELEVISION PROJECT
Eugene O'Neill Memorial Theater Center Suite 901, 234 W. 44th St., New York, NY 10036
(212) 382-2790 Contact: Peggy Vernieu, Administrator **Frequency**: annual **Award**: development, staged reading or videotaping, stipend, travel, housing and board for Conference in Waterford, CT **Works:** full-length plays, single and related one-acts **Regulations**: authors must be U.S. residents; entries must be unproduced and uncommitted; adaptations ineligible **Procedure**: request guidelines from New York office in Sept. 1989 **Deadline**: Dec. 1, 1989 postmark **Notification:** Apr. 1990 **Your chances:** 1100+/varying number of judges and readings

NATIONAL PLAYWRIGHTS SHOWCASE
Mercyhurst College, Glenwood Hills, Erie, PA 16546 (814) 825-0200 Contact: Paul C. Iddings, Director **Frequency**: annual **Award**: staged reading, production, expenses to attend reading and production, videotape **Works:** full-length plays, one-acts, musicals, children's plays **Regulations**: entries must be unproduced **Specifications**: maximum cast: 15; no more than 10 musicians; no more than 2 sets **Procedure:** send script **Deadline**: Jun. 1, 1989 **Comment:** A critique is available for $75.

NCSC AWARD IN THE ARTS
Washington, DC This contest has been discontinued.

NEW AMERICAN COMEDY FESTIVAL
Ukiah Players Theatre, Box 705, Ukiah, CA 95482 (707) 462-1210 Contact: Lesley Schisgall **Frequency**: annual **Awards**: $150 staged reading, expenses (up to $300), lodging, per diem for 3 winners; $100, production of Grand Prize winner **Works:** full-length comedies **Regulations**: entries must be unpublished and unproduced; winning playwrights must attend Festival, Aug. 1989 **Specifications**: small cast, simple set preferred **Stage:** proscenium, 133 seats **Procedure:** request guidelines and application form **Deadline**: Feb. 1, 1989 postmark **Notification**: May 1989 **Comment:** "1.5% of future royalties on any script chosen for production will become the property of Ukiah Players Theatre."

THE NEW PLAY FESTIVAL
OF THE COLONY/STUDIO THEATRE PLAYHOUSE
Los Angeles, CA This contest has been discontinued.

NEW WORLD THEATER NEW PLAY COMPETITION
7600 Red Rd. Suite 212, South Miami, FL 33143-5424 (305) 663-0208 Contact: Kenneth A. Cotthoff, Executive Director **Frequency**: annual **Awards**: $500, production for as many as 3 winners; possible public readings of finalists **Works:** full-length plays **Regulations**: entries must not be published or professionally produced **Special interests:** Florida locations or themes; interracial and/or inter-ethnic casts;

strong female roles **Specifications**: maximum cast: 4; single full set, "may have minor secondary or several minimal sets"; modest production requirements **Procedure**: request guidelines **Deadline**: May 1, 1989 **Notification**: Oct. 1989 **Comments**: "In addition to the usual elements of plot, characterization, dialogue, etc., plays will be judges in the following areas: entertainment value, relevance in today's world, broadness of appeal." "Authors must be willing to see play developed in workshop!" New World Theatre claims "customary subsidiary rights" to winning plays.

NFJC HEBREW TRANSLATION COMMISSION
National Foundation for Jewish Culture, 330 Seventh Ave. 21st Floor, New York, NY 10001 (212) 629-0500 Contact: Andrea Aronson Morgan, Program Officer **Frequency**: ongoing program **Award**: up to $1000 to be matched by producing theatre **Works**: translations **Regulations**: entries must be first translations or first stageworthy translations into English of Hebrew plays **Procedure**: nomination by theatre interested in producing translation; request guidelines

NORTHBAY PLAYWRIGHTING CONTEST
Dept. of Theatre Arts, Sonoma State University, Rohnert Park, CA 94928   (707) 664-2474 Contact: Elizabeth Craven, Project Director **Frequency**: biennial even years **Award**: $1000, production **Works**: full-length plays, adaptations **Regulations**: entries must be unpublished and unproduced; adaptations must be of material in the public domain; winning author must be available for 2-week residency **Procedure**: request guidelines and application form; $10 fee upon entry **Deadline**: inquire (Oct. 1 in 1988)

NORTH CAROLINA PLAYWRIGHTS COMPETITION
Greenville, NC   This contest has been discontinued.

OFF-OFF BROADWAY
ORIGINAL SHORT PLAY FESTIVAL
Double Image Theatre, 444 W. 56th St., New York, NY 10019 (212) 245-2489 Contact: William Talbot, Festival Coordinator **Frequency**: annual **Award**: production, publication **Works**: one-act plays, translations, adaptations, musicals and children's plays

Regulations: entries must be unpublished, 40 minutes in length and products of workshops or programs for playwrights **Stage**: proscenium, thrust, flexible—99 seats **Audience**: "New York City across the board." **Procedure**: nomination by theatres; request guidelines **Deadline**: Apr. 1989 (inquire) **Notification**: Apr. 1989 **Your chances**: 140/6 judges

ONES AT EIGHT ANNUAL ONE-ACT FESTIVAL
Virginia Beach Parks and Recreation, Virginia Beach Recreation Center, Kempsville, 800 Monmouth Ln., Virginia Beach, VA 23464-2998 (804) 495-1892 **Contact**: Eileen Gatliffe, Coordinator **Awards**: production, plaque, for each of 3 winners **Works**: one-acts **Special interests**: realistic comedies and/or dramas **Regulations**: entries must be 30-45 minutes in length **Specifications**: maximum cast: 6; no complicated technical demands; no strong language or adult situations **Audience**: family-oriented **Procedure**: request guidelines **Deadline**: fall 1989 (inquire) **Your chances**: 60-70/6/3-5

ON THEMES OF RURAL AMERICA: ARROW ROCK LYCEUM'S 3RD NATIONAL PLAYWRIGHTS COMPETITION
Main St., Arrow Rock, MO 65320 (816) 837-3311 **Contact:** Michael Bollinger, Artistic Producing Director **Frequency:** annual **Award:** $1000, possible production, transportation **Works:** full-length plays **Regulations:** entries must be unpublished and unproduced and must deal with rural or small-town America **Procedure:** request guidelines **Deadline:** Jan. 1989 (inquire) **Comment:** This competition normally receives approximately 300 entries.

PAUL T. NOLAN AWARD
Deep South Writers Conference, USL Box 44691, University of Southwestern Louisiana, Lafayette, LA 70504 Contact: Joen Fiero, Director **Frequency:** annual **Award**: $100, possible production, possible publication **Works:** one-acts **Regulations**: entries must be original plays; no more than 3 entries per author **Procedure:** request guidelines; $5 fee upon entry **Deadline**: Jul. 15, 1989 **Notification:** "Just prior to deep South Writers Conference in Sept." **Your chances:** 50/"usually 3/3 for winning play and runners-up"

PEACE PLAY CONTEST

Goshen College, Theatre Office, Goshen, IN 46526
(219) 533-3161 Contact: Lauren Friesen, Director of Theatre **Frequency**: biennial odd years **Award**: $200, possible production **Works**: single and related one-acts **Regulations**: entries must not be published or professionally produced and must deal with peace and conflict resolution **Maximum cast**: 8 **Stage**: proscenium, thrust--400 seats **Audience**: "College faculty and students." **Procedure**: request guidelines **Deadline**: inquire **Your chances**: 100/3/4

PEPPERDINE UNIVERSITY PLAY COMPETITION

Theatre Dept., Pepperdine University,
Malibu, CA 90265 This contest is inactive in 1989.

PLAYWRIGHT FOCUS

93 Sixth Ave., Brooklyn, NY 11217
(718) 638-5725 Contact: Jack Kaplan, President **Frequency**: annual **Award**: production **Works**: full-length plays, one-acts, adaptations, musicals, children's plays **Regulations**: authors must currently reside in Brooklyn **Specifications**: small cast, simple set preferred **Stage**: proscenium **Audience**: "All ages." **Procedure**: send script **Deadline**: "Plays should be submitted in the spring and will be read only May-Aug."

THE PLAYWRIGHT'S COMPANION AWARDS

Bloomington, IN This contest has been discontinued.

PLAYWRIGHT'S FORUM AWARDS

Theatreworks, University of Colorado, Box 7150, Colorado Springs, CO 80933 **(719) 593-3232, -3275 Contact**: Whit Andrews, Producing Director **Frequency**: annual **Awards**: 2 awards of $200, production, travel ($350) **Works**: single and related one-acts **Special interests**: "Experimental work and comedy." **Regulations**: entries must be unpublished and unproduced; no more than 60 minutes in length; no more than 2 entries per author **Specifications**: maximum cast: 12; modest technical requirements **Stage**: thrust, 185 seats **Audience**: "Diverse." **Procedure**: request guidelines **Deadline**: Dec. 15, 1989 **Notification**: Feb. 15, 1990 **Your chances**:

800/10/2 **Advice:** "We like passion, theatricality, risk taking; honest dialogue as opposed to an attempt to impress; plays that end instead of just petering out. A little good, old fashioned outrageousness doesn't hurt, either."

PORTLAND STATE UNIVERSITY
NEW PLAYS IN PROGRESS SERIES
Dept. of Theatre Arts, Box 751, Portland, OR 97207 (503) 229-4612
Contact: Pauline E. Peotter, Director **Frequency:** annual **Award:** production with royalty, residency **Works:** full-length plays, one-acts **Regulations:** authors must be residents of OR or WA; entries must be unproduced; no more than 1 entry per author; authors must attend at least 1 week of rehearsals (local authors must attend 6 weeks) during Oct.–Nov. 1989 **Procedure:** request guidelines **Deadline:** Jan. 11, 1989 **Notification:** spring 1989

PURGATORY THEATER
NATIONAL PLAYWRITING COMPETITION
Box 666, Durango, CO 81302
(303) 247-9000 ext. 231 **Contact:** Ron Sanford, Executive Producer **Frequency:** annual **Award:** $200, production **Works:** full-length plays **Regulations:** authors must be U.S. citizens; works must be unpublished and unproduced and must not have won a major award; no more than 1 entry per author **Specifications:** maximum cast: 10; "no nudity, no obscenity, no issues or activities included for shock value only" **Stage:** platform-thrust **Audience:** "Mainly adults, resort oriented." **Procedure:** request guidelines **Deadline:** inquire **Advice:** "Only the first 250 entries will be considered."

QRL POETRY SERIES
Quarterly Review of Literature, **Princeton University, 26 Haslet Ave., Princeton, NJ 08540 (609) 921-6976**
Frequency: annual **Award:** $1000, publication **Works:** full-length plays, single and related one-acts, translations **Regulations:** entries must be "poetic plays," 40-89 pages in length **Procedure:** request guidelines; $20 fee upon entry includes subscription **Deadlines:** May 1989, Oct. 1989 (inquire)

RADIO DRAMA AWARDS
Wisconsin Public Radio Association,
3319 W. Beltline Hwy., Madison, WI 53713
(608) 273-5500   Contact: Norman Michie, Executive Producer **Frequency**: annual **Awards**: 1st prize $500, 2nd prize $300, 3rd prize $200; production for broadcast on Wisconsin Public Radio, complimentary tape **Works:** radio plays **Regulations**: authors must be residents of IA, IL, MI, MN or WI; entries must be 30 minutes in length **Maximum cast**: 5-6 major characters **Procedure**: request guidelines and application form **Deadline**: Jan. 31, 1989 **Advice:** "Don't let the word 'drama' limit your creativity. Light comedies, verse, documentaries, even biographies may be submitted."

REGIONAL CHILDREN'S THEATRE COMPETITION 1989
Columbia Entertainment Company, 1411 St. Andrew, Columbia, MO 65203   Contact: Deborah Baldwin **Frequency:**   annual **Award**: $250, production in Dec. 1989 **Works:** full-length plays, musicals **Special interests:** "We are seeking plays for children with at least 10 major roles and roles for up to 20 children." **Regulations**: entries must be unpublished and unproduced except in staged readings and/or workshop productions **Specifications**:   large casts (maximum cast: 30) of students aged 8-15; simple sets; no "cute animal stories" or adaptations; low budget; "children will be moving set pieces; costumes can be built; however, we prefer to use what we have in stock or what the children can bring from home" **Stage:**   180 seats; "primarily we work on a thrust or proscenium" **Audience:** "Parents, general public and children median age 12 years." **Procedure:** request guidelines **Deadline**: Jun. 30, 1989 **Notification:** Aug. 15, 1989 **Your chances:** 28 1st year/5/3 **Advice:** "Please remember that young people (ages 10-15) enjoy portraying diverse human or fantastical beings. They are sophisticated and wise and have experienced many of life's lessons at earlier ages than adults (i.e. divorce, death, drugs, suicides, etc.)." **Comment:** "This is our second year."

RENATO POGGIOLI TRANSLATION AWARD
PEN American Center, 568 Broadway,
New York, NY 10012 (212) 334-1660
Contact: Christine Friedlander **Frequency**: annual **Award**: $3000 grant **Works**: translations **Special interest**: "The focus of the prize is on Italian translation, not plays." **Regulations**: award is for "a beginning and promising translator working on his or her first book-length translation from Italian into English" **Procedure:** send letters of application, curriculum vitae including the candidate's Italian studies, statement of purpose, sample of translation with original Italian text **Deadline**: Feb. 1, 1989 postmark **Notification**: May 1989 **Comment:** It is preferred that the grant period be spent in Italy.

THE RICHARD RODGERS PRODUCTION AWARD
American Academy and Institute of Arts and Letters, 633 W. 155th St., New York, NY 10032 (212) 368-5900   **Contact**: Lydia Kaim, Assistant to the Executive Director **Frequency**: annual **Award**: up to $80,000 and/or developmental grants of up to $15,000 for workshop productions by New York City not-for-profit theatres **Works**: musicals **Regulations**: authors must be citizens or permanent residents of U.S.; entries must not have been commercially produced; no more than 1 entry per author; previous entries ineligible **Procedure:** request guidelines and application form **Deadline**: Nov. 1, 1989 **Your chances:** 180/9 judges **Advice:**   "The submission of innovative and experimental work is encouraged."

ROBERT J. PICKERING AWARD
FOR PLAYWRITING EXCELLENCE
Coldwater Community Theater, 89 S. Division, Coldwater, MI 49036 (517) 278-2389, 279-7963
Contact: J. Richard Colbeck, Chairman, Play Selection Committee **Frequency**: annual **Awards**: 1st prize $200, production, housing to attend performance, production agreement; 2nd prize $50; 3rd prize $25 **Works:** full-length plays **Exclusive interest**: works of interest to a Midwestern audience **Regulations**: entries must be unproduced **Stage:**   proscenium, 500 seats **Procedure:** request guidelines **Deadline**: Nov. 15, 1989 **Notification:** Jan. 1990 **Your chances:** 125/6/6

RUBY LLOYD APSEY
NATIONAL PLAYWRITING COMPETITION
**University of Alabama at Birmingham,
Dept. of Theatre & Dance, University Station,
Birmingham, AL 35294 (205) 934-3236**
Contact: D. Ward Haarbauer, Director of Contest **Frequency**: annual **Award**: $500, possible production with residency **Works**: full-length plays **Regulations**: entries must be unproduced except in staged readings **Procedure**: request guidelines and application form **Deadline**: Jan. 1, 1989 **Notification**: Jun. 1989 **Comment**: The judges reserve the right to select no winner.

SCHOLASTIC WRITING AWARDS
**730 Broadway, New York, NY 10003
(212) 505-3404 Contact**: Chuck Wentzel
Frequency: annual **Awards**: cash prizes of $50 and $125; 2 $1000-scholarships **Works**: one-act plays, screenplays and radio and TV scripts **Regulations**: authors must be students in grades 7-12; entries must be unpublished, unproduced and 30 minutes in length **Procedure**: request guidelines and application form **Deadline**: Jan. 14, 1989 **Notification**: May 1989 **Your chances**: 1500/3/3 **Advice**: "For young playwrights: edit, edit, edit. Be medium specific when writing."

SEAGRAM'S NEW MUSIC THEATER AWARDS PROGRAM
**National Music Theater Network, 1457 Broadway
Suite 1111, New York, NY 10036 (212) 382-0984**
Contact: C. Carroll Carter, Jr., Executive Director **Frequency**: annual **Awards**: $1000 to writer/composer team; $4000 to first theatre to produce work **Works**: musicals, operas **Regulations**: authors must be American writers and composers; entries must appeal to a general audience **Procedure**: request guidelines and application form; $30 fee upon entry **Deadline**: Jun. 1989 (inquire) **Notification**: Jul. 1989

SERGEL DRAMA PRIZE
**Court Theatre, 5706 S. University Ave.,
Chicago, IL 60637 (312) 702-7005** This contest is inactive in 1989.

SETC NEW PLAY PROJECT
Dept. of Performing Arts, Clemson University, Clemson, SC 29634-1505 (803) 656-3446
Contact: Clifton S. M. Egan, Chairman, New Play Project **Frequency**: annual **Award**: $250, staged reading, travel, publicity and recommendation to the O'Neill Theater Center (see National Playwrights Conference listing in this section) **Works**: full-length plays, related one-acts **Regulations**: entries must be unpublished and unproduced **Procedure**: request guidelines **Deadline**: Jul. 31, 1989; no submission before Mar. 15 **Notification**: Oct. 1989 **Your chances**: 100/5/1 initial, 3 final

SIENA COLLEGE PLAYWRIGHT'S COMPETITION
Theatre Program, Dept. of Fine Arts, Siena College, Loudonville, NY 12211 (518) 783-2381
Contact: Mark A. Heckler, Director of Theatre **Frequency**: biennial even years **Award**: $2000, production, up to $1000 for travel and housing **Works**: full-length plays **Regulations**: entries must be unpublished and unproduced; winning author must participate in 4-week residency program, Jan.-Feb. 1991 **Specifications**: maximum cast: 10, 3-6 preferred; single or unit set; no musicals **Stages**: proscenium; thrust **Audience**: college and local community **Procedure**: before entering send notification of entry including play title, author's name, address, phone number, resume and SASE (inquire for more details after Nov. 1, 1989) **Deadline**: Feb. 1, 1990 postmark **Your chances**: 300+/3/1-3 **Advice**: "Submit scripts suitable for undergraduate theatre students who are part of a liberal arts rather than pre-professional training program."

THE SOCIETY OF MIDLAND AUTHORS DRAMA AWARD
851 Warrington Rd., Deerfield, IL 60015 (312) 945-6351 Contact: Jane R. Howard, Chairman **Frequency**: annual **Award**: $300 presented at annual banquet **Works**: full-length plays **Regulations**: authors must be current residents of IA, IL, IN, KS, MI, MN, MO, ND, NE, OH, SD or WI; entries must have been first produced professionally in 1988 **Procedure**: request guidelines and application form **Deadline**: Jan. 15, 1989 **Notification**: spring 1989 **Your chances**: varying number/3/3

SOURCE THEATRE
NATIONAL PLAYWRITING COMPETITION
1809 14th St. NW, Washington, DC 20009
(202) 462-1073   Contact: Keith Parker, Literary Manager **Frequency**: annual   **Awards**: 1st prize $250, production; finalists $50, workshop production; honorable mention $25, reading **Works**: full-length plays, one-acts, musicals **Regulations**: entries must not have been professionally produced   **Procedure**: send script with synopsis and resume   **Deadline**: Mar. 15, 1989 **Notification**: mid-Apr. 1989 **Comment**: "A play entered in the contest will be considered for the reading series and other festival production opportunities."

SOUTHEASTERN PLAYWRIGHTS COMPETITION
Greenville, NC   This contest has been discontinued.

STANLEY DRAMA AWARD
Wagner College, 631 Howard Ave.,
Staten Island, NY 10301   (718) 390-3256
Contact: Bill Bly, Director   **Frequency**: annual   **Award**: $1000, possible production **Works**: full-length plays, related one-acts, musicals **Regulations**: entries must not be published or professionally produced; former Stanley winners ineligible; entries must be recommended by a theatre professional or teacher of creative writing or drama **Procedure**: request guidelines and application form **Deadline**: Sept. 1, 1989 postmark **Notification**: Mar. 1990 **Your chances**: 100/10/1-4

SUSIE BARKER PLAYWRITING PROGRAM
Omaha, NE   This contest has been discontinued.

TCG HISPANIC TRANSLATION COMMISSION
Theatre Communications Group,
355 Lexington Ave., New York, NY 10017
(212) 697-5230   Contact: Director of Literary Services **Frequency**: ongoing program   **Award**: up to $1000 to be matched by producing TCG member theatre   **Works**: translations **Special interest:** "Hispanic drama, not in English, from all countries and historical periods." **Regulations**: entries must be either first translations or first

stageworthy translations into English of works from any Hispanic culture **Procedure:** TCG member theatre interested in producing translation may apply; no applications from translators **Your chances:** varying number/3-5/3-5 **Advice:** "Contact TCG theatres if you have a specific project in mind."

THE TEN-MINUTE MUSICALS PROJECT
Box 461194, West Hollywood, CA 90046
(213) 656-8751 Contact: Michael Koppy, Producer **Award:** $250, development towards production in a collection **Works:** musical scenes **Specifications:** entries must be 5-15 minutes in length; excerpts from full-length works must be "completely self-contained," and the full-length work must be unproduced **Procedure:** request guidelines (phone calls are accepted) **Deadline:** Feb. 1, 1989 **Comment:** "Works selected may be amalgamated with similar efforts already collected by the New York Shakespeare Festival" (see listing in Theatres).

TENNESSEE WILLIAMS/NEW ORLEANS LITERARY FESTIVAL ONE-ACT PLAY CONTEST
Dept. of English, University of New Orleans, New Orleans, LA 70148 (504) 949-9805
Contact: W. Kenneth Holditch, Board of Directors **Award:** $500, reading **Works:** one-acts **Exclusive interest:** American subjects **Regulations:** entries must not be published or professionally produced **Audience:** general **Procedure:** send script with $5 fee (check payable to Tennessee Williams Literary Festival) **Deadline:** Feb. 1, 1989 **Notification:** Apr. 1, 1989 **Your chances:** 200+/3/2

THEATRE MEMPHIS NEW PLAY COMPETITION
630 Perkins St. Extended, Memphis, TN 38117-4799 (901) 682-8323
Contact: Martha Graber, Iris Dichtel, Co-Chair, New Play Competition **Frequency:** triennial **Award:** $2500, production **Works:** full-length plays, related one-acts, musicals **Regulations:** entries must not have been professionally produced **Audience:** "Upper middle class, middle aged." **Procedure:** request guidelines; $20 fee upon entry **Deadline:** Oct. 1, 1989 **Notification:** early 1990

Your chances: 500/50/2-10 **Comments:** "We are not encouraging musicals but will accept them." "Theatre Memphis reserves the right to withhold a first place prize if the selection committee does not feel there is an entry meriting the award."

THEATRE SOUTHWEST PLAYWRITING COMPETITION

3767 Harper St., Houston, TX 77005 This contest in inactive in 1989.

THEATREWORKS/USA COMMISSIONING PROGRAM

131 W. 86th St., New York, NY 10024
(212) 595-7500 Contact: Barbara Pasternack, Literary Manager **Frequency:** ongoing program **Award:** step commissioning process, production **Works:** children's musicals **Special interests:** historical and biographical topics; adaptations of classics and contemporary literature **Regulations:** works must be 1 hour in length and relevant to young and family audiences **Specifications:** maximum cast: 5-6 with doubling; set suitable for touring **Procedure:** send script or treatment with sample scenes **Advice:** "It's a good idea to contact us for a schedule of New York City performances to see the kind of work we do."

THEODORE WARD PRIZE FOR PLAYWRITING

Columbia College Chicago, Theatre/Music Center, 72 E. 11th St., Chicago, IL 60605 (312) 663-9462
Contact: Steven Long, Facilitator **Frequency:** annual **Awards:** 1st prize $2000, production, travel, housing; 2nd prize $500, staged reading, audio tape **Works:** full-length plays **Regulations:** authors must be Afro-American residents of U.S.; entries must not be professionally produced and must be copyrighted; no more than 1 entry per author **Stage:** black box, 70 seats **Procedure:** send script, synopsis, resume, script history **Deadline:** Jul. 2, 1989 postmark **Notification:** Oct. 15, 1989 **Your chances:** 75/5/varying number

TOWNGATE THEATRE PLAYWRITING CONTEST

Oglebay Institute, Oglebay, Wheeling, WV 26003
(304) 242-4200 Contact: Debbie Hynes, Performing Arts Specialist **Frequency:** annual **Award:** $300, production,

some travel **Works:** full-length plays **Regulations**: entries must not be published or professionally produced **Specifications**: no grid or fly space **Stage:** proscenium, 171 seats **Procedure:** request guidelines **Deadline**: Jan. 1, 1989 postmark **Notification:** May 1, 1989 **Your chances:** 70-100/8-10/1 or more **Comment:** "Oglebay Institute reserves the right to withhold the award if, in the judges' opinion, no entry merits it."

TOWSON STATE UNIVERSITY PRIZE FOR LITERATURE
College of Liberal Arts, Towson, MD 21204
(301) 321-2128 Contact: Annette Chappell, Dean, College of Liberal Arts **Frequency**: annual **Award**: $1000 **Works:** single plays, collections **Regulations**: authors must be MD residents not over 40 years of age; entries must be published books **Procedure:** request guidelines and application form **Deadline**: May 1, 1989 postmark **Notification:** Aug. 1, 1989 **Your chances:** 10-15 entries/9 judges **Comment:** Books entered are not returned.

24TH STREET EXPERIMENT ANNUAL PLAYWRIGHT COMPETITION
Our Lady of the Lake University,
411 Southwest 24th St., San Antonio, TX 78285
(512) 435-2103 Contact: Lauri Bartlett **Frequency**: annual **Awards**: $200; staged reading for winner and 3 runners-up **Works:** full-length plays, one-acts, translations, adaptations, musicals, operas **Exclusive interest**: contemporary themes presented in new and interesting formats **Regulations**: entries must be unpublished, unproduced and 2 hours in length **Specifications**: small cast preferred **Procedure:** request guidelines **Deadline**: inquire (Sept. in 1988)

UNICORN THEATRE NATIONAL PLAYWRIGHT'S COMPETITION
3820 Main St., Kansas City, MO 64111
(816) 531-7529 Contact: Ernest L. Williams, Literary Manager **Frequency**: annual **Award**: $1000, production with possible residency **Works:** full-length plays **Regulations**: entries must not be published or professionally produced; no more than 2 entries per author **Specifications**: maximum

cast: 10; contemporary settings **Procedure:** send script, 1-page synopsis, cover letter with brief biography **Deadline**: Mar. 1, 1989 **Notification:** Jun. 1989 **Comment:** Theatre claims 5% subsidiary rights of winning play.

UNIVERSITY OF CINCINNATI
PLAYWRITING CONTEST/FESTIVAL OF NEW WORKS
Dept. of Theater, Mail Location 003, Cincinnati, OH 45221 (513) 475-5471
Contact: Michael Hankins, Artistic Director of Drama **Frequency**: biennial even years **Awards**: $750 for full-length play, $250 for one-act; possible production with development, royalty, travel, housing **Stage:** black box, 100 seats **Procedure:** request guidelines **Deadline**: Sept. 30, 1989 postmark **Notification:** Feb. 1990 **Your chances:** 400/4/2 **Advice:** "Write honestly."

UNIVERSITY OF LOUISVILLE GRAWEMEYER AWARD FOR MUSIC COMPOSITION
School of Music, University of Louisville, Louisville, KY 40292 (502) 588-6907
Contact: David R. Harman, Executive Secretary **Frequency**: annual **Award**: $150,000 in 5 annual installments of $30,000 each **Works:** "Large musical genre: choral, orchestral, chamber, electronic, song-cycle, dance, opera, musical theatre, extended solo work." **Regulations**: entries must have premiered between Jan. 1, 1984, and Dec. 31, 1988, and must be sponsored by professional musical organizations or individuals **Procedure:** request guidelines and application form; $30 fee upon entry **Deadline**: Jan. 27, 1989 **Notification:** late spring 1989

UNIVERSITY OF WEST FLORIDA
PLAYWRIGHT'S REPERTORY FESTIVAL
University Theatre, 11000 University Pkwy., Pensacola, FL 32514 This contest is inactive in 1989.

VERMONT PLAYWRIGHTS AWARD
The Valley Players, Box 441, Waitsfield, VT 05673
Contact: Suzanne Grosby, Chairperson **Frequency**: annual **Award**: $1000, possible production **Works:** full-length plays **Regulations**: authors must be VT residents; entries must be unpublished and unproduced; "workshop, readings are

encouraged" **Specifications**: entries must be suitable for the community and the facility (see contest guidelines) **Procedure**: request guidelines and application form **Deadline**: Aug. 1, 1989 **Notification**: Dec. 1989

VERMONT REPERTORY THEATRE
NATIONAL PLAYWRITING CONTEST
Box 366, Ft. Ethan Allen, Winooski, VT 05404
(802) 655-9620 Contact: Jeff Ryback, General Manager **Frequency**: annual **Award**: $500, production **Works**: full-length plays, translations, adaptations **Regulations**: entries must be unproduced except in showcase productions **Specifications**: no sit-coms or "cutesy" material **Stage**: 3/4 thrust, flexible--140 seats **Audience**: "Professionals and college students." **Procedure**: request guidelines **Deadline**: Nov. 21, 1989 **Notification**: Nov. 1989 **Your chances**: 400/2-3 judges **Advice**: "Professional, well-written scripts that investigate man's existence, social issues."

THE VIRGINIA PRIZE FOR PLAYWRITING
Virginia Commission for the Arts, Box 167-F Rt. 5, Staunton, VA 24401 (703) 248-1868
Contact: Kathleen Tosco, Managing Director, Shenanarts **Frequency**: annual **Award**: $2000, workshop production at Virginia Tech **Works**: full-length plays, one-acts **Regulations**: authors must have resided in VA for a major portion of the year preceding deadline; entries must be unpublished and must not have received an Equity production; students are ineligible **Procedure**: request guidelines; 3 copies of script required upon entry **Deadline**: Apr. 1, 1989 **Notification**: Jun. 1, 1989

WAREHOUSE THEATRE COMPANY
ONE-ACT COMPETITION
Box 2077, Stephens College, Columbia, MO 65215
(314) 443-0784 Contact: Jenny Friend, Artistic Director **Frequency**: annual **Award**: $200; production or staged reading **Works**: one-acts **Special interest**: works by, for or about women **Regulations**: authors must be high-school, undergraduate or graduate students; entries must be unpublished and unproduced except in staged readings or workshop productions **Procedure**: request guidelines; $7.50 fee upon entry **Deadline**: inquire (Dec. 1 in 1988)

WESTERN PUBLIC RADIO PLAYWRITING CONTEST
Ft. Mason Center, San Francisco, CA 94123
(415) 771-1160 Contact: Leo C. Lee, Project Director
Frequency: annual **Awards**: $300, production for WPR's *California Radio Theatre* series for 3 winners **Works**: one-act radio plays **Regulations**: entries must be original works, no more than 30 minutes in length **Procedure**: send script **Deadline**: Jun. 15, 1989

WHEATON COLLEGE PLAYWRITING COMPETITION
Norton, MA This contest has been discontinued.

WICHITA STATE UNIVERSITY PLAYWRITING CONTEST
University Theatre, Box 31,
Wichita State University, Wichita, KS 67208
(316) 689-3185 Contact: Bela Kiralyfalvi, Professor of Theatre **Frequency**: annual **Award**: production, expenses **Works**: full-length plays, related one-acts, musicals **Regulations**: authors must be students in U.S. colleges; entries must be unpublished, unproduced and at least 90 minutes in length **Specifications**: small theatre **Stages**: proscenium, 800 seats; flexible, 100 seats **Audience**: "Typical university audience." **Procedure**: send script **Deadline**: Feb. 15, 1989 **Notification**: Apr. 15, 1989 **Your chances**: 40-50/3/3 **Advice**: "Don't send the first draft!"

WINGS THEATRE COMPANY 1989 NEW PLAYS CONTEST
112 Charlton St., New York, NY 10014
(212) 645-9630 Contact: Jeffery Corrick, Artistic Director **Frequency**: annual **Awards**: production with royalty for as many as 3 plays; staged readings for 10 finalists **Works**: full-length plays, musicals **Special interests**: "Plays that are strong in theme and explore social, moral or philosophical issues in an intelligent and entertaining fashion." **Regulations**: authors must be U.S. playwrights; entries must not be pubished or commercially produced **Stage**: flexible, 65 seats **Procedure**: send script **Deadline**: Dec. 31, 1989 **Notification**: Jun. 1990 **Your chances**: 500/10/1-5

WRITER'S DIGEST WRITING COMPETITION
1507 Dana Ave., Cincinnati, OH 45207
(513) 531-2222 Contact: Competition Director
Frequency: annual **Awards**: overall winner: a trip to New York and lunch with 4 editors or agents; script winner: electronic typewriter; publication in booklet **Works**: 1st 15 pages of full-length plays, one-acts, children's plays **Regulations**: entries must be unpublished and unproduced; no more than 1 entry per author; previous entries ineligible **Specifications**: standard format **Procedure**: request guidelines; synopsis required upon entry **Deadline**: May 31, 1989 **Notification**: Oct. 30, 1989

YEAR-END SERIES (Y.E.S.) NEW PLAY FESTIVAL
Dept. of Theatre, Northern Kentucky University, Highland Heights, KY 41076 (606) 572-5560
Contact: Jack Wann, Project Director **Frequency**: biennial even years **Awards**: $400, production, expenses to attend opening, to each of 3 winners **Works**: full-length plays, single and related one-acts, musicals **Regulations**: entries must be unproduced; winning author must be available to visit in April; no more than 1 entry per author **Specifications**: works must be suitable for actors aged 17-25; musicals must have small orchestra demands **Stages**: proscenium; black box **Procedure**: request guidelines and application form **Deadline**: inquire (Dec. 10 in 1988) **Your chances**: 300-400/3-9/3-9

YOUNG PEOPLE'S PLAYRUSH
Perseverance Theatre, 914 3rd St., Douglas, AK 99824 This contest is inactive in 1989.

YOUNG PLAYWRIGHTS FESTIVAL
The Foundation of The Dramatists Guild, 234 W. 44th St., New York, NY 10036
(212) 575-7795 Contact: Nancy Quinn, Producing Director **Frequency**: annual **Award**: staged reading or production with royalty, travel, residency, 1-year membership in The Dramatists Guild **Works**: full-length plays, one-acts **Regulations**: authors must be under 19 years of age as of Jul. 1, 1989 **Procedure**: request guidelines **Deadline**: Oct. 1, 1989

Special Programs

Unless individual listings specify other procedures, playwrights should request guidelines and application forms for participation in all special programs. Each request for information must be accompanied by a stamped, self-addressed envelope.

ACTORS' ALLIANCE, INC.
AAI, JAF Box 7370, New York, NY 10116
(718) 768-6110 Contact: Melanie Sutherland, Juanita Walsh, Co-Artistic Directors **Program:** a resident ensemble theatre company; activities include weekly workshop meetings, productions and reading series, fundraising parties; travel expenses and small fee for performance provided **Fee:** $25 annual membership **Comments:** "Although we prefer those writers who are available for Monday night workshops, we will consider out-of-town submissions for Associate Membership." See Actors' Alliance, Inc. listing in Theatres.

THE ALLIANCE OF RESIDENT THEATRES/ NEW YORK, INC.
325 Spring St., New York, NY 10013
(212) 989-5257 Contact: Kate C. Busch, Executive Director **Program:** a membership support organization for off Broadway and off off Broadway theatre; services include resources, consultations, seminars, publications, internship program; membership categories: Theatre Members, Associate Theatre Members, Professional Affiliates **Procedure:** phone for eligibility requirements

THE AMERICAN ALLIANCE FOR THEATRE AND EDUCATION
c/o Dept. of Theatre Arts, Virginia Tech, Blacksburg, VA 24061 (703) 961-7624
Contact: Roger L. Bedard, Executive Secretary **Program:** a membership organization formed with the merger of the American Association for Theatre in Secondary Education and the American Association of Theatre for Youth; services include AATE Unpublished Play Reading Project and selection and promotion of promising new plays for elementary and secondary schools; publications include directory, quarterly newsletter and triannual *Youth Theatre Journal* **Fees:** $48 individual, $30 student or retiree

AMERICAN COLLEGE THEATRE FESTIVAL NEW PLAY PREVIEW PROGRAM

Dept. of Theater Arts, Film and Television, UCLA, 405 Hilgard Ave., Los Angeles, CA 90024
Contact: John Cauble, Professor **Program:** playwrights willing to have their works premiered as entries in ACTF are sought by the Development Committee of the Playwriting Awards Committee; donors and schools willing to sponsor and produce selected works are also sought **Comment:** See American College Theatre Festival Awards listing in Contests.

AMERICAN INDIAN COMMUNITY HOUSE

842 Broadway, New York, NY 10003
(212) 598-0100 Contact: Theater Program Director
Program: an organization for New York's American Indian population; programs include Theater Deptartment, library, newsletter, weekly radio program on WBAI-FM; resident theatre company; Native Americans in the Arts (see Theatres) develops and produces works by and about American Indians

AMERICAN PLAYWRIGHT PROGRAM

Westbeth Theatre Center, 151 Bank St., New York, NY 10014 (212) 691-2272
Contact: Script Dept. **Program:** a developmental program for full-length plays: critiques, conferences, staged readings, possible production and referral

A PLAYWRIGHTS COOPERATIVE

San Francisco, CA Our 1989 questionnaire was returned as "undeliverable," and no phone number is listed for this program.

ARIZONA STATE UNIVERSITY GUEST LECTURESHIP

Dept. of Theatre, Arizona State University, Tempe, AZ 85287 (602) 965-5359
Contact: Lin Wright, Chair **Program:** a 2-year maximum visiting professorship in beginning playwriting; maximum salary $34,000; for a published and professionally produced dramatist with an established reputation **Comment:** "The playwright has traditionally premiered a show with ASU faculty and staff and has assisted students with staged readings of their works."

ARTISTS FOUNDATION
8 Park Plaza, Boston, MA 02116 (617) 227-2787
Contact: Netta Davis, Acting Fellowship Director
Program: fellowships of $9500 or $500 to finalists in 19 categories including Playwriting & Music Composition; for playwrights at least 18 years of age who have resided for at least 6 months prior to deadline in MA and are not currently undergraduates or pursuing a graduate degree in their field of application; full-length plays and one-acts accepted
Procedure: request guidelines after Sept. 1, 1989

ARTS INTERNATIONAL
Institute of International Education,
809 United Nations Plaza, New York, NY 10017
(212) 984-5370 Contact: Barbara C. McLean, Program Director **Program:** a membership organization providing services and information on international exchange of professional artists; services include publications, technical assistance, facilitation and advocacy, data bank on sources of funding and production, work spaces and facilities for artists; newsletter; consultations ($25 per hour)

ASOLO TOURING THEATER COMMISSIONS
Drawer E. Sarasota, FL 33578 (813) 355-7115
Contact: Robert G. Miller, Artistic Director **Program:** a step-commissioning process of script development for 1-hour plays (maximum cast: 5; new plays and adaptations of classics) for touring to upper elementary, junior high and high schools; workshop production; commission negotiable
Procedure: request Information Sheet for Playwrights

ASSITEJ/USA
Theatre & Film Dept. Brigham Young University,
Provo, UT 84602 (801) 378-4574
Contact: Harold R. Oaks, President **Program:** an international membership organization for professional theatre for young audiences; services include international networks, New Plays program, information resources, exchanges, forums, festivals; publications include *TYA Today* **Fees:** $30 individual; $15 student or retiree; $40 organization; $50 individual or organization outside U.S.A.

THE ASSOCIATED WRITING PROGRAMS
Old Dominion University, Norfolk, VA 23529
(804) 440-3839 Contact: Gale Arnoux, Director of Services **Program:** a national membership organization serving as an advocate for authors and students and encouraging growth in university and college creative writing programs; *Job List* includes opportunities for playwrights

ASSOCIATION FOR THEATRE IN HIGHER EDUCATION
c/o Theatre Service, Box 15282,
Evansville, IN 47716 (812) 474-0549
Program: a membership organization serving university and college theatres, teachers and students; programs include playwriting (see Christina Crawford Awards listing in Contests); annual conference features playwriting sessions and staged readings **Fees:** $50 individual; $30 student or retiree

ATLANTA NEW PLAY PROJECT
Atlanta, GA See Southeast Playwrights Project.

AT THE FOOT OF THE MOUNTAIN PROGRAMS
2000 S. 5th St., Minneapolis, MN 55454
(612) 375-9487 Contact: Rebecca Rice, Co-Artistic Director **Program:** collaboration by women of color on works to be performed by people of color; plays by and about women; "interested in scripts by or directed by women from all cultural communities"

THE AUTHORS LEAGUE FUND
AND THE DRAMATISTS GUILD FUND
234 W. 44th St., New York, NY 10036
(212) 391-3966 Contact: Susan Drury, Administrator
Program: interest-free loans to meet the immediate and demonstrated needs of published or produced working professional writers **Response:** 4-6 weeks

BMI/LEHMAN ENGEL
MUSICAL THEATRE WORKSHOP
Broadcast Music, Inc., 320 W. 57th St.,
New York, NY 10019 (212) 586-2000 ext. 258
Contact: Jean Banks, Senior Director, Musical Theater Dept.
Program: 2-year workshops for composers and lyricists;

activities include weekly meetings, writing assignments, 2-person team participation, discussions and analyses, collaboration with librettists, public presentation of selected material, advanced workshop for selected 2nd-year participants **Deadlines:** May 1, 1989 librettists; Aug. 1, 1989 composers and lyricists

BRITISH THEATRE ASSOCIATION
Regent's College, Inner Circle, Regent's Park, London NW1 4NW, England Phone: (01) 935-2571 Contact: Sally Meades, Director **Program:** a membership organization acting as a clearinghouse for information on theatre; services and activities include comprehensive theatre reference library of over 250,000 holdings, training courses in all theatre skills, playwrights' workshops, script assessment, discounts on theatre tickets and theatre supplies, lectures and events and quarterly publication *Drama Magazine*

BRODY ARTS FUND
California Community Foundation, 3580 Wilshire Blvd. Suite 1660, Los Angeles, CA 90010 (213) 413-4042 Contact: Jack Shakely, President **Program:** a $2500 fellowship awarded to a resident of Los Angeles County, awarded triennially to emerging artists in the literary and media arts (including playwrights); artists in "expansion arts" field (inner-city, rural, minority or tribal arts) preferred; artists in visual and performing arts are eligible in 2 intervening years **Procedure:** applications available summer 1990 **Deadline:** fall 1990 for 1991 fellowship

CALIFORNIA THEATRE COUNCIL
1824 N. Curson Ave., Los Angeles, CA 90046; Box 48320, Los Angeles, CA 90048 (213) 874-3163 Contact: Teresa A. Gregory, General Manager **Program:** a membership organization for individuals and theatres; programs and services include annual California Theatre Conference, publications including *West Coast Theatre News* (journal, free to members), *West Coast Plays* (anthology, $12.95; $10.35 members; see Publishers), *West Coast Theatre Directory* ($10; $8 members) **Fee:** $30

CENTER FOR ARTS INFORMATION
1285 Avenue of the Americas 3rd Floor,
New York, NY 10019 (212) 977-2544
Contact: Laura Green, Executive Director **Program:** a resource center for the not-for-profit arts; 6500-volume library has books, pamphlets, directories and information on funding agencies and service organizations; publication program offers information on grants, jobs and arts management and administration; publications include newsletters *FYI* and *Spaces*

CENTER THEATRE YOUTHEATRE PROGRAM
1346 W. Devon, Chicago, IL 60660 (312) 508-0200
Contact: Hilary Hammond, Literary Manager **Program:** workshop productions of plays performed by young people, including mentally and physically handicapped young people; most works are created by improvisation; works which may be adapted to performers' needs will be considered **Procedure:** send script

CHICAGO DRAMATISTS WORKSHOP
1105 W. Chicago Ave., Chicago, IL 60622
(312) 633-0630   Contact: Russ Tutterow, Artistic Director **Program:** a developmental process for members' works; programs include workshops, productions, marketing services; selective admission of Chicago-area playwrights; participation in programs required **Fee:** $75 per year

CINTAS FOUNDATION FELLOWSHIP PROGRAM
Arts International Program, Institute of
International Education, 809 United Nations Plaza,
New York, NY 10017-3580 (212) 984-5370
Contact: Rebecca A. Abrams, Associate Program Officer **Program:** fellowships designed "to foster and encourage the professional development and recognition of talented artists" of direct Cuban lineage **Deadline:** Mar. 1, 1989

COLUMBIA COLLEGE CHICAGO
NEW MUSICALS PROJECT
Music/Theater Center, 72 E. 11th St.,
Chicago, IL 60605 (312) 663-9462
Contact: Sheldon Patinkin, Artistic Director **Program:** a year-round program of development for composer-writer

teams with full-length works in first stages of development; weekly stipends provided **Procedure:** submit a rough draft of libretto and songs or full treatment with samples of previous work, history of project, tape of music, biographies **Notification:** 2-3 months after receipt of material **Comment:** Formerly Columbia College Chicago Musical Theater Workshop.

COMPOSERS/LIBRETTISTS STUDIO
New Dramatists, 424 W. 44th St.,
New York, NY 10036 (212) 757-6960
Contact: Ben Krywosz, Special Projects Director **Program:** a 3-week exercise workshop (Sept.-Oct. 1989) dealing with the composer-librettist relationship **Deadline:** Jun. 1989 (inquire) **Notification:** late Aug. 1989

COORDINATING COUNCIL
OF LITERARY MAGAZINES LIBRARY
666 Broadway 11th Floor, New York, NY 10012
(212) 614-6551 Program: a library of magazines, useful to playwrights interested in publication; *Catalogue of Literary Magazines* ($6.95) **Procedure:** phone for appointment

CORNELL CENTER FOR THE PERFORMING ARTS
NEW WORKS PROGRAM
430 College Ave., Cornell University,
Ithaca, NY 14850 (607) 254-2700
Contact: Janet Salmons-Rue, Outreach Director **Program:** residencies of 7-10 days for rehearsals and staged readings of new plays; honorarium, housing, travel provided **Procedure:** send query/synopsis; no unsolicited script **Deadline:** Apr. 30, 1989

DENVER CENTER THEATRE PLAYWRIGHTS' UNIT
Denver, CO This program is inactive in 1989.

DISCOVERY '89
Choate Rosemary Hall, Box 788,
Wallingford, CT 06492 (203) 269-1113
Contact: Terrence Ortwein **Program:** a 4-week summer residency (Jul. 9-Aug. 2, 1989) for development of previously

unproduced 1-hour scripts specifically for production by secondary schools; $700 stipend, housing, board provided **Procedure:** submit script or request guidelines **Deadline:** Mar. 1, 1989 **Notification:** May 1, 1989

DORSET COLONY HOUSE FOR WRITERS
Box 519, Dorset, VT 05251   (802) 867-2223
Contact: John Nassivera, Director **Program:** 1 week-2 month residencies (Sept.-May) for writers of serious purpose and "record of professional achievement" **Procedure:** submit query with resume and description of proposed project; indicate desired dates of residency **Fee:** $45 per week maximum, plus meals

DRAMA PROJECT
Box M 151 First Ave., New York, NY 10003
(212) 674-1166   Contact: Doug Moston, Artistic Director **Program:** Drama Project is a workshop of actors, directors and playwrights who collaborate in the development of new plays; during sessions lasting 10 weeks, the playwright's works are read by actors and regularly critiqued as the development progresses; roles are cast from actors within the group, and staged readings are created for public audiences including the industry (also literary agents); the best of these readings are given workshop productions which are held at the Riverside Shakespeare **Fee:** $110.

THE DRAMATISTS GUILD, INC.
234 W. 44th St., New York, NY 10036
(212) 398-9366   Contact: David E. LeVine, Executive Director **Program:** the professional association of playwrights (produced and unproduced); services include use of standard contracts, contract counseling, advice on relationships with producers and agents, emergency toll-free number, script-retrieval and royalty collection, symposia in New York and other major U.S. cities, reference library, Committee for Women, Young Playwrights Festival (see Contests) and The Dramatists Guild Exchange which helps to locate directors for members' works; The Dramatists Guild Fund (See The Authors League Fund and The Dramatists Guild Fund listing in this section); publications include quarterly journal and monthly newsletter **Fee:** $50 per year

THE EDWARD F. ALBEE FOUNDATION, INC.
14 Harrison St., New York, NY 10013
(212) 226-2020 Program: 1-month residencies at the William Flanagan Memorial Creative Persons Center ("The Barn") in Montauk, Long Island, for writers and artists demonstrating talent and need;   private room provided **Deadline:**   Apr. 1, 1989 for Jun.-Sept. 1989 season **Notification:** May 1989

FAIRCHESTER PLAYWRIGHTS PROJECT
5 Olmstead Rd., West Redding, CT 06896
(203) 431-4408 Contact: Lawrence Geddie, Director **Program:** membership organization for playwrights residing in Fairfield County, CT, or Westchester County, NY; readings and/or staged readings (with professional actors, audience discussion) of 18 new works per year **Fee:** $6 per month **Procedure:**   submit script of 1 full-length or 2 one-act plays-in-process, with self-addressed postcard for response **Comment:** Formerly   Fairchester   Playwrights   and Screenwriters.

FEEDBACK SERVICES/FEEDBACK THEATREBOOKS
305 Madison Ave. Suite 411, New York, NY 10165
(212) 687-4185 Contact: Walter J. Meserve, Vice President   **Program:**   a resource information service providing   script   critiques,   correspondence   courses   in playwriting, query letter and synopsis preparation, script preparation, topical research

FIRSTSTAGE
6817 Franklin Ave., Los Angeles, CA 90028
(213) 850-6271   Contact: Gwenn Victor, Literary Coordinator **Program:** a membership organization "dedicated to bringing together writers, actors and directors in the development of new material for stage and film"; weekly readings and discussions; possible workshop productions **Fee:** $30 per quarter **Procedure:**   send script and resume

FLORIDA STUDIO THEATRE ARTISTS COLONY
1241 N. Palm Ave., Sarasota, FL 34236
(813) 366-9017 Contact: Dorean Pucciatti **Program:** residencies (Apr.-Nov.) of varying length for up to 6 writers,

directors and designers in FST living-center; program includes private work time and opportunity for interaction with staff and administrative and technical involvement in FST activities and productions; bedroom, common living area, shared kitchen and bath provided **Fee:** $7.50 per day **Deadline:** applications due 1 month prior to expected residency

THE FOUNDATION CENTER
79 Fifth Ave./16th St., New York, NY 10003
(212) 620-4230 Program: an independent national service organization providing information on private philanthropic giving; national network of library reference collections available; publications include *Grants for Arts and Cultural Programs* and *Grants to Individuals*

FRANK SILVERA WRITERS' WORKSHOP
317 W. 125th St. 3rd Floor, New York, NY 10027
(212) 662-8493 Contact: Karen Baxter, Executive Director **Program:** an annual Writers' Laboratory for Afro-American authors, other minorities and women; Monday readings/critiques (Sept.-Jun.), staged readings, full production of works-in-progress, seminars, technical assistance training program **Fees:** $25 seminar registration; $10 per session

FREDERICK DOUGLASS CREATIVE ARTS CENTER WRITING WORKSHOPS
168 W. 46th St., New York, NY 10036
(212) 944-9870 Contact: Fred Hudson, Artistic Director **Program:** 12-week workshops in beginning and advanced playwriting; weekly meetings; advanced session includes readings, possible production (produced playwright receives $300) **Deadlines:** early Sept. 1989 for Oct. 1989-Jan. 1990; inquire for deadline for Mar.-Jun. 1990

FUND FOR AMERICAN PLAYS
John F. Kennedy Center, Washington, DC 20566
(202) 254-3490 Contact: Deborah Dixon, Project Director **Program:** fund to assist not-for-profit professional, non-professional and college/university theatres in the production of American plays; financial assistance for the creation of excellence in production (4-week

rehearsal periods, residencies for playwrights, possible guest actors and theatre artists, $10,000 award to playwright); no funds for technical requirements **Procedure:**   producing company may submit as many as 3 original American plays with detailed budgets outlining ordinary production expenses and additional funds needed for each play in the competition **Deadline:**   Feb. 14, 1989   **Notification:**   Jun. 30, 1989 **Comment:**   This program is supported by the John F. Kennedy Center for the Performing Arts, American Express and the President's Committee on Arts and Humanities.

THE GATHERING
The Whole Theater, 544 Bloomfield Ave.,
Montclair, NJ 07042   (201) 744-2996
Contact: Pat Andrews   **Program:**   a project meeting for readings on the last Monday of each month; open to all women; purpose is "to share and promote women's activities in the theatre"   **Procedure:**   call for information

THE HENRY FONDA YOUNG PLAYWRIGHTS PROJECT
Very Special Arts, Education Office,
John F. Kennedy Center, Washington, DC 20566
(202) 662-8899   Contact: Michael Anderson, Administrator, Field Services   **Program:**   annual playwriting workshops for students aged 12-18 (with and without disabilities) to develop plays addressing some aspect of disability; Royal Court Young People's Theatre Exchange international program for exchange of productions of winning plays **Deadline:** Feb. 15, 1989 **Comment:** See The Henry Fonda Young Playwrights Project listing in Contests.

INSTITUTE OF OUTDOOR DRAMA
CB #3240, Graham Memorial,
University of North Carolina, Chapel Hill, NC 27599
(919) 962-1328 Contact: Mark R. Sumner, Director
Program: a research/resource and advisory agency providing communications services for producers and information for those interested in outdoor drama, encouraging established playwrights and composers to create new outdoor dramas and advising new playwrights interested in writing outdoor dramas; services and activities include a roster of artists and production personnel, professional consultation and

feasibility study appraisal, annual auditions for summer employment in outdoor drama, conferences, lectures, symposia, occasional reading of scripts by produced playwrights (query/synopsis required prior to submission); publications include books, bulletins, visual aids and monthly newsletter

INTAR HISPANIC AMERICAN MUSIC THEATRE LABORATORY

Box 788, New York, NY 10108 (212) 695-6134, -6135 **Contact:** Graciela Daniele, Program Director **Program:** an annual 4-month residency program which "nurtures the creation of original Hispanic musical theatre by combining latin music with theatrical traditions"; for Hispanic playwrights working mainly in English; readings, possible workshop production; $1000 stipend provided **Deadline:** Sept. 30, 1989

INTAR HISPANIC PLAYWRIGHTS-IN-RESIDENCE LABORATORY

Box 788, New York, NY 10108 (212) 695-6134, -6135 **Contact:** Maria Irene Fornes, Program Director **Program:** a 25-week residency program for professional Hispanic playwrights writing mainly in English; readings, staged readings, possible workshop productions; $100 weekly stipend provided **Procedure:** submit script with biography **Deadline:** Jun. 30, 1989 **Notification:** early fall 1989

INTERNATIONAL THEATRE INSTITUTE OF THE UNITED STATES (ITI/US)

220 W. 42nd St., New York, NY 10036 (212) 944-1490 **Contact:** Elizabeth Burdick, Library Director **Program:** an organization with centers in 70 countries, founded by UNESCO "to promote the exchange of knowledge and practice in the theatre arts"; programs and services include assistance for theatre artists traveling internationally, reference library documenting theatre activities in 150 countries and housing 10,000 plays from 92 countries, information and consultation service on international theatre activities and on international copyright, Theatre of Nations biennial international festival

THE INTERNATIONAL WOMEN'S WRITING GUILD
Drama Consortium, Box 810 Gracie Station,
New York, NY 10028 (212) 737-7536
Contact: Hannelore Hahn, Executive Director **Program:** an alliance of women writers in U.S., Canada and abroad; programs include workshops; annual 1-week conference/retreat at Skidmore College, Saratoga Springs, NY; contracts with agents; insurance programs; legal aid; newsletter; script-reading program with cooperating theatres **Fees:** $25 U.S.; $31 foreign membership

THE JAMES THURBER
PLAYWRIGHT-IN-RESIDENCE
The Thurber House, 77 Jefferson Ave.,
Columbus, OH 43215 (614) 464-1032
Contact: Michael J. Rosen, Literary Director **Program:** a 1-quarter teaching residency for a playwright who has had at least 1 play published and/or produced by a significant company and who shows aptitude for teaching; resident teaches 1 course in The Ohio State University's Dept. of Theatre; possible public reading or production of resident's work; $5000 stipend (not available in summer 1989), housing in Thurber's boyhood home; book center, local writers' center, museum available **Deadline:** Jan. 15, 1989 for Autumn 1989 and Winter or Spring 1990 **Notification:** Mar. 15, 1989

JEROME PLAYWRIGHT-IN-RESIDENCE
FELLOWSHIPS
The Playwrights' Center, 2301 Franklin Ave. E,
Minneapolis, MN 55406 (612) 332-7481
Program: 6 annual fellowships of $5000; access to The Playwrights' Center services, for playwrights who have not had more than 2 professionally produced plays; Fellows must spend fellowship period (Jul.-Jun.) in residence **Deadline:** Feb. 1, 1989 **Notification:** Mar. 31, 1989 **Comment:** See The Playwrights' Center listing in this section.

JOHN SIMON GUGGENHEIM
MEMORIAL FOUNDATION FELLOWSHIPS
90 Park Ave., New York, NY 10016
(212) 687-4470 Program: 6 month-1 year fellowships to assist scholars and artists in research and creation; fellows

must "have already demonstrated exceptional capacity for productive scholarship or exceptional creative ability in the arts"

LEAGUE OF CHICAGO THEATRES/ CHICAGO THEATRE FOUNDATION
67 E. Madison Suite 2116, Chicago, IL 60603
(312) 977-1730 Contact: Diane O. Economos, Executive Director **Program:** a trade and service organization for Chicago artists, theatres and theatre personnel, providing programs and services in marketing, promotion, advocacy and general resources; publications include bimonthly *Theatre Chicago* magazine, monthly *Theatre Chicago Guide, Marketing Promotions Guide* and annual *Theatre Chicago Reference Book* **Membership dues:** $250-$1500, based on theatre's budget **Affiliate Fees:** $35 individual; $100 organization

THE LEE STRASBERG THEATRE INSTITUTE
115 E. 15th St., New York, NY 10003
(212) 533-5500; 7936 Santa Monica Blvd.,
Los Angeles, CA 90046 (213) 650-7777 Program:
Playwrights & Company: a forum in which acting students write scenes and/or one-act plays; works in progress are presented for discussion and critique, possible staged readings, productions **Procedure:** Institute registration required

THE LEHMAN ENGEL MUSICAL THEATRE WORKSHOP
1605 N. Cahuenga Blvd. #216, Hollywood, CA 90028
(213) 465-8818 Contact: John Sparks, Co-Director **Program:** workshop and in-house staged reading program (Sept. 1989-May 1990) **Fee:** $100 (including $25 application fee); possible work-study program **Deadline:** Aug. 15, 1989

LITERARY MANAGERS AND DRAMATURGS OF AMERICA
c/o CASTA, CUNY Graduate Center, 33 W. 42nd St.,
New York, NY 10036 (212) 642-2657
Contact: David Copelin, President **Program:** a national membership organization offering job referral, information

resources, a quarterly newsletter, insurance; activities include workshops and symposia, public panels, membership meetings, annual conference **Fees:** $25 voting member; $20 associate (associate membership open to playwrights, artistic directors, agents, other theatre professionals and members of the public concerned with dramaturgy); $15 student

LOS ANGELES THEATRE ALLIANCE/ LEAGUE OF PRODUCERS
644 S. Figueroa, Los Angeles, CA 90017
(213) 614-0556 Contact: Karen Rushfield, Executive Director **Program:** a membership service organization of theatres and producers in Los Angeles; services include resource center, lectures, workshops, audience development and marketing services, advocacy, information hotline, monthly newsletter, professional job bank

LOS ANGELES THEATRE CENTER PROGRAMS
514 S. Spring St., Los Angeles, CA 90013
(213) 627-6500 Contact: Bill Bushnell, Artistic Producing Director **The Women's Project:** a workshop for Los Angeles women playwrights **Young Playwrights Lab:** a developmental workshop for Los Angeles residents aged 15-22 **Latino Theatre Lab:** a workshop for Latino actors, playwrights and directors; collaborative projects; works may be included in LATC season **Playwrights' Unit:** regular sessions for established, Los Angeles playwrights **Asian American Theatre Project:** an access point for emerging Asian artists to "mainstream" theatre **Black Theatre Artists Workshop:** a forum for research and presentation of new plays by black writers; a contact point for writers, directors and actors **Music Theatre Lab:** playwrights, composers and lyricists explore a musical expression of "the kind of cutting-edge theatre for which LATC is known"

MANHATTAN PLAYWRIGHTS UNIT
338 W. 19th St., New York, NY 10011
(212) 989-0948 Contact: Saul Zachary, Co-Founder/ Director **Program:** organization of experienced, active playwrights; works-in-progress shared at weekly meetings **Procedure:** send cover letter and resume

MARY ROBERTS RINEHART FUND
Dept. of English, George Mason University, 4400 University Dr., Fairfax, VA 22030 (703) 323-2220 Contact: Roger Lathbury **Program:** a grant of ("amount varies depending upon income generated by the fund--currently around $900") presented biennially in odd years to an unpublished dramatist who needs assistance to complete a work with strong narrative quality **Procedure:** nomination by established writer and/or editor who should submit 30-page sample of nominee's work; written recommendation not necessary **Deadline:** inquire for 1990 deadline for 1991 grant

McKNIGHT FELLOWSHIPS
The Playwrights' Center, 2301 Franklin Ave. E, Minneapolis, MN 55406 (612) 332-7481 Contact: Lisa Stevens **Program:** six fellowships of $10,000 with provisions for professional workshops, "to recognize playwrights whose work has made a significant impact on the contemporary theatre"; subsidy, supplementary assistance and professional encouragement; 2-month residency in Minnesota; selection based on resume and plan for Fellowship year **Procedure:** request guidelines after Oct. 2, 1989 **Deadline:** inquire (Dec. 1 in 1988) **Comment:** See The Playwrights' Center listing in this section.

MERELY PLAYERS
Box 606, New York, NY 10108 (212) 799-2253 Contact: Monica Hays, President **Program:** a membership organization of actors, directors and writers; activities include script development through semi-monthly readings and critiques, Second Step staged readings and full productions **Procedure:** submit script; playwright who has had 2 scripts accepted may become member

MIDWEST PLAYLABS
The Playwrights' Center, 2301 Franklin Ave. E, Minneapolis, MN 55406 (612) 332-7481 Program: a 2-week retreat (Jul. 30-Aug 12, 1989) during which 6 new, unpublished full-length plays are developed with assistance from professional acting company and nationally recognized directors and dramaturgs; travel, room, board,

stipend provided; revised plays receive public readings; for playwrights who have an association with Midwestern states, or are members of The Playwrights' Center; Pre-Conference (May 12-14, 1989) **Procedure:** guidelines and application forms available after Jan. 2, 1989 **Deadline:** Mar. 1, 1989 **Notification:** Apr. 14, 1989 **Comment:** See The Playwrights' Center listing in this section.

MILDRED I. REID WRITERS COLONY
Penacook Rd., Contoocook, NH 03229
(603) 746-3625   Contact: Mildred I. Reid, Director **Program:** 1-6 week residencies (Jul.-Aug.) providing single or double rooms and kitchen facility for beginning writers who wish to work under a director's guidance and for professionals and semi-professionals; room and breakfast provided **Fee:** at least $115 per week

MONEY FOR WOMEN/
BARBARA DEMING MEMORIAL FUND, INC.
Box 40-1043, Brooklyn, NY 11240
Contact: Pam McAllister, Administrator **Program:** semi-annual grants averaging $500-$1000 for U.S. residents who are feminists "active in the arts whose work speaks for peace and social justice and in some way sheds light upon the condition of women or enhances self-realization" **Deadlines:** Feb. 1, 1989; Jul. 1, 1989

MOUNT SEQUOYAH NEW PLAY RETREAT
Dept. of Drama, 406 Kimpel Hall, University of Arkansas, Fayetteville, AR 72701 (501) 575-2953
Contact: Thomas R. Jones **Program:** summer residency/ workshop: play development with directors and actors, staged reading with critique by theatre professional; housing, meals provided. **Fee:** $10 upon application **Deadline:** inquire

MUSICAL THEATRE LAB
Agassiz House, Radcliffe College, 10 Garden St., Cambridge, MA 02138 (617) 495-8676
Contact: Stuart Ostrow, Producer **Program:** a developmental workshop for new, production-ready works; public workshop performances; weekly stipend provided for 6 weeks

NATIONAL ENDOWMENT FOR THE ARTS
OPERA MUSICAL THEATER PROGRAM
**NEA, Nancy Hanks Center, 1100 Pennsylvania Ave.
NW, Washington, DC 20506 (202) 682-5447**
Contact: Gertrude J. Saleh **Program:** annual grants or commissions awarded to professional producing organizations, independent producers, artist-producers, artistic associates and national and regional service organizations **Procedure:** request guidelines and "Intent to Apply Card" **Deadline:** card must be returned to NEA by Feb. 1, 1989

NATIONAL ENDOWMENT FOR THE ARTS
THEATER PROGRAM
**NEA, Nancy Hanks Center Room 608,
1100 Pennsylvania Ave. NW, Washington, DC 20506
(202) 682-5425 Contact:** Eleanor Moncure
Program: 1-year fellowships of $10,000-$17,500 plus additional $2500 for residency at a professional theatre; awarded to playwrights whose work has been professionally produced within the past 5 years **Deadline:** Jun. 30, 1989

THE NATIONAL FOUNDATION
FOR JEWISH CULTURE
**330 Seventh Ave. 21st Floor, New York, NY 10001
(212) 629-0500 Contact:** Andrea Aronson Morgan, Program Officer **Program:** an umbrella organization for programs and services in contemporary Jewish theatre in North America; services include information resources and consultation for theatres interested in producing plays on Jewish topics, advocacy, communication services, newsletter and catalogue, NFJC Playwrights' Travel Grant Program (see listing in this section), NFJC Hebrew Translation Commission (see Contests)

NATIONAL INSTITUTE FOR MUSIC THEATER
**John F. Kennedy Center, Washington, DC 20566
(202) 965-2800 Contact:** Maria L. Thompson, Program Manager **Program:** a not-for-profit arts organization that supports American creators and performers during the early stages of their careers

THE NATIONAL MUSIC THEATER NETWORK
1457 Broadway Suite 1111, New York, NY 10036
(212) 382-0984   Contact: Jay Stephens, Executive Director **Program:** a service organization "committed to the discovery, evaluation and promotion of new music theatre"; services include professional evaluations, listing of selected works in national catalogue, Sampler Series of excerpt concert performances, Seagrams New Music Theater Awards programs (see Contests) **Fee:** $30 for evaluation

NEW AMERICAN THEATRE PROJECT
The New York Theatre Group, Box 1557,
New York, NY 10011   (718) 624-4680
Contact: William Neish   **Program:** a long-term developmental process of readings, workshops and full productions designed to explore different facets of contemporary American writing for the theatre; Phase II Apr.-Oct. 1989: new 2-character one-act American plays; Phase III Apr.-Dec. 1989: new plays by West Coast Writers; Phase IV Nov.1989-Feb. 1990: The New York Gay Theatre Festival

NEW CITY THEATER DIRECTOR'S FESTIVAL
1634 11th Ave., Seattle, WA 98122
(206) 323-6801   Contact: John Kazanjian, Artistic Director **Program:** an annual spring showcase for Seattle directors, playwrights and actors; one-act plays receive 1 performance, after which the 5 best plays run in repertory for 2 weeks **Procedure:** director should submit project (director is responsible for finances including playwright's royalty); all projects are accepted **Fee:** $30 **Deadline:** Jan. 1, 1989

NEW DRAMATISTS
424 W. 44th St., New York, NY 10036
(212) 757-6960 Contact: Thomas G. Dunn, Executive Director **Program:** a membership organization open to all playwrights residing in New York City area and those residing elsewhere who can advantageously use membership; services include developmental laboratory, library, loan fund, free ticket service for Broadway and off Broadway shows, international exchanges, ScriptShare national distribution

service, Arnold Weissberger Award (see Contests), Composer/ Librettists Studio (see listing in this section); publications include bimonthly newsletter and monthly bulletin providing information on funding, competitions and other opportunities **Deadline:** Jul. 15, 1989 **Notification:** Spring 1990

NEW WORKS THEATRE
San Diego, CA Our 1989 questionnaire was returned as "undeliverable," and no phone number is listed for this program.

NEW YORK FOUNDATION FOR THE ARTS
5 Beekman St. Suite 600, New York, NY 10038
(212) 233-3900 Program: a service organization offering Artists-Residencies in New York schools and communities, Artists' New Works Program, consultation services for arts in education, fiscal and advisory services for artists working on individual projects, fellowships, loans, conferences, workshops, seminars, publications

NFJC PLAYWRIGHTS' TRAVEL GRANT PROGRAM
330 Seventh Ave. 21st Floor, New York, NY 10001
(212) 629-0500 Contact: Andrea Aronson Morgan, Program Officer **Program:** a travel grant of up to $250 for a playwright to work with a not-for-profit theatre in the U.S. or Canada during rehearsal of a previously unproduced play with a Jewish theme **Procedure:** theatre must request guidelines and application form **Deadline:** application due at least 1 month prior to 1st rehearsal

NORTH CAROLINA ARTS COUNCIL
VISITING ARTIST PROGRAM
Community Development Section, North Carolina Arts Council, Dept. of Cultural Resources, Raleigh, NC 27611 (919) 733-7897
Program: residencies of 9 months-1 year (maximum term of participation: 4 years) for professional, committed artists at 58 community and technical colleges; artists-in-residence work for the communities in which the institutions are located, presenting workshops, lecture/demonstrations, in-school activities, readings and productions; "self-development time is set aside for artists to devote to their own work"; negotiable

salary ($14,000-$24,000) plus benefit package; masters degree or equivalent experience and training required, possible interview **Deadline:** Feb. 1, 1989

NORTHWEST PLAYWRIGHTS GUILD
Box 95259, Seattle, WA 98145 (206) 365-6026
Contact: Sharon Glantz, Administrator **Program:** a service organization and information resource for playwrights; support services include in-house staged readings, public readings, writer's forum with members' critiques, bank of members' scripts, newsletter; discounts on Guild seminars, workshops, symposia, publications, script preparation services **Fees:** $20 1st year, $10 per year thereafter

OLLANTAY CENTER FOR THE ARTS
Box 636, Jackson Heights, NY 11372
(718) 565-6499   Contact: Pedro R. Monge, Director
Program: a multi-art center serving mainly the Hispanic population of Queens, NY; programs include staged readings, full bilingual traveling productions, visual arts, literature, publications, folk arts, writing workshops include playwriting

O'NEILL OPERA/MUSIC THEATER CONFERENCE
Eugene O'Neill Memorial Theater Center,
234 W. 44th St. Suite 901 New York, NY 10036
(212) 382-2790   Contact: Paulette Haupt, Artistic Director **Program:** annual 4-week conference (Aug.) "for the purpose of exploring new works and developing new writers"; for U.S. citizens with unproduced, unoptioned opera and music-theatre work; program includes public staged readings and non-public readings; $250 stipend, room, board, transportation provided; adaptors must have permissions from copyright holders; participants must be in residence for entire conference period **Deadline:** May 1, 1989 **Procedure:** applications accepted Nov. 1-Mar. 1

PADUA HILLS PLAYWRIGHTS' WORKSHOP/ FESTIVAL
Box 461450, Los Angeles, CA 90046
(213) 281-6799   Contact: Cheryl Bianchi, Executive Director **Program:** 6-week summer workshop in playwriting "with emphasis on developing the voice of the playwright"; program includes student readings with professional actors and

participation in Padua Playwrights Festival; instructors include Maria Irene Fornes, Murray Mednick, David Henry Hwang, Eric Overmyer **Fee:** $750 **Deadline:** May 15, 1989

PALENVILLE INTERARTS COLONY
2 Bond St., New York, NY 10012 (212) 254-4614
Contact: Patrick Schiarratta, Colony Director **Program:** 1-8 week residencies (Jun. 1-Sept. 30) for artists with at least 3 years' professional experience in their fields who "demonstrate a high level of artistic ability"; private or semi-private room or cabin, studio space, meals provided; special interest: "artists who possess an appreciation of the global implication of their efforts" **Fee:** $160 per week suggested **Deadline:** Apr. 1, 1989 **Notification:** 4 weeks

PEN AMERICAN CENTER
568 Broadway, New York, NY 10012
(212) 334-1660 Contact: Karen Kennerly, Executive Director **Program:** a member of International PEN association of writers; activities include Freedom to Write and Freedom to Read; readings, symposia and other public events; translator-publisher resources; publisher-writer programs; publications include *Grants and Awards Available to American Writers* annual awards include Renato Poggioli Award (see Contests); the PEN Writers' Fund (see listing in this section)

PEN TO STAGE PRODUCTIONS
441 W. 24th St. #2, New York, NY 10011
Contact: W. Squier **Program:** a developmental collective of 50 New York City area actors, directors, designers and writers meeting weekly for cold readings; possible public presentation **Fee:** contribution **Procedure:** send dialogue sample (10 page maximum) typical of playwright's work

PEN WRITERS' FUND
PEN American Center, 568 Broadway,
New York, NY 10012 (212) 334-1660
Contact: Christine Friedlander, Program Coordinator **Program:** interest-free loans and grants of up to $1000 in emergency assistance for published or produced writers in financial difficulties

PERFORMING ARTS RESEARCH CENTER
**The New York Public Library at Lincoln Center,
111 Amsterdam Ave., New York, NY 10023**
**(212) 870-1639 (Billy Rose Theatre Collection),
870-1663 (Rodgers & Hammerstein Archives of
Recorded Sound) Contact:** Richard M. Buck, Assistant to
the Chief   **Program:** extensive collection of non-circulating
research materials on theatre, music, dance, film, radio and
TV; for in-depth research by advanced students, professionals,
authors and specialists

PHILADELPHIA DRAMA GUILD
PLAYWRIGHTS' PROJECT
112 S. 16th St. Suite 802, Philadelphia, PA 19102
(215) 563-7530   Contact: Charles Conwell, Director
Program: staged readings, possible production in Playwrights
of Philadelphia (POP) Festival for playwrights residing within
25 miles of Philadelphia City Hall; $100 stipend provided
Deadline: Dec. 31,1989 **Notification:** Jan. 31, 1990

PLAYFORMERS
New York, NY   (212) 685-5394
Program: "a limited membership group of congenial and
committed theatre people who meet every 2 weeks to read and
critique plays," program serves the playwriting interests of
its membership   **Fee:** voluntary contribution of $90 per year
to support "a wine and cheese buffet at each meeting and
clerical expenses" **Procedure:** call above number for details
Comment: Membership is limited to 15.

PLAYMARKET
Box 9767, Wellington, New Zealand
Phone: Wellington (04) 758-405
Contact: Ann Paetz, Administrator **Program:** a New
Zealand's principle agency for playwrights; services include
script advisory and critiquing, arrangements for workshop
productions of promising scripts, script preparation and
distribution, contract negotiation and royalty collection;
publications include *The Playmarket Directory of New Zealand
Plays and Playwrights* and *New Zealand Theatrescripts*

THE PLAYWRIGHT/DIRECTOR WORKSHOP

c/o **Charles Maryan, Director,**
777 West End Ave. Apt. 6C, New York, NY 10025
(212) 864-0542 Program: a course designed for developing directors and playwrights, dealing with the process of a play from manuscript to production; 2 terms of 16 weeks each are held from Oct.-May **Procedure:** send script; interview required **Fee:** $320 per 16-week term **Comment:** "By design this is a very small group: no more than 12 including both directors and playwrights."

THE PLAYWRIGHTS' CENTER

2301 Franklin Ave. E, Minneapolis, MN 55406
(612) 332-7481 Program: a service organization for playwrights; programs include developmental services (readings, staged readings, workshops, classes); exchanges with theatres and other programs; Jones Commissioning Program for one-acts; Playwrights-in-the Schools Residency Program; Storytalers professional touring company; Young Playwrights program for writers under 19 (see listing in this section); fellowships: 6 annual Jerome Playwrights-in-Residence Fellowships of $5000 (see listing in this section), 6 annual McKnight Fellowships of $10,000 (see listing in this section); Midwest PlayLabs (see listing in this section)

PLAYWRIGHTS' CENTER OF CHICAGO

3716 N. Clark St., Chicago, IL 60613
(312) 271-3468 Contact: James W. MacDowell, Artistic Director **Program:** a membership organization for Chicago-area playwrights; activities include workshops, classes and showcase productions of original scripts

THE PLAYWRIGHTS FOUNDATION

Box 1191, Mill Valley, CA 94942 (415) 381-3311
Contact: Scott Wren, Vice-President **Program:** a developmental support organization for northern CA playwrights; programs include annual Bay Area Playwrights Festival: 4-6 workshop productions of new plays; Staged Reading Series: readings of 8-12 scripts per year (unsolicited scripts accepted), panel discussions and workshops led by established artists, publication of *Re:Write* newsletter, playwright-in-residence fellowships

THE PLAYWRIGHTS FUND OF NORTH CAROLINA
Greenville, NC   Our 1989 questionnaire was returned as "undeliverable," and no phone number is listed for this program.

PLAYWRIGHTS' PLATFORM
164 Brayton Rd., Boston, MA 02135
(617) 254-4482, 427-7450
Contact: Beverly Creasey, President **Program:** a membership organization for authors with unpublished, unproduced plays; activities include a developmental program of weekly workshops, staged readings, referral and dramaturgical services, summer festival productions; participants are encouraged to become members **Fee:** $15

PLAYWRIGHT'S PREVIEW PRODUCTIONS
1160 Fifth Ave. #304, New York, NY 10029
(212) 289-2168   Contact: Frances W. Hill, Artistic Director **Program:** developmental program (Sept.-May) for plays not previously produced in the New York City area; activities include staged readings, workshops, possible productions, Emerging Playwright Award (see Contests) **Procedure:** submit script

PLAYWRIGHTS THEATRE OF NEW JERSEY
33 Green Village Rd. Madison, NJ 07940
(201) 514-1787   Contact: Buzz McLaughlin, Producing Artistic Director **Program:** a service organization for playwrights and a theatre producing new plays; services and activities include New Play Development Program (see listing immediately following), Geraldine R. Dodge Foundation New American Play Award (see Contests), Playwrights Information Center offering advice to writers and sponsoring playwriting symposiums, state-wide playwriting-in-the-schools program and playwriting-for-teachers project, Madison Young Playwrights Festival (productions of works by 4th-12th grade participants in city-wide playwriting-in-the-schools program), special needs projects for playwrights (work with senior citizens, the physically handicapped, teenage substance abusers, juvenile offenders; playwriting-in-prisons initiative), "gifted and talented playwriting symposiums" for students from various school districts, adult playwriting classes

PLAYWRIGHTS THEATRE OF NEW JERSEY
NEW PLAY DEVELOPMENT PROGRAM
33 Green Village Rd., Madison, NJ 07940
(201) 514-1787 Contact: Kate Clark, Literary Manager
Program: development of unproduced plays by American playwrights; activities include readings, staged readings and workshop productions; liaison with other theatres; housing, expenses provided

THE PLAYWRIGHTS' UNIT
1733 Kilbourne Pl. NW, Washington, DC 20010
(202) 667-3623 Contact: Ernest Joselovitz, Administrator **Program:** Two programs for DC, MD and VA playwrights: The Unit, the permanent professional playwrights workshop; and The Forum, apprenticeship program of continual 3-month sessions; both offer biweekly meetings with roundtable discussions, in-house and public readings, Intensive Workshop readings, free theatre ticket privileges, Playwrights-Read-Playwrights discussions, Production Observerships at cooperating theatres, classes in Acting for Playwrights and in Re-writes **Fees:** The Unit $60 for 6 months; The Forum $80 per session; Associate Membership $25 per year

THE PRESTON JONES NEW PLAY SYMPOSIUM
Chocolate Bayou Theater Company, Box 270363, Houston, TX 77277 This program is inactive in 1989.

PRIMAFACIE
Denver Center Theatre Company, 1050 13th St., Denver, CO 80204 (303) 893-4200
Contact: Barbara Sellers, Producing Director **Program:** an annual new play festival in which 8-10 unproduced scripts (maximum cast: 12) are selected for development; 2-week residency includes rehearsal and staged reading by members of DCTC Acting Company; 3-4 scripts from series are chosen for full production **Deadline:** inquire (Dec. 30 in 1988)

PRIMARY STAGES COMPANY
584 Ninth Ave., New York, NY 10036
(212) 582-7862, 333-7471 Contact: Casey Childs, Artistic Director **Program:** a developmental program of

readings, workshop productions, full productions; for American playwrights with unproduced plays; stipend provided for full production **Comment:**   See 45th Street Theatre listing in Theatres.

PROFESSIONAL ASSOCIATION OF CANADIAN THEATRE/PACT COMMUNICATIONS CENTER

64 Charles St. E, Toronto, Ontario, Canada M4Y 1T1 (416) 968-3033 Contact: Catherine Smalley, Executive Director   **Program:**   the national service and trade association for professional English-language theatres in Canada; services include government advocacy, negotiation of collective agreements, public awareness programs, PACT Communications Center serving as charitable wing to improve and expand communications and information services; publications include *Behind the Scenes: A guide to Canadian non-profit professional theatres and theatre-related resources,* monthly *Artsboard* bulletin of job opportunities, *Canada on Stage* yearbook of theatrical activity and bimonthly *PACT News*

PUERTO RICAN TRAVELING THEATRE PLAYWRIGHTS' WORKSHOP

141 W. 94th St., New York, NY 10025 (212) 354-1293 Contact: Allen Davis III, Director **Program:** workshop with beginning and professional units for New York City area residents; Hispanic writers preferred; activities include readings, weekly meetings (Oct.-Jun.) **Deadline:** Sept. 30, 1989

RED OCTOPUS THEATRE COMPANY ORIGINAL SCRIPTS WORKSHOP

Box 1403, Newport, OR 97365 (503) 265-9231 Contact: Edward Van Aelstyn, Director **Program:**   2-3 week developmental workshop for as many as 10 unproduced works (one-acts or excerpts from full-length plays); program includes collaboration with director and actors, staged readings, possible production; small honorarium, housing provided **Procedure:** submit script **Deadline:** Nov. 1, 1989 **Notification:** Dec. 15, 1989

THE ROCKEFELLER FOUNDATION GRANTS
**1133 Avenue of the Americas, New York, Ny 10036
(212) 869-8500 Contact:** Karen Kaplan **Program:** program is undergoing changes in 1989; interested playwrights should contact Karen Kaplan

ROUNDABOUT THEATRE'S CREATIVE CONNECTION
**Roundabout Theatre Conservatory, 100 E. 17th St., New York, NY 10003 (212) 420-1360
Contact:** Janet McCall, Conservatory Director **Program:** playwriting classes offered each fall and spring **Fee:** inquire

THE SCRIPT REVIEW
**Box 925, Arlington Heights, IL 60006
Contact:** Timothy Mooney **Program:** a new newsletter providing reports on new manuscripts to literary managers, dramaturgs, artistic directors, producers, theatre programs and agents; reader's fee: $10; subscription: $20

SHENANDOAH VALLEY PLAYWRIGHTS RETREAT
**ShenanArts, Box 167-F, Route 5, Staunton, VA 24401 (703) 248-1868
Contact:** Robert Graham Small, Director **Program:** a fellowship for a 3-week residency (Jul-Aug.) for purpose of providing "a stimulating, challenging environment for playwrights to test and develop new work"; activities include personal writing time; readings by writers of their own works, discussions with directors and dramaturgs, workshops providing "on-the-feet/on-the page exploration of each play" with acting company, public staged readings, discussions **Procedure:** send 2 bound copies of script typed in standard format, personal statement of writing background, sas postcard, $10 fee **Deadline:** Apr. 1, 1989 **Notification:** Jul. 1, 1989 **Comments:** See Virginia Playwriting Fellowships listing in this section. Fellowships are available, based on competition for admission: The Jack Morrison Playwriting Fellowship, The Retreat Alumni Fellowship, American College Theatre Festival Fellowships (see American College Theatre Festival listing in Contests).

SOURCEWORKS
**Source Theatre Company, 1809 14th St. NW,
Washington, DC 20009 (202) 462-1073**
Contact: Pat Murphy Sheehy, Artistic Director **Program:**
at least 20 evenings (Oct.-May) of script-in-hand productions
of original new works or "theatre rarities"; host organization
for emerging projects from Washington area playwright
support groups and new production companies

SOUTHEAST PLAYWRIGHTS PROJECT
Box 14252, Atlanta, GA 30324 (404) 242-5906
Contact: Gayle Austin, Executive Director **Program:** a
service organization for playwrights who reside, or who have
resided, in the Southeast; programs include script development
(cold readings, rehearsed and staged readings, non-
performance workshops and bi-monthly Writers' Lab) and
career development (dramaturgical advice, retreats,
networking, mentor program, free theatre tickets); programs
planned for the future include script circulation service,
fellowships, emergency loan fund, internships, classes,
publications of directories of dramaturgs and directors **Fee:**
$25 General Member **Comment:** Formerly Atlanta New Play
Project.

SOUTHERN ILLINOIS UNIVERSITY PLAYWRIGHT'S WORKSHOP
Theater Dept., SIU, Carbondale, IL 62901
Contact: Christian H. Moe, Head, Playwriting Program
This program is inactive in 1989.

SOUTHWEST THEATRE ASSOCIATION/ MARIE LAYTON BLISS NEW PLAYS PROGRAM
**School of Drama, University of Oklahoma,
Norman, OK 73019 Contact:** Theodore Herstand, Chair,
STA New Plays This program is inactive in 1989.

S.T.A.G.E.
**Box 214820, 3614 Cole Ave., Dallas, TX 75221
(214) 559-3917 Contact:** Robin Stanton, Executive
Director **Program:** a membership organization for
playwrights, actors, designers and directors in southwestern
U.S.; services include resource and script library, audition

callboards, career counseling, advice on resume preparation and contracts, publication of Center Stage, collaboration with The Plaza Theatre in operating the Playwrights Project script development program and Festival of New Plays summer workshop productions **Fee:** $35

STAGES
The Philadelphia Theatre Company,
The Bourse Bldg. Suite 734, 21 S. 5th St.,
Philadelphia, PA 19106 (215) 592-8333
Contact: Lynn M. Thompson, Literary Manager **Program:** a 2-week developmental program of rehearsals, workshop production of unproduced or substantially revised full-length plays or one-acts; pre-program Weekend Writers Retreat for selected playwrights (Apr. 1990); stipend, travel, housing provided **Deadline:** Dec. 15, 1989 **Notification:** Apr. 1990

STAGE II WORKSHOPS
Long Wharf Theatre, 222 Sargent Dr.,
New Haven, CT 06511 (203) 787-4284
Contact: James Luse, Literary Analyst **Program:** a developmental residency providing 3 weeks of rehearsals, 3 weeks of performances before an audience, with playwright in residence for the entire time **Procedure:** agent submission

SUMMER SOLSTICE THEATRE CONFERENCE
Brooklyn, NY   Our 1989 questionnaire was returned as "undeliverable," and no phone number is listed for this program.

THE SUNDANCE INSTITUTE
PLAYWRIGHTS LABORATORY
19 Exchange Pl., Salt Lake City, UT 84111
(801) 521-9330 Contact: David Kirk Chambers, Managing Director **Program:** a 3-week developmental program (Jul.) providing intensive workshops and readings of unproduced full-length plays and one-acts; stipend, room, board, travel provided **Procedure:** nomination of playwright and specific script by a committed not-for-profit theatre **Deadline:** Dec. 15, 1990

TCG OBSERVERSHIP PROGRAM

**Theatre Communications Group, 355 Lexington Ave.,
New York, NY 10017 (212) 697-5230
Contact:** Arthur Bartow, Associate Director **Program:**
semi-annual grants in 3 categories: Category I/Affiliated
Artists (artists holding salaried positions with TCG affiliated
theatres) and Category II/Unaffiliated Artists offer grants of
up to $2000 for inter-city travel in U.S. and Canada, per diem
to enable "theatre artists to extend their artistic boundaries by
exploring the work of colleagues in other locations," trips of at
least 1 week including visits to no fewer than 3 theatres;
Category III/Rehearsal Observerships offers grants for
inter-city travel to enable writers whose work is receiving full
production at a TCG Constituent theatre to be in residence for a
minimum of 2 weeks during rehearsal period **Procedure:**
application or nomination by TCG Constituent theatres

THEATER IN THE WORKS

**112 Fine Arts Center, University of Massachusetts,
Amherst, MA 01003 (413) 545-3490, -0681
Contact:** Virginia Scott, Resident Dramaturg **Program:** a
2-week residency for development of substantially unproduced
plays with limited practical requirements and/or small-scale
musicals; $325 weekly stipend, housing, travel provided.
Procedure: submit script **Deadline:** Feb. 15, 1989 for
Jul. 1989 program **Notification:** May 15, 1989

THEATRE ARTISTS WORKSHOP OF WESTPORT, INC.

**17 Morningside Dr. S, Westport, CT 06880
(203) 227-5836 Contact:** Doug Scott, President
Program: a not-for-profit membership organization with
Monday meetings of actors and playwrights; activities include
readings, staged readings, workshop productions **Procedure:**
submit script for approval

THEATRE BAY AREA

**2940 16th St. Suite 102, San Francisco, CA 94103
(415) 621-0427 Contact:** Jean Schiffman,
Communications Director **Program:** a membership and
resource organization for theatre artists in the San Francisco
area; support services available; publications include
Callboard monthly magazine and *Theatre Directory of the San*

Francisco Bay Area ($13.50 for non-members, $11.50 for members) which includes resources for playwrights   **Fees:** $27 per year individual, $32 per year organization

THEATRE COMMUNICATIONS GROUP
355 Lexington Ave., New York, NY 10017
(212) 697-5230   Contact: Peter Zeisler, Director **Program:**   the national organization for America's professional not-for-profit theatres; programs and services include conferences, seminars, TCG Hispanic Translation Commissions (see Contests), TCG Observership Program (see listing in this section), a theatre resource library and computerized data bank; publications include *Dramatists Sourcebook* (see The Playwright's Library), *American Theatre* magazine (see Publishers and The Playwright's Library) and *Plays in Process/New Plays USA* (see Publishers), *ArtSEARCH* bulletin of job opportunities, *Theatre Profiles* reference guide to constituent theatres

THIRD STEP THEATRE COMPANY
SPRING FESTIVAL OF STAGED READINGS
308 W. 103rd ST. #3C, New York, NY 10025
(212) 865-1094   Contact: Margit Ahlin, Literary Manager   **Program:** annual festival of staged readings followed by discussions; possible cash award to best play **Procedure:**   request guidelines available in fall 1989 **Deadline:** Dec. 31, 1989 **Notification:** 3 months

UNIVERSITY OF ALABAMA
NEW PLAYWRIGHTS' PROGRAM
Dept. of Theatre & Dance, Box 870239, University of Alabama, Tuscaloosa, AL 35487-0239
(205) 348-9032   Contact: Director   **Program:**   a developmental residency for emerging playwrights; activities include staged reading, workshop for full production of unproduced scripts; resident may offer limited workshops; stipend, travel, expenses provided **Procedure:** submit script with cover letter **Response time:** 2 months

VIRGINIA PLAYWRIGHTS FELLOWSHIPS
ShenanArts, Box 167F, Route 5,
Staunton, VA 24401 (703) 248-1868
Contact: Kathleen Tosco, Managing Director **Program:** 2 annual fellowships of $2000 and acceptance to 1989 Shenandoah Valley Playwrights Retreat (see listing in this section) for playwrights who have resided in VA for a major portion of the past year; students ineligible **Deadline:** Apr. 1, 1989 **Notification:** Jun. 1, 1989

VOLUNTEER LAWYERS FOR THE ARTS (VLA)
1285 Avenue of the Americas 3rd Floor,
New York, NY 10019 (212) 977-9270
Program: a national organization arranging free legal representation and counseling for artists and not-for-profit organizations unable to afford private counsel and with arts-related legal problems; services include educational program of seminars on not-for-profit incorporation, legal workshops, national conferences; publications include *Law & the Arts* quarterly journal ($30 annual subscription) and guides covering issues in copyright, contracts, privacy and libel

THE WASHINGTON THEATRE FESTIVAL
Source Theatre Company, 1809 14th St. NW,
Washington, DC 20009 (202) 462-1073
Contact: Pat Murphy Sheehy, Artistic Director **Program:** annual program (Jul.-Aug.) involving small professional theatres "on and around 14th Street"; The New Play Showcase: 10 evenings of full productions of full-length plays or evenings of one-acts, Theatre Row Events: 10 workshop productions receive 1-3 performances each, The Ten-Minute Play Competition: 3-night event with at least 25 entries and $75 grand prize; awards presented at Festival Awards Ceremony

WHETSTONE THEATRE COMPANY PLAYWRIGHTS PROGRAM
Box 800, Putney, VT 05346 (802) 387-4355
Contact: Tamara Tormohlen, Managing Director **Program:** a developmental program for plays not professionally produced; public workshops, staged readings, discussions, possible production; stipend, housing, possible travel provided **Procedure:** submit script

WOMEN IN THEATRE FESTIVAL
64 Wyman St.; Jamaica Plain, MA 02130
(617) 524-0971   Contact: Sophie Parker, Festival Director **Program:** organization providing exposure for women in theatre arts and nurturing women's theatre network; services include publication of *Women in Theatre Resource Guide* and annual multi-cultural/multi-racial festival of previously mounted productions of new works **Deadline:** Sept. 30, 1989

THE WOMEN'S PROJECT AND PRODUCTIONS
220 W. 42nd St. 18th Floor, New York, NY 10036
(212) 382-2750   Contact: Suzanne Bennett, Literary Manager **Program:** a producing organization serving largely women playwrights and directors; activities include staged readings, workshops, productions and forums; members receive *Dialogues* newsletter **Procedure:** submit full-length script, Sept.–Jun. **Notification:** 5-9 months

WOW (WOMEN ONE WORLD) CAFE
59 E. 4th St., New York, NY 10003
(212) 460-8067   Contact: Claire Moed, Wowette-at-large **Program:** a cooperative membership organization for women playwrights, producers, directors and performers (men are welcome if event is coordinated by a women); program provides an opportunity for playwrights to see and work in plays that may be presented in readings, staged readings or workshops; members may share in box office receipts and are expected to cooperate in all aspects of the program; meetings generally take place on Tuesday evenings

YADDO
Box 395, Saratoga Springs, NY 12866
(518) 584-0746 Contact: Myra Sklarew, President **Program:** 1-2 month residencies for artists of "professional standing and achievement as evidenced by publication or performance of works"; room, studio space, meals provided **Deadlines:** Jan. 15, 1989 for 1989-90; Aug. 1, 1989 for remaining winter 1989-90 space

THE YARD
325 Spring St., New York, NY 10013
(212) 206-7885   Contact: Walt Sado, Administrative
Director **Program:** 6-8 week residencies (May 15-Jun. 30)
in Chilmark, Martha's Vineyard, for collaborations of
choreographer and artist from any other discipline on new
work; 2 selected teams work with performing artists; works
premiere in 100-seat Barn Theater; possible Boston and/or
New York performance in Sept.; stipend provided **Procedure:**
submit joint proposal **Deadline:** Dec. 15, 1989
Notification: Feb. 1989

YELLOW SPRINGS INSTITUTE
Art School Rd., Chester Springs, PA 19425
(215) 827-9111   Contact: Kimberly Niemela Duggan,
Assistant to the Director **Program:** annual Artists'
Residency Fellowships in dance, performance art, new music,
experimental theatre and interdisciplinary forms for the
development of new works **Deadline:** inquire (Dec. 18 in
1988)

YOUNG PLAYWRIGHTS
The Playwrights' Center, 2301 Franklin Ave. E,
Minneapolis, MN 55406 (612) 332-7581
Contact: Gail Smogard **Program:** year-round activities
for playwrights under 19 years of age: Young Playwrights
Contest & Festival, Summer Playwriting Conference
(scholarships and college credit available), mentorships with
professional playwrights; readings and workshops with theatre
professionals, Playwrights Center classes, Play Readings and
Shoptalks, Young Playwrights Newsletter, teacher training
Comment: See The Playwrights' Center listing in this
section.

Publishers

Guidelines for submitting materials to the publishers listed in *The Playwright's Companion 1989*:

Read each listing thoroughly and carefully and follow any advice offered.

Do not expect a publisher to alter its exclusive interests or specifications in order to publish your play.

Comply exactly with each publisher's stated submission policy.

Be sure that appropriate materials accompany every submission (see The Playwright's Checklist).

Do not expect any publisher to return materials, or respond to any correspondence, not accompanied by self-addressed mailers or envelopes, adequately stamped and large enough to accommodate the materials to be mailed.

ACTION THEATRE PRESS
96 Madbury Rd., Durham, NH 03824
This publisher is not accepting scripts in 1989.

AMELIA MAGAZINE
329 E St., Bakersfield, CA 93304 (805) 323-4064
Contact: Frederick A. Raborg, Jr., Editor
See Frank McClure One-Act Play Award listing in Contests.

AMERICAN THEATRE MAGAZINE
Theatre Communications Group, 355 Lexington Ave., New York, NY 10017 (212) 697-5230
Contact: Jim O'Quinn, Editor **Works**: full-length plays, one-acts, translations, adaptations, children's plays **Special interests**: significant contemporary works; translations from all periods **Readership**: "General circulation." **Policy**: solicited script **Remuneration**: negotiable fee; 10 copies **Advice:** "The vast majority of plays published have been produced in a TCG theatre, so writer should concentrate on obtaining production." **Comment:** 5 plays are published each year.

THE AMERICAS REVIEW
Room 429-AH University of Houston, 4800 Calhoun, Houston, TX 77004 (713) 749-4768 **Contact:** Nicolás Kanellos, Publisher **Works**: full-length plays, one-acts, adaptations, musicals, children's plays **Guidelines**: authors must be Hispanic; works must be unpublished and written in either Spanish or English **Policy**: unsolicited script **Response**: 3 months **Remuneration**: fee; 2 copies

ANCHORAGE PRESS, INC.
Box 8067, New Orleans, LA 70182 (504) 283-8868 **Contact:** Orlin Corey, Editor **Works**: children's plays: full-length plays, one-acts, translations, adaptations, musicals **Guidelines**: works must be previously produced plays (at least 3 productions required, 5 preferred) written for trained actors **Readership**: "All working theatres, whether educationally based, community or professional." **Policies**: unsolicited script with proof of productions (reviews, programs); professional recommendation; agent submission **Response**: 30 days query; 120 days script **Remuneration**: 50% of royalties, 10% of play sales; 10 copies **Your chances**: 1000+/10 **Advice**: "Read the literature in the field; see a current Anchorage Press catalogue; work in the theatre in general; master the development of plays through productions first."

ARAN PRESS
1320 S. Third St., Louisville, KY 40208 (502) 636-0115 Contact: Tom Eagan, Editor & Publisher **Works**: full-length plays, one-acts **Special interests**: "We concentrate on 5 markets: professional theatre, community theatre, summer stock, dinner theatre and college/university theatre." **Guidelines**: "Standard play format; typed. All subjects." **Readership**: "Hopefully our readers are producers!" **Policy**: query/synopsis **Response**: 2 weeks **Remuneration**: 50% production royalty, 10% book royalty **Your chances**: 200-300/50 in 1988 **Advice**: "We issue a catalogue each year of the plays we publish."

ART CRAFT PUBLISHING COMPANY/
HEUER PUBLISHING COMPANY

233 Dows Bldg., Cedar Rapids, IA 52406
(319) 364-6311   Contact: C. E. McMullen, President
Works: 3-act plays, one-acts, musicals   **Guidelines:**
"Material must be within the scope of high school students."
Policies: unsolicited script; query/synopsis   **Best time:**
early spring **Response:** 5-6 weeks **Remuneration:** "Either
outright payment or percentage; 12 copies."

ARTE PUBLICO PRESS

University of Houston, 4800 Calhoun,
Houston, TX 77004   (713) 749-4768
Contact: Nicolás Kanellos, Publisher   **Works:** full-length
plays, one-acts **Guidelines:** Authors must be U.S. Hispanic
playwrights; works must be produced **Readership:** Hispanic
Policies: unsolicited script; query/synopsis; professional
recommendation **Response:** 4 months **Your chances:** 50/1

BAKER'S PLAYS

100 Chauncy St., Boston, MA 02111
(617) 482-1280   Contact: John B. Welch, Editor
Works: full-length plays, one-acts, adaptations, musicals,
children's plays **Special interests:** religious plays; "mature
plays for teen actors" **Guidelines:** previously produced plays
preferred; works must be 24-80 pages in length **Readership:**
"High school, community, university and children's theatre;
religious theatre."   **Policies:** unsolicited script; query/
synopsis; agent submission **Response:** 1 week query; 4
months script   **Remuneration:** "Varies from 50%-80%; 6
copies." **Your chances:** 800/20-15 **Advice:** "Get it
produced. Collaborate with an understanding director and
actors." **Comment:** Baker's publishes as many as 25 scripts
for the amateur market each year.

BROADWAY PLAY PUBLISHING INC.

357 W. 20th St., New York, NY 10011
(212) 627-1055   Contact: Christopher Gould, President
Works: full-length plays, musicals **Special interest:**
contemporary American works **Guidelines:** works must be 80
minutes in length **Policies:** unsolicited script; query/synopsis
with   dialogue   sample   and   resume;   professional

recommendation; agent submission **Response**: immediate query; 4 months script **Remuneration**: advance; 10%/20%; 10 copies **Advice**: "Write something we've never seen before."

CALLALOO
Dept. of English, Wilson Hall, University of Virginia, Charlottesville, VA 22903 (804) 924-6637
Contact: Charles H. Rowell, Editor **Works**: full-length plays, one-acts, translations, adaptations **Special interest**: "African American works." **Guidelines**: previously produced works preferred **Readership**: "African American." **Policies**: unsolicited script with resume; query/synopsis with dialogue sample and resume; professional recommendation; agent submission **Response**: 1 week query; 1 year script **Remuneration**: $150 **Your chances**: 10/1

CASTA-INSTITUTE FOR CONTEMPORARY EAST EUROPEAN DRAMA AND THEATRE
Graduate Center of the City University of New York, 33 W. 42nd St. Room 1222, New York, NY 10036 (212) 790-4209, -4464 Contact: Daniel C. Gerould, Alma H. Law, Co-directors **Works**: translations of Eastern European plays written since 1945 **Special interests**: published or unpublished translations for listing in bibliographies; translations-in-progress; previously published bibliographies of Polish and Soviet plays **Policy**: query/synopsis

CHARLES RIVER CREATIVE ARTS PRESS
Dover, MA   See Freelance Press.

CHILD LIFE MAGAZINE
Box 567, Indianapolis, IN 46206 (317) 636-8881
Works: children's plays **Special interest**: works for classroom or living-room staging, for children aged 8-11 **Policy**: unsolicited script **Remuneration**: approximately 6 cents per word; magazine buys all rights

CHILDREN'S PLAYMATE MAGAZINE
**1100 Waterway Blvd., Box 567,
Indianapolis, IN 46206** (317) 636-8881 ext. 249
Contact: Elizabeth Rinck, Editor   **Works**: children's plays
Special interest: "Health-related themes."   **Guidelines**:
works must be 500-800 words in length **Policy**: unsolicited
script **Response**: 10 weeks **Remuneration**: approximately
6 cents per word

COACH HOUSE PRESS, INC.
Box 458, Morton Grove, IL 60053 (312) 967-1777
Contact: David Jewell, Publisher **Works**: full-length plays,
one-acts, translations, adaptations, musicals, children's plays,
plays for senior adults **Special interests**: "Human
intelligence, our caring and cooperative natures, and our innate
zest for life." **Readership**: "Most of our plays will be
produced by adult or high school actors for audiences K-8, in
schools and on tours to schools—urban, rural and suburban."
Policies: unsolicited script with resume; query/synopsis with
resume; professional recommendation; agent submission;
"include notes on experience with production: observations,
changes made" **Best times**: Nov.-Mar., summer **Response**: 1
month query; 3-4 months script **Remuneration**: 10% script
sales, 50% performance royalty **Your chances**: 150/3-8
Advice: "Get at least 1 first-class production of your play and
rewrite/tighten based on your observations with an audience."

CONTEMPORARY DRAMA SERVICE
**Meriwether Publishing, Ltd., Box 7710,
Colorado Springs, CO 80907** (303) 594-4422
Contact: Ted Zapel, Associate Editor   **Works**: one-acts,
adaptations, musicals, children's plays   **Special interest**:
"One-act comedies or musicals that can be performed by young
people in church or school." **Guidelines**: works are usually 35
pages in length **Specifications**: "No serious, legitimate-
theatre plays; no excessive profanity or x-rated subject
matter." **Readership**: "Youngsters and non-denominational
church folk." **Policies**: unsolicited script; query/synopsis
Response: 2 weeks-1 month **Remuneration**: flat payment of
$200-$600; 10% royalty or negotiable fee; 3 copies **Your
chances**: 1200/50-60 **Advice**: "Send for our catalogue and
guidelines; enclose $1 for postage."

DRAMA BOOK PUBLISHERS
260 Fifth Ave., New York, NY 10001
(212) 725-5377 Contact: Ralph Pine, Editor-in-Chief
Works: full-length plays, translations, musicals **Special interest**: plays previously produced on Broadway **Guidelines**: works must be produced on Broadway, off Broadway or in London **Policy**: professional recommendation **Remuneration**: advance against royalties

DRAMATIC PUBLISHING COMPANY
311 Washington St., Box 109, Woodstock, IL 60098
(815) 338-7170 Contact: Sally Fyfe, Editor
Works: full-length plays, one-acts, adaptations, musicals, children's plays **Guidelines**: one-acts must be at least 30 minutes in length **Readership:** "Elementary, junior high, high school, college, community and professional teachers/ directors." **Policies**: unsolicited script; professional recommendation; agent submission **Response**: 3 months **Remuneration**: "By contract." **Your chances**: 500-600/ 8-12 "of unsolicited scripts" **Advice**: "If produced, include reviews and photos."

DRAMATICS MAGAZINE
3368 Central Pkwy., Cincinnati, OH 45225-2392
(513) 559-1996 Contact: Don Corathers, Editor
Works: full-length plays, one-acts, translations, adaptations **Special interests**: produced plays preferred; "roles that are within the range of high school students and plays that address the concerns of young people aged 16-20" **Guidelines**: "No photocopies of dot matrix printouts, please." **Readership**: "Teens to young adults, generally brighter than average, very interested in theatre; also 3500 high school and college theatre directors." **Policies**: unsolicited script; query/synopsis; professional recommendation; agent submission; solicited script **Response**: 2 weeks query; 6 weeks script **Remuneration**: flat payment of $100-$200; 5 copies (negotiable); "we buy first serial rights only" **Your chances**: 500/5

DRAMATIKA
429 Hope St., Tarpon Springs, FL 34689
Contact: John Pyros, Editor **Works**: one-acts **Guidelines**: scripts must be camera ready, 8"x11" **Policy**: unsolicited script **Response**: 1 month **Remuneration**: copies

DRAMATISTS PLAY SERVICE
440 Park Ave. S., New York, NY 10016
(212) 683-8960 Contact: F. Andrew Leslie, President **Works**: full-length plays, one-acts **Guidelines**: works must be produced **Policies**: professional recommendation; agent submission

ELDRIDGE PUBLISHING COMPANY, INC.
Box 216, Franklin, OH 45005 (513) 746-6531
Contact: Nancy Vorhis, Editor **Works**: full-length plays, one-acts, adaptations, musicals, children's plays, Christmas plays **Special interests**: "Fun, light-hearted material as well as some serious works. Larger-cast plays do better for schools, so more students can become involved." **Guidelines**: produced works preferred **Specifications**: "Nothing x-rated!" **Readership**: "Elementary, middle and high schools; community theatres; churches. We have a widely varied marked, but do not reach inner city." **Policies**: unsolicited script; query/synopsis **Response**: 3 weeks query; 3 months script **Remuneration**: flat payment of $125 or more; 35% collected royalties; 12 copies **Your chances**: 350/20; "99% of our submissions are unsolicited" **Advice**: "Have the play produced locally to work out any 'bugs' before submission. Remember, stage action is critical. Keep dialogue snappy."

FREELANCE PRESS
Box 548, 56 Center St., Dover, MA 02030
(617) 785-1260 Contact: Priscilla B. Dewey, Managing Editor **Works**: musicals for young audiences **Guidelines**: entries must be unpublished and less than 50 pages in length; scores must be camera ready **Policy**: unsolicited script **Response**: 1-2 months **Remuneration**: royalty $50/$35 **Your chances**: 10-15/6 **Comment**: Formerly Charles River Creative Arts Press.

GEORGE SPELVIN'S THEATRE BOOK
Box 361, Newark, DE 19715
Contact: Kathleen Danaher Parks, Managing Editor **Works**: full-length plays, one-acts, translations, adaptations **Guidelines**: works must be unpublished **Policy**: unsolicited script **Response**: 3 months **Remuneration**: copies

HEUER PUBLISHING COMPANY
Cedar Rapids, IA   See Art Craft Publishing Company/Heuer Publishing Company.

I. E. CLARK, INC., PUBLISHERS
St. John's Rd., Box 246, Schulenburg, TX 78956
(409) 743-3232   Contact: M. A. Berckenhoff, Manager, Editorial Dept.   **Works**: full-length plays, one-acts, translations, adaptations, musicals, children's plays **Guidelines**: works must have had "2 or 3 previous productions directed by someone other than the author" **Policy**: unsolicited script   **Response**: 6 months-1 year **Remuneration**: royalty **Your chances**: 1000/10-15 "over half of which are by our established authors" **Advice**: "Get produced by a superb director and polish your play according to his advice. Ask yourself: why, with thousands of good plays available, would anybody want to do my play?"

INSTRUCTOR MAGAZINE
7500 Old Oak Blvd., Cleveland, OH 44130
(216) 243-8100   Works: children's plays   **Special interest**: holiday and seasonal themes   **Policy**: unsolicited script **Response**: 6-8 weeks **Remuneration**: $75-$125 **Advice**: "Submit seasonal plays 4-6 months before season."

LILLENAS PUBLISHING COMPANY
Box 419527, Kansas City, MO 64141
(816) 931-1900 ext. 319   Contact: Paul M. Miller, Editor   **Works**: full-length plays, one-acts, adaptations, musicals, children's plays, sketches   **Special interests**: unproduced plays preferred; "scripts must reflect a philosophical/religious point of view, in keeping with Christianity" **Guidelines**: full-length plays must be 90 minutes-2 hours in length, one-acts 30-45 minutes, sketches shorter **Readership**: "Somewhat conservative Christians of

all ages." **Policies**: unsolicited script; query/synopsis **Best time**: "Christmas plays in fall for following year." **Response**: 2 weeks query; 2-3 months script **Remuneration**: flat payment: $5 per page; 10% royalty; 25 copies **Your chances**: 200/12-15 **Advice**: "Know our market; if Christmas is your thing, find a new angle; visit a Christian bookstore and look over Lillenas script formats."

MODERN INTERNATIONAL DRAMA
Theatre Dept., SUNY, Binghamton, NY 13905
(607) 777-2704 Contact: George E. Wellwarth, Co-editor **Works**: translations of previously untranslated plays **Guidelines**: "Consult inside front cover for format." **Readership**: "Academic and professional theatre." **Policy**: unsolicited script with author's permission **Response**: 1 week query; 1 month script, if submitted Sept.-May **Remuneration**: 3 copies **Your chances**: 20/4

MODERN LITURGY
160 E. Virginia St. Suite 290, San Jose, CA 95112
(408) 286-8505 Contact: Ken Guentert, Editor **Works**: "Short sketches suitable for presentation during worship services." **Guidelines**: works should be no more than 10 minutes in length **Specifications**: "Minimum props." **Readership**: "Worship planners and artists." **Policy**: unsolicited script **Best time:** 1 year before issue date **Response**: 2 months **Remuneration**: subscription

NEW PLAYS INCORPORATED
Box 273, Rowayton, CT 06853
(203) 866-4520 Contact: Patricia Whitton, Publisher **Works**: children's plays, translations, adaptations and musicals **Special interest**: "Out of the ordinary plays to be performed for young audiences by adults and teens." **Guidelines**: works must be produced ("by someone other than the author") and 90 minutes in length **Readership**: "Looking for high-quality writing, depth of theme." **Policies**: unsolicited script; professional recommendation **Remuneration**: 50% production royalties, 10% script sales; 6 copies **Your chances**: 300-500/2-4 "often from writers we are already working with" **Advice**: "Read our catalogue; it will give a better idea of our interests."

ORACLE PRESS
5323 Heatherstone Dr., Baton Rouge, LA 70820
(504) 766-5577 Contact: Cj Stevens, Director
Works: full-length plays, one-acts, translations, adaptations
Special interest: works for colleges, high schools and other non-professional groups **Guidelines**: works must be unproduced, uncollected or out-of-print **Policy**: unsolicited script **Response**: 2 weeks-2 months **Remuneration**: 10% book royalty; 3-10 copies **Comment:** See *Plays* listing in this section.

PERFORMING ARTS JOURNAL
PAJ Publications, 325 Spring St. Room 318, New York, NY 10013 (212) 243-3885, -3974
Contact: Bonnie Maranca, Gautam Dasgupta, Co-Publishers/ Editors **Works**: full-length plays, one-acts, translations, adaptations **Special interests**: plays, critical literature on the performing arts **Policy**: query/synopsis **Response time**: 1-2 months **Remuneration**: advance; option and/or royalty **Comment:** PAJ Publications is interested in "20th century modernist fiction, nature and gardening books with literary bent and other literary titles."

PIONEER DRAMA SERVICE, INC.
Box 22555, Denver, CO 80222 (303) 759-4297
Contact: Shubert Fendrich **Works**: full-length plays, musicals **Special interest**: "We deal primarily in the educational theatre market." **Guidelines**: "All material should be produced prior to submission; 60-90 minutes playing time; large casts." **Specifications**: "Single set preferred; no obscene language or overly mature situations." **Policies**: unsolicited script; query/synopsis **Best time**: Nov.-Mar. **Response**:1 week-1 month **Remuneration**: varies **Your chances**: 150/15 **Advice**: "Check our catalogue to make sure your play is the type of thing we use; query."

PLAYERS PRESS, INC.
Box 1132, Studio City, CA 91604 (818) 789-4980
Contact: Robert W. Gordon, Senior Editor **Works**: full-length plays, one-acts, translations, adaptations, musicals, children's plays; performing arts books **Guidelines**: works must be produced **Specifications**: "No pornography or objectionable

material." **Readership**: "Professional, semi-professional and amateur theatres and the reading public." **Policy**: query/ synopsis **Response**: 2 months query; 12 months script **Remuneration**: negotiable royalty **Your chances**: 300-2000/5-25

PLAYS
Oracle Press, 5323 Heatherstone Dr., Baton Rouge, LA 70820 (504) 766-5577 **Contact**: Cj Stevens, Senior Editor **Works**: full-length plays, one-acts, translations, adaptations **Guidelines**: works must be unpublished **Policy**: unsolicited script **Response**: 2 weeks-2 months **Remuneration**: 3 copies **Comments**: *Plays* normally publishes 16-20 new scripts each year. Oracle Press (see listing this section) reserves the right to republish plays in book form.

PLAYS IN PROCESS (PIP)
Theatre Communications Group, 355 Lexington Ave., New York, NY 10017 (212) 697-5230 **Contact**: Director of Literary Services **Works**: full-length plays, one-acts, translations, adaptaitons, musicals, children's plays **Guidelines**: works must have been produced during the current season by a TCG member theatre **Readership:** "PIP subscribership (mainly non-profit theatres in U.S., Canada and abroad, college and university theatres and libraries.)" **Policy**: nomination by artistic director or literary manager of producing theatre; request nomination form from Literary Services Dept. **Best time:** "As early in season as possible." **Deadline:** Jun. 30, 1989 **Response**: 3 months **Remuneration**: international circulation of script; 10 copies **Your chances**: 100-150/12 **Advice**: "Submit work to TCG member theatres and hope for the best." **Comment:** Related program: *New Plays USA* biennial anthology series of plays selected from PIP circulation and *American Theatre* magazine (see listing in this section); playwright receives royalty and 6 copies.

PLAYS, THE DRAMA MAGAZINE FOR YOUNG PEOPLE
120 Boylston St., Boston, MA 02116 (617) 423-3157 Contact: Elizabeth Preston, Managing Editor **Works**: one-act children's plays and adaptations

Guidelines: adaptations must be of works in public domain; 20-30 minutes playing time preferred for junior-senior high, 15-20 minutes for middle grades, 8-15 minutes for lower grades **Specifications**: "Sets should be simple enough for young people to erect without too much trouble; low-cost materials, nothing elaborate." **Policies**: unsolicited script; query/synopsis for adaptation **Response**: 2 weeks **Remuneration**: "Rates vary on acceptance; we buy all rights." **Your chances**: 250-300/25-30 **Advice**: Request style sheet.

RESOURCE PUBLICATIONS
160 E. Virginia St. #290, San Jose CA 95112
(408) 286-8505 Contact: Ken Guentert, Editorial Director
Works: short plays, collections **Exclusive interest**: works for religious education classes, youth ministry or celebrations **Guidelines**: works must be unpublished and 7-15 minutes in length **Policy**: unsolicited script **Response**: 2 months

SAMUEL FRENCH, INC.
45 W. 25th St., New York, NY 10010
(212) 206-8990 Contact: Lawrence Harbison, Editor
Works: full-length plays, one-acts, translations, adaptations, musicals, children's plays **Special interests**: "Light comedies, mysteries, Broadway and off Broadway hits." **Guidelines**: "We prefer professional stageplay format, an example of which is our publication *Guidelines* ($3 including postage)." **Policies**: unsolicited script; query/synopsis; professional recommendation; agent submission **Response**: 1 week query; 2-8 months script **Remuneration**: 80% amateur, 90% stock royalty **Your chances**: 1500/"few" **Advice**: "Have it succeed on the Island of Manhattan."

SCHOLASTIC SCOPE
730 Broadway, New York, NY 10003
(212) 505-3000 Contact: Fran Claro, Editor
Works: plays for teenagers **Guidelines**: works must be 800-6000 words in length and suitable for classroom readings by junior and senior high students **Policy**: unsolicited script **Remuneration**: $200 or more

SCRIPTS AND SCRIBBLES
141 Wooster St., New York, NY 10012
(212) 473-6695 Contact: Daryl Chin, Consulting Editor
Works: full-length plays, one-acts, performance-art texts and scenarios **Policy**: query/synopsis **Response**: 3-4 months **Remuneration**: 25 copies

SWIFT KICK
1711 Amherst St., Buffalo, NY 14214
(716) 837-7778 Contact: Robin Kay Willoughby, Editor
Works: full-length plays, one-acts **Exclusive interest**: experimental works **Guidelines**: works must be unproduced **Readership**: "Very small, crosses all category lines." **Policies**: unsolicited script; query/synopsis **Best time**: summer **Response**: 3 months **Remuneration**: "Varying number of complimentary copies." **Your chances**: 1/"1 in 1 of 7 issues" **Advice**: "Order sample copy ($7);   have the philosophical outlook of Tzara or Beckett."

TEJAS ART PRESS
207 Terrell Rd., San Antonio, TX 78209
(512) 826-7803 Contact: Robert Wilson, Editor
Works: full-length plays **Guidelines**: authors must be American Indians; works must be unpublished and scheduled for first production **Policy**: unsolicited script **Response**: 1 month **Remuneration**: negotiable royalty; copies

THEATER
222 York St., New Haven, CT 06520
(203) 436-1417   Contact: Joel Schechter, Editor
Works: full-length plays, one-acts, translations, adaptations **Guidelines**: works must have received 1 production only **Policy**:   query/synopsis   **Response**:   2   months **Remuneration**:   approximately $100   and/or   copies **Comment:** *Theater* publishes 1 new script per issue.

UNITED ARTS
141 Wooster St., New York, NY 10012
(212) 473-6695 Contact: Daryl Chin, Editor
Works: one-acts,   translations **Exclusive   interest:** unconventional, avant garde works **Policy:** query/synopsis **Response:** 6-8 weeks **Remuneration**: copies

WEST COAST PLAYS
California Theatre Council, Box 48320, Los Angeles, CA 90048 (213) 874-3163
Works: full-length plays, one-acts, translations, adaptations, musicals, children's plays, performance art **Guidelines**: works must have received their first U.S. production west of the Rockies **Policy**: unsolicited script **Remuneration**: up to $100 advance against royalty; copies **Comment**: See California Theatre Council listing in Special Programs.

WOMEN IN PERFORMANCE: A JOURNAL OF FEMINIST THEORY
New York University, Tisch School of the Arts, 721 Broadway 6th Floor, New York, NY 10003 (212) 663-7025 **Contact**: Katheryn White, Theatre Co-Editor **Works**: full-length plays, one-acts, translations **Special interest**: "Feminist performance theory." **Guidelines**: works must be unpublished, unproduced and by, for and about women **Policies**: query/synopsis preferred; unsolicited script **Response**: 6 months **Advice**: Request guidelines; inquire for details of monthly staged reading program. **Comment:** This journal normally publishes 2 new scripts each year.

The Playwright's Companion 1990

- **To be published in December 1989.**

- **More than 1,000 up-to-date listings** of theatres, contests, programs, publishers and agents--plus the marketing tips and cross references that have helped to make *The Playwright's Companion* **"an indispensable resource for playwrights"** (*Library Journal*) and **"a goldmine"** (*Dramatics*).

- **Spotlight** on a professional theatre or program committed to new plays and playwrights.

- **Publisher's price:** **$18.95** (shipping and handling included).

- To order your copy ot *The Playwright's Companion 1990*, complete the form below and mail it, along with your check or money order to **Feedback Theatrebooks, 305 Madison Ave., Suite 411, New York, NY 10165**. Please allow 3-4 weeks for delivery.

The Playwright's Companion 1990

Reservation Form

Name: _____

Address: _____

City, State, Zip: _____

Phone: (_____)_____

No. copies: _____ Payment enclosed: $_____

**Feedback Theatrebooks, 305 Madison Ave.,
Suite 411, New York, NY 10165. Thank you!**

Agents

The Playwright's Library

Contest Entry Calendar

Cross Reference to Special Interests

Cross Reference to Special Programs

Index to Listings

A playwright hoping to secure the services of an agent should send a brief query letter describing his or her work and a resume providing details of plays produced or published and awards and honors received. Agents do not welcome unsolicited scripts or phone calls from playwrights whose work they do not know. "The Literary Agent," an informational brochure on the standard practices of and services offered by agents (see The Playwright's Library) is available free from the Society of Author's Representatives, Box 650 Old Chelsea Station, New York, NY 10113.

Agency for the Performing Arts, 888 Seventh Ave., New York, NY 10106 (212) 582-1500;
Agents: Richard Krawetz, Rick Leed

Alan Willig and Associates, 337 W. 43rd St. Suite 1B, New York, NY 10036 (212) 586-4300

Anna-Marie McKay, 400 W. 43rd St. #3A,
New York, NY 10036 (212) 564-6990

Ann Elmo Agency, 60 E. 42nd St., New York, NY 10165 (212) 661-2880

Artists Agency, Inc., 230 W. 55th St. Suite 29D,
New York, NY 10019 (212) 245-6960;
Agent: Jeannine Edmunds

Bertha Klausner International Literary Agency,
71 Park Ave., New York, NY 10016 (212) 685-2642

Bret Adams, 448 W. 44th St., New York, NY 10036
(212) 765-5630; Agents: Bret Adams, Mary Harden

Dorese Agency, 41 W . 82nd St, New York, NY 10024
(212) 580-2855; Agent: Alyss Dorese

The Dramatic Publishing Company, 311 Washington St., Woodstock, IL 60098 (815) 338-7170; Agent: Susan Sergel

Elisabeth Marton Agency, 96 Fifth Ave.,
New York, NY 10011 (212) 255-1908;
Agents: Elisabeth Marton, Tonda Marton

Ellen Neuwald, 902 N. Ronda Sevilla, Laguna Hills, CA 92653
(714) 380-7987

Evelyn J. Powers, 2311 Windingbrook Ct.,
Bloomington, IN 47401 (812) 336-5643
This agent is not currently representing playwrights but may do
so in the future.

Fifi Oscard Associates, 19 W. 44th St.,
New York, NY 10036 (212) 764-1100

Flora Roberts, Inc., 157 W. 57th St., New York, NY 10019
(212) 355-4165

The Gersh Agency, 103 W. 42nd St., New York, NY 10036
(212) 997-1818; Agent: Jaime Wolff

Graham Agency, 311 W. 43rd St., New York, NY 10036
(212) 489-7730; Agent: Earl Graham

Harold Matson Company, 276 Fifth Ave. Suite 303W,
New York, NY 10001 (212) 679-4490
This agency is not accepting new playwrights in 1989 but may
do so in the future.

Helen Harvey Associates, 410 W. 24th St.,
New York, NY 10011 (212) 675-7445;
Agents: Helen Harvey, Marion Matera

Helen Merrill, 435 W . 23rd St. #1A, New York, NY 10011
(212) 691-5326

Hutto Management, 405 W. 23rd St., New York, NY 10011
(212) 807-1234; Agent: Jack Hutto

International Creative Management, 40 W. 57th St., New
York, NY 10019 (212) 556-5600;
Agents: Bridget Aschenberg, Kay Brown, Mitch Douglas, Wiley
Hausam, Steve Sultan

Jack Lenny Associates, New York City and Los Angeles
Neither branch of this agency is accepting new clients.

Joyce P. Ketay, 334 W. 89th St. #4F, New York, NY 10024
(212) 799-2398

Kathe Telingator, 435 Bergen St., Brooklyn, NY 11217
(718) 230-4910

The Lantz Office, 888 Seventh Ave. Suite 2500,
New York, NY 10106 (212) 586-0200; Agents: Robert Lantz,
Edward Betz, Joy Harris

Lester Lewis Associates, New York City
This agency no longer represents playwrights.

Lois Berman, 240 W. 44th St., New York, NY 10036
(212) 575-5114

Lucy Kroll, 390 West End Ave. Suite 9B,
New York, NY 10024 (212) 877-0627, -0556;
Agents: Barbara Hogenson, Lucy Kroll

Marion Searchinger Associates, 327 Central Park W.,
New York, NY 10025 (212) 865-5777
This agency only occasionally represents playwrights.

Michael Imison Playwrights, New York Office: Box 1006
Ansonia Station, New York, NY 10023 (212) 874-2671;
Agent: Abbe Levin
London Office: 28 Almeida St., London N1 1TD, England
(01) 354-3174; Agents: Alan Brodie, Michael Imison

Paramuse Artists Associates,
1414 Avenue of theAmericas, New York, NY 10019
(212) 758-5055; Agent: Shirley Bernstein

Peregrine Whittlesey, 345 E. 80th St., #31F,
New York, NY 10021 (212) 737-0153

Robert A. Freedman Dramatic Agency, Inc.,
1501 Broadway #2310, New York, NY 10036
(212) 840-5760; Agents: Robert A. Freedman, Selma Luttinger

Rosenstone/Wender, 3 E. 48th St., New York, NY 10017
(212) 832-8330; Agents: John Gersten, Howard Rosenstone

Samuel French, Inc., 45 W. 25th St., New York, NY 10010
(212) 206-8990; Agents: Lawrence Harbison, William Talbot

Scott Hudson, 215 E. 76th St., New York, NY 10021
(212) 570-9645

The Shukat Company, 340 W. 55th St. #1A,
New York, NY 10019 (212) 582-7614; Literary
Representatives/Personal Managers: Scott Shukat, Larry
Weiss

Suhrkamp Verlag, 792 Columbus Ave., New York, NY 10025
(212) 865-0409; Agent: Kurt Bernheim

Susan Schulman Literary Agency, 454 W. 44th St.,
New York, NY 10036 (212) 713-1633

The Tantleff Office, 360 W. 20th St. #4F,
New York, NY 10011 (212) 627-2105; Agent: Jack Tantleff

William Morris Agency, Inc.,
1350 Avenue of the Americas, New York, NY 10019
(212) 586-5100; Agents: Leo Bookman, Peter Franklin, George
Lane, Owen Laster, Biff Liff, Gilbert Parker, Esther Sherman,
Jerome Talbert

Writers & Artists Agency, 70 W. 36th St. #501,
New York, NY 10018 (212) 947-8765; Agent: William Craver

The Playwright's Library

The Playwright's Library is a selective list of articles, periodicals, books and brochures which we believe to be valuable to dramatists at various stages in their careers.

Articles

Catron, Louis E., "One to One: The Art and Science of Writing Monologues," *Dramatics* (Oct. 1988), 29-37; presents ideas on the value of the theatrical monologue, writing techniques and "Rules" of the monologue.

Costa, Carol, "Marketing Your Play," *The Writer* (May 1988), 22-24; offers tips on polite and effective submission practice.

Dietz, Steven, "Developed to Death?," *American Theatre* (May, 1987), 42-43.

Kennedy, Adrienne, "Becoming a Playwright," *American Theatre* (Feb. 1988), 26-27.

Rosenthal, Lois, "Marsha Norman," *Writer's Digest* (Sept. 1988), 34-38; presents Norman's theories of playwriting as seen through her own experience.

Periodicals

American Theatre, New York: Theatre Communications Group; a monthly magazine dealing with the professional not-for-profit theatre in the U.S.; special "Plays and Playwrights" section provides information on opportunities and announces results of playwriting competitions.

Dramatics, Cincinnati: The International Thespian Society; a monthly magazine aimed at teachers and students of drama.

The Writer, Boston: The Writer, Inc.; a monthly magazine aimed at aspiring writers; each Sept. issue focuses on play markets.

Books

Archer, William. *Play-Making: A Manual of Craftsmanship.* Boston: Small, Maynard and Co., 1912.

Busfield, Roger M. Jr. *The Playwright's Art.* Westport, CT: Greenwood Press, 1958.

Catron, Louis E. *Writing, Producing, and Selling Your Play.* Englewood Cliffs, NJ: Prentice-Hall, Inc., 1984.

Charles, Jill, ed. *Directory of Theatre Training Programs.* Dorset, VT: Dorset Theatre Festival & Colony House, Inc. 1987.

Cohen, Edward M. *Working on a New Play.* New York: Prentice-Hall, Inc., 1988.

Cole, Toby, ed. *Playwrights on Playwriting.* New York: Hill and Wang, 1960.

Egri, Lagos. *The Art of Dramatic Writing.* New York: Simon and Schuster, 1960.

Else, Gerald F. (trans. and intro.). *Aristotle Poetics.* Ann Arbor, MI: The University of Michigan Press, 1967.

Grebanier, Bernard. *Playwriting: How to Write for the Theatre.* New York: Barnes & Noble, 1961.

Griffiths, Stuart. *How Plays Are Made: The Fundamental Elements of Play Construction.* Englewood Cliffs, NJ: Prentice-Hall, Inc., 1982.

Lawson, John Howard. *Theory and Technique of Playwriting.* New York: G. P. Putnam's Sons, 1949.

MacGowan, Kenneth. *A Primer of Playwriting.* New York: Random House, 1951.

Richards, Gillian and Ray Sweatman, eds. *Dramatists Sourcebook 1988-89 Edition.* New York: Theatre Communications Group, 1988.

Rowe, Kenneth Thorpe. *Write That Play.* New York: Funk & Wagnalls Co., 1939.

Smiley, Sam. *Playwriting: The Structure of Action.* Englewood Cliffs, NJ: Prentice-Hall, Inc., 1971.

Weales, Gerald. *A Play and Its Parts.* New York: Basic Books, 1964.

Brochures

"Copyright Basics" (R1), Register of Copyrights, Library of Congress, Washington, DC 20559 (202) 287-9100; free brochure of the U.S. Copyright Office.

"Guidelines," Samuel French, Inc., 45 W. 25th St., New York, NY 10010; sample of format preferred by Samuel French ($3).

"A Handbook for Literary Translators," PEN American Center, 568 Broadway, New York, NY 10012; free brochure containing a model contract, information on "The Responsibilities of Translation" and a "Manifesto on Translation."

"Highlights of the New Copyright Law" (R99), Register of Copyrights, Library of Congress, Washington, DC 20559 (202) 287-9100; free brochure of the U.S. Copyright Office.

"The Literary Agent," Society of Authors' Representatives, Inc., Box 650 Old Chelsea Station, New York, NY 10113; free brochure explaining services provided by agents, standard practices of agents, a list of tasks which agents cannot perform, advice on "How to Find an Agent" and a list of SAR members with addresses.

Contest Entry Calendar 1989

Contests listed in this calendar are those whose specific 1989 deadlines were announced prior to publication of *The Playwright's Companion 1989*. For information on ongoing competitions, deadlines yet to be announced and deadlines falling after 1989, playwrights should consult individual listings and request guidelines from contest sponsors.

January

1 Gallery Players of the Leo Yassenoff Jewish Center Playwriting Contest
Kumu Kahua/University of Hawaii at Manoa Drama Department Playwriting Contest
The Lee Korf Playwriting Awards
Mill Mountain Theatre New Play Competition
Ruby Lloyd Apsey National Playwriting Competition
Towngate Theatre Playwriting Contest
6 Chicano Literary Contest
11 Portland State University New Plays in Progress Series
14 Scholastic Writing Awards
15 Geraldine R. Dodge Foundation New American Play Award
James D. Phelan Literary Award
Lois and Richard Rosenthal New Play Prize
Maude Adams Playwriting Contest
The Society of Midland Authors Drama Award
23 Margaret Bartle Annual Playwriting Award
27 University of Louisville Grawemeyer Award
31 Atlantic Community College Playwrights' Weekend
Dubuque Fine Arts Players 12th Annual One-Act Contest
Radio Drama Awards

February

1 Aggie Players Playwriting Competition
Arnold Weissberger Award
Christina Crawford Awards
Columbia Theatre Players' Annual New Play Contest
Margo Jones Playwriting Competition
Merrimack Repertory Theatre Playwriting Contest
New American Comedy Festival
Renato Poggioli Translation Award
The Ten-Minute Musicals Project
Tennessee Williams/New Orleans Literary Festival One-Act Play Contest
15 The Henry Fonda Young Playwright's Project
Wichita State University Playwriting Contest

March
1 Golden Gate Actors Ensemble Playwrights Competition
   Unicorn Theatre National Playwright's Competition
15 Cornerstone: Penumbra Theatre Company Competition
   Lewis Galantiere Literary Translation Prize
   Source Theatre National Playwriting Competition
31 Bob Clark New Playwright Contest
   Mystery Play Competition
   National One-Act Playwriting Competition

April
1 Charlotte Repertory Theatre Play Commission
   David James Ellis Memorial Award
   George R. Kernodle Playwriting Competition
   Marc A. Klein Playwriting Award
   Midsouth Playwrights Contest
   The Virginia Prize for Playwriting
15 Hispanic Playwrights Project
   John Gassner Memorial Playwriting Award
   Mixed Blood Versus America
   National One-Act Play Contest
30 Feat Playwriting Festival

May
1 California Young Playwrights Project
   New World Theater New Play Competition
   Towson State University Prize for Literature
15 Frank McClure One-Act Play Award
   International New Music Composers Competition
   Marvin Taylor Playwriting Award
31 Writer's Digest Writing Competition

June
1 ASF Translation Prize
   National Playwrights Showcase
15 Western Public Radio Playwriting Contest
30 Regional Children's Theatre Competition 1989

July
2 Theodore Ward Prize
15 The Dogwood National One-Act Play Competition
   Miller Award 1989
   Paul T. Nolan Award
31 SETC New Play Project

August
1 Arnold and Dorothy Burger Playwriting Competition
   Vermont Playwrights Award

September
1 Stanley Drama Award
30 Actors Alley Repertory Theatre's Annual Competition
Annual At the Uprising Playwright's Award
University of Cincinnati Playwriting Contest

October
1 Anna Zornio Memorial Children's Theatre Award
Drama League of New York Plays-in-Progress Competition
Ferndale Repertory New Works Competition
The International Society of Dramatists Awards: Lincoln
Theatre Memphis New Play Competition
Young Playwrights Festival
12 Letras de Oro (Spanish Literary Contest)
15 American College Theatre Festival Awards: David Library
Bloomington Playwrights Project Contest
CAC New Play Competition
Illinois State Fine Arts Playwriting Contest
Multicultural Playwrights Festival

November
1 Beverly Hills Theatre Guild-Julie Harris Award
The Inside from the Outside International Contest
The International Society of Dramatists Awards: Adriatic
The Richard Rodgers Production Award
15 The Ann White Theatre 6th Annual Contest
Robert J. Pickering Award
18 Forest A. Roberts/Shiras Institute Playwriting Award
21 Vermont Repertory Theatre National Playwriting Contest
30 Dayton Playhouse Playwriting Competition

December
1 American College Theatre Festival Awards: ASCAP
Foundation, Columbia Pictures, Lorraine Hansberry,
National Student Playwriting, The Short Play Program
Celebration of One-Acts
Dramarama89
National Playwrights Conference
6 The International Society of Dramatists Awards: Perkins
15 Festival of Southern Theatre
JCC Theatre of Cleveland Playwriting Competition
Playwright's Forum Awards
31 Harold Morton Landon Translation Award
Wings Theatre Company 1989 New Plays Contest

Cross Reference to Special Interests

While the theatres, contests, programs and publishers included in this cross reference express a special or exclusive interest in the topics under which they are listed, many of them have other interests as well. Some theatres, contests, programs and publishers not listed below also accept works indicated by the following headings. Some special interests noted in individual listings are so specific as to preclude their inclusion here, and those special interests which call for value judgments are not included.

American Works & Themes
Theatres: **About Face Theatre Co., American Folk** Theater, **American Living History** Theater, **American Renaissance** Theatre, **American Stage Company** (NJ), **American Stage Festival, Apple Corps** Theatre, The **Arts at St. Ann's, City Theatre** Co., **East West Players, 45th Street** Theatre, **Gloucester Stage** Co., The **Immediate Theatre, Intermountain** Actors Ensemble, **Ironbound** Theatre, **Lakewood** Little Theatre, The **Philadelphia Theatre Co., Rendezvous** Productions, **St. Bart's** Playhouse, **Studio Arena** Theatre, The **Studio Theatre, Tennessee Repertory** Theatre, **Theater for The New City, Virginia Stage** Co., **WPA** Theatre
Contests: **Aggie Players** Playwriting Competition, **American College Theatre Festival** Awards: David Library, **David James Ellis** Memorial Award, **National Archives** Playwriting Competition, **Tennessee Williams/ New Orleans Literary Festival** Contest
Programs: **Fund for American Plays, New American Theatre** Project
Publisher: **Broadway Play Publishing Inc.**

Avant Garde, Experimental & Innovative Works
Theatres: **Academy Theatre, Actors Alley** Repertory Theatre, The **American Place** Theatre, **American Stage Festival, At the Foot of the Mountain, Burbage Theatre** Ensemble, The **Changing Scene**, The **Chicago Theatre Co., Clavis** Theatre, **Contemporary Arts Center, Creation Production** Co., **Dixon Place, Dreiske Performance** Co., **45th Street** Theatre, **Jacksonville University** Department of Theatre Arts, **Just Us** Theater Co., **La Mama** Experimental Theatre,

Music-Theatre Group/Lenox Arts Center, **New York Theatre Workshop, Omaha Magic** Theatre, **One Act** Theatre Co., **Playmakers, Playwright's Alliance, The Road Co., Round House** Theatre, The **Salt Lake Acting Co.,** San Diego Repertory Theatre, **Seven Stages,** Soho Repertory Theatre, **Storefront** Theatre, **Theater for The New City, Theatre X, T.W.E.E.D., Woolly Mammoth** Theatre Company
Contests: **Playwright's Forum** Awards, The **Richard Rodgers Production** Award, 24th Street Experiment Annual Playwright Competition
Publishers: **Swift Kick, United Arts**

Biblical/Christian/Religious Themes
Theatres: **Acacia** Theatre, **A.D. Players, Chicago Medieval** Players, **Company** Theatre, **Lamb's Players** Theatre
Publishers: **Baker's** Plays, **Lillenas** Publishing Co., **Modern Liturgy, Resource** Publications

Biographical & Historical Works
Theatres: **AMAS** Repertory Theatre, **American Living History** Theater, **Artreach** Touring Theatre, **Boston Shakespeare** Co., **Bristol Riverside** Theatre, **Dixie College** Theatre, **Great North American History** Theatre, **Intermountain** Actors Ensemble, **N.C. Black Repertory** Co., **New Voices, The Old Slocum House** Theatre, **Shakespeare & Company, Theatre West Virginia, Theatreworks/USA, Walnut Street** Theatre, **Young People's Theatre** Company of Delaware Valley
Contests: **Festival Theatre of Biography & History** Commissions, **Margaret Bartle** Annual Playwriting Award, **Miller** Award 1989, **National Archives** Playwriting Competition, **Theatreworks/USA** Commissioning Program

Children's Plays, Concerns of Youth
Theatres: **Academy** Theatre, **A Contemporary Theater Southwest, A.D. Players, Artreach** Touring Theatre, **Arvada Center** for The Arts & Humanities, **California Theatre Center,** The **Children's Theatre Co., Community Children's Theatre,** The **Coterie** Inc., **Creative Arts Team, Creative** Theatre, **Dell'Arte Players** Co., **Emmy Gifford** Children's Theater, The

Delray Beach Playhouse, The Fuller Young People's Theatre, The Great-American Theatre Co., Honolulu Theatre for Youth, Little Broadway Productions, Looking Glass Theatre, Market House Theatre, Marriott Lincolnshire Theatre, Merry-Go-Round Playhouse, Miami Beach Community Theatre, The New Conservatory, Northside Theatre Co., Old Creamery Theatre Co., Pennyrile Players Theatre, Periwinkle National Theatre for Young Audiences, Prairie Players Youth Theatre, Pushcart Players, Seattle Children's Theatre, Stage One: Louisville Children's Theatre, Stop-Gap Co., The Street Theater, Synthaxis Theatre Co., The Theater at Monmouth, Theatre IV, Theatre of Youth Co., TheatreWorks/USA, The Thirteenth Street Children's Theatre Ensemble, Young People's Theatre Company of Delaware Valley, Young Performers Theatre

Contests: Anna Zornio Memorial Children's Theatre Playwriting Award, Margaret Bartle Annual Playwriting Award, Indiana University-Purdue University at Indianapolis Children's Theatre Playwriting Competition, Regional Children's Theatre Competition 1989, Theatreworks/USA Commissioning Program

Programs: The American Alliance for Theatre & Education, Asolo Touring Theater Commissions, ASSITEJ/USA, Playwrights Theatre of New Jersey

Publishers: Anchorage Press, Child Life Magazine, Children's Playmate Magazine, Coach House Press, Dramatics Magazine, Eldridge Publishing Co., Freelance Press, Instructor Magazine, New Plays Incorporated, Plays: The Magazine for Young People, Scholastic Scope

Contemporary & Social/Political Issues

Theatres: About Face Theatre Co., Academy Theatre, Actors Alliance Theatre, Actors for Themselves, The Actors Space, Actors' Workshop, The Adelphian Players, American Ensemble Co., American Folk Theater, American Stage Festival, Art & Work Ensemble, The Arts at St. Ann's, Barter Theatre, BoarsHead: Michigan Public Theater, Bond Street Theatre, Boston Shakespeare Co., Bristol Riverside Theatre, Burbage Theatre Ensemble, City Theatre Co., Clavis Theatre, Coney Island USA, Contemporary Arts

Center, Dell'Arte Players Co., Dordt College Theatre, Eureka Theatre Co., Experimental Theatre of The Puertorican Atheneum, Free Street Theater, Fulton Opera House, Gnu Theatre, Hudson Guild Theatre, The Immediate Theatre, Independence Theater Co., Intermountain Actors Ensemble, Invisible Theatre, Irondale Ensemble Project, Janus Theatre Co., The Julian Theatre, Horizon Theatre Co., Lace Productions, The Lamb's Theatre Co., Light Opera of Manhattan, Long Wharf Theatre, Looking Glass Theatre, Los Angeles Theatre Center, Mabou Mines, Marin Theatre Co., N.C. Black Repertory Co., New City Theater, The New Conservatory, New Federal Theatre, New Voices, New York Shakespeare Festival, The New York Theatre Group, New York Theatre Studio, New York Theatre Workshop, Oakland Ensemble Theatre, Off Center Theatre, Ohio Theater, One Act Theatre Co., On Stage Productions: On Stage Children, Periwinkle National Theatre for Young Audiences, Philadelphia Drama Guild, The Philadelphia Theatre Co., Playhouse West, The Play Works Co., Playwright's Alliance, Potomac Theatre Project, Puerto Rican Traveling Theatre, Pushcart Players, Remains Theatre, The Repertory Theatre of St. Louis, The Road Co., Round House Theatre, The Salt Lake Acting Co., Sandcastle Players, Seattle Children's Theatre, The Second Stage, Seven Stages, Shakespeare & Company, Spectrum Theatre, Stage West (TX), Stop-Gap Co., Studio Arena Theatre, Theatre Exchange, Theater for The New City, Theatre of Youth Co., Theatre Rapport, Underground Railway Theater, Unicorn Theatre, Vetco, Victory Gardens Theater, Virginia Stage Co., The Will Geer Theatricum Botanicum, Wisdom Bridge Theatre, Woodstock Playhouse Association., WPA Theatre, Young Performers Theatre Adult Wing, Zephyr Theatre Complex

Contests: Frank McClure One-Act Play Award, Merrimack Repertory Theatre Playwriting Contest, New World Theater New Play Competition, 24th Street Experiment Annual Playwright Competition, Vermont Repertory Theatre National Playwriting Contest, Wings Theatre Company 1989 New Plays Contest

Ethnic & Minority Authors & Themes

Theatres: **American Jewish** Theatre, **Asian American** Theater Co., **At the Foot of the Mountain** , The **Bilingual Foundation** of the Arts (Hispanic), The **Chicago Theatre** Company (African American), **Contemporary Arts Center**, **Crossroads** Theatre Company (Afro-American, African, W. Indian), **Duo** Theatre (Hispanic American), **East West Players** (Asian American), **Experimental Theatre** of The Puertorican Atheneum (Puerto Rican, Hispanic), **Folksbeine Theater** (Jewish), **Havurat Yisrael** Theatre Group (Jewish), **INTAR Hispanic American** Theatre, **JCC Center Stage** (Jewish), **Jewish Repertory** Theatre, **Just Us** Theater Company (Black American), **Los Angeles Theatre Center**, **National Jewish** Theater, **Native Americans** in the Arts, **N.C. Black Repertory** Co., **Negro Ensemble** Co., **New Federal** Theatre, **New Mexico Repertory** Theatre (Hispanic), **Oakland Ensemble** Theatre (Black American), **One Act** Theatre Co., **Pan Asian Repertory** Theatre, The **Penumbra** Theatre Company (African American), **Puerto Rican Traveling** Theatre (Hispanic), **Repertorio Español** (Hispanic), **Rites & Reason** (Afro-American), **San Diego Repertory** Theatre, **Studio Arena** Theatre, **Theatre Rhinoceros**, **Three Brothers Theatre** (Black), **University of Arizona** Department of Drama (Hispanic, Native American), **Victory Gardens** Theater, **Wisdom Bridge** Theatre

Contests: **American College Theatre Festival** Awards: Lorraine Hansberry (Black), **Chicano** Literary Contest, **Cornerstone:** Penumbra Theatre Company National Playwright Competition (Afro-American), **Dayton Playhouse** Playwriting Competition, **Emerging Playwright** Award, **Helen Eisner** Award for Young Playwrights (Jewish), **Hispanic Playwrights** Project, **JCC Theatre** of Cleveland Playwriting Competition (Jewish), **McDonald's** Literary Achievement Awards (Black), **Multicultural Playwrights** Festival, **Theodore Ward** Prize for Playwriting (Afro-American)

Programs: **American Indian Community House, At the Foot of the Mountain** Programs, **Brody Arts Fund, Cintas Foundation** Fellowship Program (Cuban), **Frank Silvera** Writers' Workshop, **INTAR** Hispanic American Music Theatre Laboratory, **INTAR** Hispanic Playwrights-in-

Residence Laboratory, **Los Angeles Theatre Center** Programs (Latino, Asian American, Black), The **National Foundation for Jewish Culture, NFJC Playwrights Travel Grant** Program (Jewish), **Ollantay Center** for the Arts (Hispanic), **Puerto Rican Traveling Theatre** Playwrights' Workshop (Hispanic)

Publishers: The **Americas Review** (Hispanic), **Arte Publico** Press (Hispanic), **Callaloo** (African American), **Tejas Art** Press (American Indian)

Gay & Lesbian Themes & Characters
Theatres: **Actors Alliance** Theatre, **Celebration** Theatre, The **Glines, Order Before Midnight, Stonewall** Repertory Theater, **Theatre Rhinoceros**
Program: **New American** Theatre Project

Health & Disability
Theatre: **Stop–Gap** Company
Contest: The **Henry Fonda** Young Playwrights Project
Programs: The **Henry Fonda** Young Playwrights Project, **Playwrights Theatre of New Jersey**
Publisher: **Children's Playmate** Magazine

Multi–Media Works
Theatres: **Contemporary Arts Center, Mettawee River** Co., **Music–Theatre Group**/Lenox Arts Center, **Soho Repertory** Theatre, **Theater for The New City, T.W.E.E.D., Underground Railway** Theater, **Vineyard** Theatre
Contest: **International New Music Composers** Competition

Multi–Ethnic Casting
Theatres: **American Folk** Theater, **Apple Corps** Theatre, **Detroit Repertory** Theatre, **Mill Mountain** Theatre, The **New Rose** Theatre, **On Stage Productions:** On Stage Children
Contests: **Aggie Players** Playwriting Competition, **Mill Mountain Theatre** New Play Competition, **New World Theater** New Play Competition
Program: **At the Foot of the Mountain** Programs

Musicals, Operas

Theatres: **Allenberry** Playhouse, **AMAS** Repertory Theatre, **American Music Theatre Festival**, **Barksdale** Theatre, **Barn** Players, **Broadway Tomorrow** Musical Theatre, **Coconut Grove** Playhouse, **Country Dinner** Playhouse, **Creative** Theatre, The **Delray Beach** Playhouse, **Derby** Dinner Theatre, **Dixie College** Theatre & Pioneer Players, **Fairbanks Light Opera** Theatre, **Firehouse** Dinner Theatre, **Firelite** Dinner Theatre, **Ford's** Theatre, **Goodspeed** Opera House, **Kalamazoo** Civic Players, **Lake George** Dinner Theatre, **Lakewood** Little Theatre, **Lawrence Welk** Dinner Theatre, **Light Opera** of Manhattan, **Little Broadway** Productions, **Marriott Lincolnshire** Theatre, **Musical Theatre Works**, **Music Hall** Theatre, **Music-Theatre Group**/Lenox Arts Center, **New Tuners** Theatre, **Omaha Magic** Theatre, **Paper Mill** Playhouse, **PCPA Theaterfest**, **Royal Court** Repertory, St. **Bart's** Playhouse, **Soho Repertory** Theatre, **Stages**, **Stanley Hotel** Theatre, **Tennessee Repertory** Theatre, **Theatre on The Square**, **TheatreWorks**, **Triangle** Theatre Co., **Upstairs** Dinner Theatre, **Vineyard** Theatre, **West End** Dinner Theatre, **Young People's Theatre** Company of Delaware Valley, **Zephyr** Theatre Complex

Contests: American College Theatre Festival Awards: ASCAP Foundation, **American Musical Theater** Festival, **BMI University Musical Show** Competition, **International New Music Composers** Competition, The **Richard Rodgers** Production Award, **Seagram's** New Music Theater Awards Program, The **Ten-Minute Musicals** Project, **University of Lousiville Grawemeyer** Award for Music Composition

Programs: **BMI/Lehman Engel** Musical Theatre Workshop, **Columbia College Chicago** New Musicals Project, **Composers/Librettists Studio**, **INTAR** Hispanic American Theatre Laboratory, The **Lehman Engel** Musical Theatre Workshop, **Los Angeles Theatre Center** Programs, **Musical Theatre Lab**, **National Endowment for the Arts** Opera Musical Theater Program, **National Institute** for Music Theater, The **National Music Theater Network**, **O'Neill Opera/Music Theater** Conference

Publishers: **Contemporary Drama Service**, **Freelance** Press

Mysteries
Theatres: Coconut Grove Playhouse, The Delray Beach Playhouse, Market House Theatre, New Phoenix, Royal Court Repertory, Stanley Hotel Theatre
Contest: Mystery Play Competition
Publisher: Samuel French Inc.

One-Acts & Short Plays
Theatres: Academy Theatre, The Acting Group, American Living History Theater, Arvada Center for The Arts & Humanities, Atlantic Community College Theatre, Barn Players, Brooklyn Theatre Ensemble, Cheyenne Little Theatre Players, Clavis Theatre, Manhattan Punch Line Theatre, One Act Theatre Co., Pennsylvania Stage Co., Senior Acting Program of the Barn Players
Contests: American College Theatre Festival Awards: The Short Play Awards Program, Carol Burnett Young Playwrights' Competition, Celebration of One-Acts, Chicano Literary Contest, Christina Crawford Awards, The Dogwood National One-Act Play Competition, Drury College 1-Act Playwriting Contest, Dubuque Fine Arts Players 12th Annual One-Act Playwriting Contest, Frank McClure One-Act Play Award, George R. Kernodle Playwriting Competition, The Inside from the Outside International Prose/Poetry Contest, The International Society of Dramatists Awards: Lincoln, National One-Act Play Contest, National One-Act Playwriting Competition, Off-Off Broadway Original Short Play Festival, Ones at Eight Annual One-Act Festival, Paul T. Nolan Award, Peace Play Contest, Playwright's Forum Awards, Scholastic Writing Awards, The Ten-Minute Musicals Project, Tennessee Williams/New Orleans Literary Festival One-Act Play Contest, Warehouse Theatre Company One-Act Competition, Western Public Radio Playwriting Contest
Programs: Discovery `89, New American Theatre Project
Publishers: Dramatika, United Arts

Published Works
Contests: ATA Award for Literary Translation from the German, Harold Morton Landon Translation Award,

Lewis Galantiere Literary Translation Prize, **Towson State University** Prize for Literature

Puppetry
Theatres: Center for Puppetry Arts, **Mettawee River** Co., **Underground Railway** Theater

Radio Plays
Contests: **Radio Drama** Awards, **Scholastic** Writing Awards, **Western Public Radio** Playwriting Contest

Regional/Local Writers & Themes
NORTHEAST
Theatres: **Atlantic Community College** Theatre, **Brooklyn Theatre** Ensemble, **Contemporary Theatre** of Syracuse, The **Gallery Players** of Park Slope, **Huntington Guild** Theatre Co., **Oldcastle** Theatre Co., **Vermont** Theatre Company
Contests: **Clauder** Competition for Excellence, **Merrimack Repertory Theatre** Playwriting Contest, **Playwright Focus, Vermont** Playwrights Award
Programs: **American Indian Community House, Artists Foundation, Fairchester Playwrights** Project, **New Dramatists, Ollantay Center** for the Arts, **Philadelphia Drama Guild** Playwrights' Project, **Playwrights' Workshop, Puerto Rican Traveling Theatre** Playwrights' Workshop
SOUTH/SOUTHEAST
Theatres: **Adademy** Theatre, **Cumberland County** Playhouse, The **Road** Co., **Roadside** Theater, **Southern Appalachian** Repertory Theatre, **Theatre-in-the-Works**
Contests: **CAC** New Play Competition, **FIU** Playwrights' Festival, **New World Theater** New Play Competition, **Towson State University** Prize for Literature,   The **Virginia Prize** for Playwriting
Programs: The **Playwrights' Unit, Southeast Playwrights** Project, **Southwest Theatre Association/** Marie Layton Bliss New Plays Program,   **Virginia Playwrights Fellowships**
MIDWEST
Theatres: **BoarsHead:** Michigan Public Theater, **Brown Grand** Theatre, **Coldwater** Community Theater, The

Cricket Theatre, **Detroit Center** for the Performing Arts , **Free Street Theater, Horse Cave** Theatre, **Northlight** Theatre, **Players Theatre** of Columbus, **Remains** Theatre, **Victory Gardens** Theater

Contests: Arnold & Dorothy Burger Playwriting Competition, **Radio Drama** Awards, **Robert J. Pickering** Award, The **Society of Midland Authors** Drama Award

Programs: Chicago Dramatists Workshop, **League of Chicago Theatres/**Chicago Theatre Foundation, **Midwest PlayLabs, Playwrights' Center** of Chicago

WEST/SOUTHWEST

Theatres: Arizona Theatre Co., **Cheyenne** Little Theatre Players, **Denver Center** Theatre Co., **Intermountain** Actors Ensemble, The **Julian** Theatre, The **Salt Lake Acting Co., Stages** Repertory Theatre, **Tale Spinners** Theater

Contests: California Young Playwrights Project, **James D. Phelan** Literary Award

Programs: Brody Arts Fund, **Los Angeles Theatre Center** Programs, **New American Theatre Project,** The **Playwrights Foundation, S.T.A.G.E., Theatre Bay Area, Southwest Theatre Association**

Publisher: West Coast Plays

NORTHWEST

Contests: Allen Clark Memorial Award, **Portland State University** New Plays in Progress Series

Programs: New City Theater Director's Festival, **Northwest Playwrights Guild**

Publisher: West Coast Plays

OUTSIDE CONTINENTAL U.S.A.

Theatres: Experimental Theatre of the Puertorican Atheneum, **Honolulu Theatre** for Youth, **One Act** Theatre Co., **Shakespeare & Company**

Contests: Allen Clark Memorial Award, **Kumu Kahua/** University of Hawaii at Manoa Drama Dept. Playwriting Contest

Program: Playmarket   *Publisher:* CASTA

Rural or Small-Town Settings & Themes

Theatres: Arrow Rock Lyceum Theatre, **Cumberland County** Playhouse, **Mad River** Theater Works, The **Road Company**

Contest: On Themes of Rural America

Program: Brody Arts Fund

Second Productions, Previously Produced Works

Theatres: Music Hall Theatre, The Second Stage
Contests: American College Theatre Festival
Awards, Breakthrough Series, The Society of Midland
Authors Drama Award, University of Louisville
Grawemeyer Award for Musical Composition
Program: Women in Theatre Festival
Publishers: American Theatre Magazine, Anchorage
Press, Arte Publico Press, Baker's Plays, Callaloo,
Drama Book Publishers, Dramatics Magazine,
Dramatists Play Service, Eldridge Publishing Co., I. E.
Clark Publishers, New Plays Incorporated, Pioneer
Drama Service, Players Press, Plays in Process (PIP),
Samuel French Inc., Theater, West Coast Plays

Seniors' Issues, Older Actors & Audiences

Theatres: The Adelphian Players, Art & Work
Ensemble, Barn Players, Senior Acting Program of the
Barn Players, Stop-Gap Co., Sunset Playhouse, Synthaxis
Theatre Company

Spanish-Language Plays

Theatres: Duo Theatre (playwrights' unit), Repertorio
Español, Thalia Spanish Theatre
Contests: Chicano Literary Contest, Letras de Oro
(Spanish Literary Contest), TCG Hispanic Translation
Commission
Publisher: The Americas Review

Student Authors, Young Playwrights

Theatre: A Contemporary Theater Southwest
Contests: American College Theatre Festival
Awards, BMI University Musical Show Competition,
Carol Burnett Young Playwrights Competition, California
Young Playwrights Project, Christina Crawford
Awards, Henry Fonda Young Playwrights Project, Marc A.
Klein Playwriting Award, Scholastic Writing Awards,
Warehouse Theatre Company One-Act Competition,
Wichita State University Playwriting Contest, Young
Playwrights Festival
Programs: The Associated Writing Programs,
Association for Theatre in Higher Education, The
Henry Fonda Young Playwrights Project, Los Angeles

Theatre Center Programs, **Playwrights Theatre of New Jersey**, **Young Playwrights**

Translations (into English), Adaptations

Theatres: **Alabama Shakespeare** Festival (tr. 17th–19th century European), The **Arkansas Arts Center** Children's Theatre (ad. classics), **Chicago Medieval** Players (ad. medieval, Renaissance), The **Children's Theatre Company** (ad.), The **Clarence Brown** Company (classics, E. European, Latin American), **CSC**: Classic Stage Company (ad. other genres; European classics), **Drama Committee** Repertory Theatre (ad. prose classics), The **Empty Space** Theatre (tr. contemporary European), The **Fuller** Young People's Theatre (ad.), The **Great-American Theatre** Company (ad. children's classics), **INTAR** Hipanic American Theatre, **Intiman** Theatre Company (classics), **Little Broadway** Productions (musical ad. fairy tales), **Marin** Theatre Company (tr. classics), **Mettawee River** Company (ad. myths, legends), **Nebraska Theatre Caravan** (classics), The **New Rose** Theatre (classics), **Paper Mill** Playhouse (musical ad.), **Remains** Theatre (ad.), **Round House** Theatre (tr. classics), **Shakespeare & Company** (ad. E. Wharton, H. James & contemporaries), **The Shakespeare Theatre** at the Folger (classics), **Stage One**: Louisville Children's Theatre (ad.), **Stage West** (MA) (ad. other genres; neglected classics, 20th century European), The **Studio Theatre** (tr. new Asian, European), **Theatre West Virginia** (ad. well-known works), **Three Rivers** Shakespeare Festival (classics), **Ubu Repertory** Theater (tr. French), The **Will Geer Theatricum Botanicum** (tr. classics), **Women in Theatre** Network (tr.), **Yale Repertory** Theatre (tr.)

Contests: **ASF** Translation Prize (Scandinavian), **ATA Award** for Literary Translation from German, **Harold Morton Landon** Translation Award (verse), **Lewis Galantiere** Literary Translation Prize (any language), **Margaret Bartle** Annual Playwriting Award (ad. children's classics), **NFJC Hebrew Translation** Commission, **Renato Poggioli** Translation Award (Italian), **TCG Hispanic Translation** Commission

Publishers: **American Theatre** Magazine (tr.), **CASTA** (tr. East European since 1945), **Modern International Drama** (tr.), **Plays**: The Drama Magazine for Young People (ad. children's)

Urban Settings & Themes
Theatres: The **Adelphian** Players, **Free Street Theater, Ironbound** Theatre, **The Power Theatre**
Program: **Brody** Arts Fund

Women Authors, Women's Issues, Women's Roles
Theatres: **Actors Alliance** Theatre, **At the Foot of the Mountain, Horizons:** Theatre from a Woman's Perspective, **Horizon** Theatre Co., The **Immediate Theatre, Kalamazoo** Civic Players, **Lace** Productions, **Los Angeles Theatre Center, Mary Baldwin College** Theatre, **One Act** Theatre Co., **Order Before Midnight, San Diego Repertory** Theatre, **Springboard** Theatre, **Studio Arena** Theatre, **Synthaxis** Theatre Co., **Texas A & I University** Theatre, The **Tower Players** of Hillsdale College, **Wisdom Bridge** Theatre, **Women in Theatre** Network, **Women's Interart Center**
Contests: **Dayton Playhouse** Playwriting Competition, **Margaret Bartle** Annual Playwriting Award, **Margo Jones** Playwriting Competition, **Maude Adams** Playwriting Contest, **New World Theater** New Play Competition, **Warehouse Theatre Company** One-Act Competition
Programs: **At the Foot of the Mountain** Programs, **Frank Silvera** Writers' Workshop, **The Gathering**, The **International Women's Writing Guild, Los Angeles Theatre Center** Programs, **Money for Women/**The Barbara Deming Memorial Fund Inc., **Women in Theatre** Festival, **The Women's Project** & Productions, **WOW (Women One World) Cafe**
Publisher: **Women in Performance:** A Journal of Feminist Theory

Cross Reference to Special Programs

Membership, Service & Support Organizations, Resource Information Services
Actors' Alliance Inc., The **Alliance of Resident Theatres**/New York, The **American Alliance for Theatre and Education, American Indian Community House, Arts International,** ASSITEJ/USA, The **Associated Writing Programs,** Association for **Theatre in Higher Education,** British **Theatre** Association,

California Theatre Council, Center for Arts Information, Chicago Dramatists Workshop, Coordinating Council of Literary Magazines Library, The Dramatists Guild, Fairchester Playwrights Project, Feedback Services/Feedback Theatrebooks, FirstStage, The Foundation Center, Institute of Outdoor Drama, International Theatre Institute of the United States, The International Women's Writing Guild, League of Chicago Theatres/Chicago Theatre Association, Literary Managers and Dramaturgs of America, Los Angeles Theatre Alliance/League of Producers, Manhattan Playwrights Unit, Merely Players, National Foundation for Jewish Culture, National Institute for Music Theater, The National Music Theater Network, New Dramatists, New York Foundation for the Arts, Northwest Playwrights Guild, Ollantay Center for the Arts, PEN American Center, Pen to Stage Productions, Performing Arts Research Center, Playformers, Playmarket, The Playwrights' Center, Playwrights' Center of Chicago, Playwrights' Platform, Playwrights Theatre of New Jersey, The Playwrights' Unit, Professional Association of Canadian Theatre/PACT Communications Center, Southeast Playwrights Project, S.T.A.G.E., Theatre Artists Workshop of Westport, Theatre Bay Area, Theatre Communications Group, The Thirteenth Street Repertory Company Playwrights Unit, Volunteer Lawyers for the Arts (VLA), Women in Theatre Festival, WOW (Women One World) Cafe

Play Development Programs (for theatres and contests offering play development programs, see individual listings) Actors' Alliance Inc., American Playwright Program, Asolo Touring Theatre Commissions, At the Foot of the Mountain Programs, BMI/Lehman Engel Musical Theatre Workshops, Center Theater Youtheatre Program, Chicago Dramatists Workshop, Columbia College Chicago New Musicals Project, Composers/Librettists Studio, Cornell Center for the Performing Arts New Works Program (residency), Discovery '89 (residency), Fairchester Playwrights Project, Firststage, Frank Silvera Writers' Workshop,

Frederick Douglass Creative Arts Center Writing Workshops, **Drama Project, The Gathering, Henry Fonda** Young Playwrights Project, **INTAR Hispanic American Music Theatre** Laboratory (residency), **INTAR Hispanic Playwrights-in-Residence** Laboratory (residency), The **Lee Strasburg Theatre Institute,** The **Lehman Engel Musical Theatre** Workshop, **Los Angeles Theatre Center** Programs, **Manhattan Playwrights Unit, Merely Players, Midwest PlayLabs** (residency), **Mount Sequoyah** New Play Retreat (residency), **Musical Theatre Lab, New American Theatre Project, New York Foundation** for the Arts, **O'Neill Opera/Music Theater Conference** (residency), **Padua Hills** Playwrights' Workshop/Festival (residency), **Pen to Stage** Productions, **Philadelphia Drama Guild** Playwrights' Project, **Playformers,** The **Playwright/Director Workshop,** The **Playwrights' Center, Playwrights' Center of Chicago,** The **Playwrights Foundation, Playwrights' Platform, Playwright's Preview** Productions, **Playwrights Theatre of New Jersey** New Play Development Program (residency), **The Playwrights' Unit, PrimaFacie** (residency), **Primary Stages Co., Puerto Rican Traveling Theatre** Playwrights' Workshop, **Red Octopus Theatre Company** Workshop (residency), **Shenandoah Valley** Playwrights Retreat (residency), **SourceWorks, Southeast Playwrights Project, Stages** (residency), **Stage II Workshops** (residency), The **Sundance Institite** Playwrights Laboratory (residency), **Theater in the Works** (residency), **Theatre Artists Workshop** of Westport, **Third Step Theatre Company** Spring Festival of Staged Readings, **University of Alabama** New Playwrights' Program (residency), The **Washington Theatre Festival, Whetstone Theatre Company** Playwrights Program (residency), **Women in Theatre** Festival, The **Women's Project and Productions, Young Playwrights, WOW (Women One World) Cafe**

Professional Appointments
Arizona State University Guest Lectureship, The **James Thurber Playwright-in-Residence, New York Foundation for the Arts, North Carolina Arts Council** Visiting Artist Program, The **Playwrights' Center** Playwrights-in-the-Schools

Script Services: Critiques, Script Preparation, Marketing/Distribution (for theatres and contests offering script services, see individual listings)

American College Theatre Festival New Play Preview Program, **American Playwright Program**, **Chicago Dramatists** Workshop, **Feedback Services/** Feedback Theatrebooks, **Frank Silvera** Writers Workshop, **The International Women's Writing Guild**, **Merely Players**, **Mount Sequoyah** New Play Retreat, **New Dramatists**, **Northwest Playwrights Guild**, **Playmarket**, The **Script Review**, **Southeast Playwrights Project** (future plans)

Sources of Financial Support

Artists Foundation, The Authors League Fund and **The Dramatists Guild Fund**, **Brody** Arts Fund, **Cintas Foundation** Fellowship Program, **Fund for American Plays**, **Jerome Playwright-in-Residence** Fellowships, **John Simon Guggeheim** Memorial Foundation Fellowships, **Mary Roberts Rinehart** Fund, **McKnight Fellowships**, **Money for Women/**Barbara Deming Memorial Fund Inc., **National Endowment for the Arts Opera Musical Theater** Program, **National Endowment for the Arts Theater** Program, **New York Foundation** for the Arts, **NFJC** Playwrights' Travel Grant Program, **PEN** Writers' Fund, The **Playwrights' Center**, **Rockefeller Foundation** Grants, **TCG Observership** Program, **Virginia Playwrights Fellowships**

Writers' Colonies, Retreats (also see residencies indicated under Play Development Programs)

Dorset Colony House for Writers, The **Edward F. Albee Foundation** Inc., **Florida Studio Theatre** Artists Colony, **Mildred I. Reid** Writers Colony, **Palenville** Interarts Colony, **Shenandoah Valley** Playwrights Retreat, **Yaddo**, **The Yard**, **Yellow Springs** Institute

Index to Listings

ADVERTISEMENTS